WELDED DECK
HIGHWAY BRIDGES

Editor

James G. Clark

Professor of Civil Engineering

University of Illinois

Price

This Book may be ordered direct from

THE JAMES F. LINCOLN ARC WELDING FOUNDATION

Cleveland 1,   Ohio

Published by

THE JAMES F. LINCOLN ARC WELDING FOUNDATION

First Printing November, 1950

Printed in USA

Preface

This book, "Welded Deck Highway Bridges," is devoted exclusively to information obtained from the designs entered in the "Welded Bridges of the Future, 1949 Award Program." It has been written in order that many of the good ideas incorporated in the designs of this program might be made available to structural engineers. The members of the Jury of Award recognized the value of the material in these designs and unanimously recommended to the Trustees of The James F. Lincoln Arc Welding Foundation that a book such as this be prepared and published.

The Rules and Conditions of the program stated that each exhibit entered should present an original, all-welded design for a two-lane deck highway bridge supported on two end piers 120 feet apart. To this extent, the designs were similar. As to the basic structural type of the primary longitudinal members and the kind of floor system used, the designs differed greatly. The arrangement and the make-up of individual members, the choice of the floor slab material, and the connection details are some of the other items of the designs which varied to a considerable extent.

Because of the number and length of the papers, it is impracticable to publish all of them in their entirety. The selection of material presented in this book is based on the intention of discussing enough designs to insure that most of the new and important ideas are included; nevertheless, it is impossible to mention some of the proposed design features.

"Welded Deck Highway Bridges" is divided into chapters, and most of the chapters into specific classifications. This arrangement was chosen to permit an easy comparison of similar structural types, similar floor systems, etc. Such a division of subject matter has made it necessary to discuss some designs in more than one chapter.

The editor gratefully acknowledges the helpful suggestions he has received, especially those from Professor Thomas C. Shedd.

James G. Clark

Urbana, Illinois

May, 1950

DEDICATED TO

WILBUR M. WILSON

Research Professor of Structural Engineering, Emeritus

UNIVERSITY OF ILLINOIS

This volume on Welded Bridges of the Future is a review of the 1949 Award Program. It summarizes the contributions the many contestants made to the design of welded bridges. Since Professor Wilson conceived the program and conducted much of the research on which the designs submitted were based, it is entirely appropriate that this volume be dedicated to him.

There can be no real measure of the great significance of his research in this field. However, as the years go by and welded bridges assume increasing importance, it will become more and more clear that it was he who constructed a solid base on which to build.

[signature]

Head of Department of
Civil Engineering,
University of Illinois

CONTENTS   Pages

Preface III

Dedication V

Contents Page VII

Chapter   I—Introduction
          The James F. Lincoln Arc Welding Foundation........................... 1
          The 1949 Award Program... 1
          The Awards 4
          Summary of Results and Data.. 6

Chapter II—Structural Types
          Vertical Girders With Single Webs...................................... 8
          Inclined Girders 30
          Box Girders 36
          Single Longitudinal Members... 45
          Vertical Trusses 64
          Inclined Trusses 83
          Vierendeel Trusses 114
          Other Types 127

Chapter III—Floor Systems
          Reinforced Concrete 168
          Steel Grid 183
          Steel Plates 193

Chapter IV—New Sections
          Plates 206
          Angles 210
          Tees 214
          Beams, Channels, Miscellaneous Shapes................................. 219

Chapter V—Special Connections And Details.. 227

Chapter VI—Quantities And Costs 239

CHAPTER I

INTRODUCTION

The James F. Lincoln Arc Welding Foundation

Many programs have been sponsored by The James F. Lincoln Arc Welding Foundation since it was established in 1936. This book is restricted to the "Welded Bridges of the Future, 1949 Award Program", which was only one of the many programs. As all programs must, this program did satisfy the requirement from the Deed of Trust of the Lincoln Foundation,

"The object and purpose of The James F. Lincoln Arc Welding Foundation is to encourage and stimulate scientific interest in, and scientific study, research and education in respect of the development of the arc welding industry through advance in knowledge of design and practical application of the arc welding process."

The Trustees of the Foundation are pleased with the results of this 1949 Award Program and in accordance with their adopted policy are making available to the public, by publishing this book, the information disclosed by the designs submitted. The Trustees were so impressed by the good results of the 1949 Award Program that they approved a "Welded Bridges of the Future, 1950 Award Program", which offered awards for the best designs of a welded 240 ft. through highway bridge. This program closed in July 1950.

The Trustees and Officers of the Foundation are:

Trustees:
E. E. Dreese, Chairman, Columbus, Ohio
H. R. Harris, Cleveland, Ohio
T. V. Koykka, Cleveland, Ohio
Officers:
A. F. Davis, Secretary, Cleveland, Ohio
C. G. Herbruck, Assistant Secretary, Cleveland, Ohio

The 1949 Award Program

The purpose of this program was to stimulate original and creative thinking on the design of bridges. Unlike any other program sponsored by the Foundation, this program was limited to the design of a bridge with a specified span and loading. The exact description of the bridge to be designed was:

A two-lane deck highway bridge supported on two end piers 120 feet apart, centerline to centerline of bearings.

To be in accordance with common bridge design practice and in order that the designs submitted would be more competitive, specifications for the

1

two-lane deck highway bridge were given in the Rules and Conditions. These specifications were as follows:

Inasmuch as the substructure is not included in this competition, the competitor may assume that suitable piers or abutments are available. However, he will show the outline of their upper parts in the general drawings (plans, sections and elevations) of the super-structure.

The bridge shall be designed for ASTM-A7-46 steel. The significant requirements for base metal specifications are published in appendix E of the 1947 edition of the standard specifications for welded Highway and Railway bridges of the American Welding Society.

Recent editions of the American Association of State Highway Officials Standard Specifications for Highway Bridges are out of print and therefore not generally available to the competitors. For this reason, the design competition will be governed by the following abbreviated specifications as to the loads to be used in computing the stresses. The proportioning of the members, the allowable unit stresses, and the size and type of welds to be used in fabricating them will be in accordance with the 1947 Edition of the Standard Specifications for Welded Highway and Railway Bridges of the American Welding Society.

The loads to be used in the design are as follows: The dead load shall consist of the weight of the steel super-structure and of the floor and floor system. Each traffic line will be 10 feet wide but the distance inside to inside of curb will be not less than 26 feet. Each curb shall be 1'-6" wide.

The live load for each lane shall consist of a uniform load of 640 lbs. per linear foot of traffic lane combined with a single concentrated load, both so placed on the bridge, both longitudinally and transversely, so as to produce maximum stress. This concentrated load shall have a value of 18,000 lbs. for moment and 26,000 lbs. for shear. The concentrated load shall be considered as uniformly distributed across one lane on a line normal to the center line of the lane. In addition, the floor system shall be designed for truck wheel concentrations as follows: 1 front axle of 8,000 lbs. (4,000 lbs. per wheel), and 1 rear axle of 32,000 lbs. (16,000 lbs. per wheel); distance between axles of 14 feet; distance between wheels on the same axle of 6 feet.

The impact load allowance is expressed as a fraction of the live load stress and shall be determined by the formula:

$$I = \frac{50}{L + 125}$$ but not to exeed 30 per cent, in which L is the span length in feet.

The wind force on the structure shall be assumed as a moving horizontal load equal to 30 lbs. per sq. ft. on 1½ times the area of the structure as seen in elevation, including the floor system and railings.

The lateral force due to the moving live load shall be 200 lbs. per linear foot and shall be considered as acting 6 feet above the roadway.

Structures designed for these lateral forces in combination with dead load, live load and impact forces may be proportioned for the normal unit stresses increased by 25 per cent. However, the resulting sections shall not be less than those required for dead load, live load and impact at the normal unit stresses.

Any type of floor adequately attached to its supports may be assumed to resist the lateral forces specified above.

A floor which serves only as such and does not participate in the strength of the supporting structure shall be designed only so far as is necessary to indicate the dimensions from which the gross weight is determined. A floor which is designed to contribute to the strength of the supporting structure shall be designed in sufficient detail to indicate the extent and manner of its participation.

The exhibit shall include the allowable unit stresses which were used in the design of this floor, if it is not of steel.

Some portions of the Standard Specifications for Welded Highway and Railway Bridges of the American Welding Society are based on the results of fatigue tests of welded joints described in Bulletins of the University of Illinois Engineering Experiment Station. Three of these bulletins, Nos. 344, 350 and 377, which might be of value in making the design, may be obtained free by contestants upon addressing a request to Dr. L. A. Rose, Editor, Engineering Experiment Station, Room 112 Engineering Hall, University of Illinois, Urbana, Illinois, in which it is stated that the bulletins are wanted in connection with the 1949 Award Program on Welded Bridges of the Future.

Features of the design not definitely covered by the specifications should be explained by the contestant. Moreover, it will be entirely in order for a contestant to call attention to and briefly describe any special feature of his design that he believes to have special merit.

Normally the designers of bridges have much more comprehensive specifications to follow, but as the object of this award program was "to encourage designers to explore the future of bridge design unfettered by the restrictions of tradition that now limit work in their field", these very brief specifications were considered to be appropriate.

One qualification of all entries in this program was that the manuscripts and drawings of all exhibits had to be in English and must have been completely executed within the period of the competition, January 1, 1949 to June 30, 1949. Exhibits had to represent the work of the designer or designers submitting them, but they could have been based on the designers' previous studies, experience and thinking.

In rating the merits of exhibits the Jury of Award gave consideration to the following factors:

INTRODUCTION

Compliance with the specifications;

The ingenuity exercised in developing shapes, sections and connections.

As indicated by the Dedication, Wilbur M. Wilson, Research Professor of Structural Engineering, Emeritus, University of Illinois, conceived this program and presented it to the Trustees of the Foundation for their approval. Professor Wilson served as Chairman of the Rules Committee and Chairman of the Jury of Award. In order to have representation of highway bridge engineers, steel fabricators, consulting engineers, university professors with practical experience, and the Foundation, Professor Wilson selected the following members for the Rules Committee and Jury of Award:

Dr. E. E. Dreese
Chairman Board of Trustees, Lincoln Foundation
Chairman, Department of Electrical Engineering
Ohio State University, Columbus, Ohio

Harry C. Boardman, Director of Research
Chicago Bridge and Iron Company
Chicago, Illinois

Professor James G. Clark
Department of Civil Engineering
University of Illinois, Urbana, Illinois

John I. Parcel, Consulting Engineer
Sverdrup and Parcel
St. Louis, Missouri

Lee E. Philbrook, Asst. Bridge Engineer
Illinois State Division of Highways
Springfield, Illinois

Professor Frank W. Stubbs, Jr.
School of Civil Engineering and Engineering Mechanics
Purdue University, Lafayette, Indiana

The Awards

The completely confidential handling of all exhibits by the Officers of the Foundation and the extreme precautions they took to assure that each exhibit should receive fair and proper consideration impressed every member of this Jury.

Following the rating of the exhibits by the Jury of Award, the exhibits were returned to the Office of the Foundation and the identity of the author of each exhibit was determined. Notifications of awards as determined by the Jury were sent then to the entrants and an announcement of the awards was made in various trade and technical journals.

A total of $6250 was paid to the authors of the thirteen designs which received awards. A list of the award winners with a very brief description of each design is as follows:

First Award—$3000

Thomas C. Kavanagh, Professor of Civil Engineering, Pennsylvania State College, State College, Pennsylvania. Design—One space truss of triangular cross section with two top chords and one bottom chord, employing new steel shapes in both chords for easier welding and economy of metal.

Second Award—$1500

Angel R. Lazaro, Jr., Malabon, Rizal, Republic of the Philippines (c/o U.S. Army District Engineers, Portland, Oregon).
Design—Two vertical girders with steel deck of ⅝″ floor plate welded to Y shaped stringers, composite action between steel deck and girders.

Third Award—$750

Fred C. Miller, 319 Capistrano Avenue, Toledo, Ohio. Design—Two vertical trusses using 12″ and 10″ pipe as members and new shapes (Pipe Adapter Bars) to facilitate making the welded connections.

Ten Honorable Mention Awards—$100 each

Kiser E. Dumbauld, 1844 Chatfield Road, Columbus 12, Ohio.
Design—Two vertical girders with new T sections used as flanges, continuous stringers, new section used in details.

Carl W. Otto, R.F.D #1, Box 467, Norfolk, Virginia; and Earle M. Cassidy, 913 East Weldon, Phoenix, Arizona.
Design—A single rectangular box section, five feet wide, with cantilever floorbeams.

Francis W. Cox, 3010 Lafayette Avenue, Omaha, Nebraska; and Lawrence W. Cox, 4115 North 33rd Street, Omaha, Nebraska.
Design—Three vertical girders using one longitudinal stiffener and vertical stiffeners for each girder.

R. W. Ullman, 3057 Edgehill Road, Cleveland Heights, Ohio.
Design—Interconnected triangular trusses using four top chords and three bottom chords, all chords made of new angle sections.

Paul Johan Tupker, 2/22 Van Starkenborghstraat, Groningen, Holland.
Design—A closed box section 26 feet wide with the top, bottom, and sides of the box composed of rectangular tubes or cells, each 4″ x 4″ running longitudinally the length of the bridge. Tubes made of thin sheet.

C. J. Pimenoff, 2045 Grey Avenue, Montreal, P. Q., Canada.
Design—Two vertical trusses with WF sections used as truss members.

INTRODUCTION

James H. Jennison, 1612 Coolidge Avenue, Pasadena, California.
Design—Two vertical trusses with curved bottom chord.

Hans H. Bleich, 127 West 79th Street, New York, New York; and
John R. Schwarting, 214 West Merrick Road, Bellmore, Long Island,
New York.
Design—Two vertical girders with horizontal stiffeners, two-way
concrete slab has composite action with both floorbeams and girders.

Harold H. Gilbert, 1655 San Carlos Avenue, San Carlos, California.
Design—Tied arch, with two tubular arch ribs made of $\frac{1}{2}''$ plate,
each 3 feet in diameter, 8" pipe used as verticals at floorbeams.

J. R. Daymond, Professor; and M. S. Zakrzewski, both of Civil Engineering Department, The University of Natal, Howard College, Durban, South Africa.
Design—Five longitudinal frames of special shape the top flanges
of which are connected with arched $\frac{3}{8}''$ curved plates on which the
concrete roadway is placed.
These are but thirteen of the many good designs entered in this program.

Summary of Results and Data

In all respects, this program was extremely successful. The caliber of the
participants was unusually high. Many are outstanding structural engineers
of great renown. They include bridge engineers of state highway depart-
ments, consulting engineers, designers of steel fabricating companies, structural engineers of research organizations, and professors of structural engineering. The authors represent 24 states and the District of Columbia in
this country and 19 other countries.

The quality of exhibits was very good. The designs reflected the wealth
of knowledge and experience of the entrants and also their creative thoughts.
Although only thirteen designs won awards, there were many other good
ones which were well designed, complete, and original. The many excellent
bridge designs submitted contained new ideas which the Jury of Award
believes will influence engineering and specifications in the bridge field.
Many of the new shapes evolved for the program indicate clearly the fact
that present structural shapes were not designed for the most economical
distribution of metal now possible with welding, but were dictated by
means of fabrication which existed at the time they were developed.

This program brought out many facts that will be valuable to designers
of "Welded Bridges of the Future". The shape or form of the primary
structure of a bridge should be one which utilizes the economy of metal
made possible by employing welding as the means of attachment of
its individual members. In many of the designs, the primary structure was
not confined so as to lie in a vertical plane; the web systems of trusses or

webs of girders were inclined. Some designers utilized parts of the steel floor systems as effective chord or flange material. In some cases, reinforced concrete floors participated as effective material for the primary structure or floorbeams, or both. It was not uncommon for designers to use steel floor plates or reinforced concrete slabs as effective material for stringer flanges.

Many new shapes were suggested which permitted a decrease in the amount of detail material necessary. By using a participating floor system, some designers eliminated the use of lateral bracing members in the plane of the top chords; others, by having a single tension chord, had no bottom lateral bracing.

In the chapters that follow, the details of some of the exhibits are shown and discussed. While it would be expected that all engineers should not agree as to what the best design should contain, and that an individual designer in his design may create some expensive details while eliminating other more expensive details, it is bound to be true that the publication of some of the excellent ideas presented in this program will benefit the field of bridge engineering and enable many designers to add this information to that which they already have.

CHAPTER II

STRUCTURAL TYPES

The structural types used by the participants in this program have been divided into the eight classifications of this chapter for the convenience of presentation. The order of listing bears no relationship to the number or quality of exhibits. Some designs could have correctly been included in more than one classification. By no means does this chapter refer to all of the designs submitted, neither does it include all the data from any one design. The material presented here represents only what is considered to be the most feasible information for a book of this nature.

Vertical Girders With Single Webs

This common structural type was used in more designs than was any other type. Twenty-six percent of the designs employed vertical girders with single webs. Sixty-five percent of these used two girders for the bridge, but the number of girders per bridge varied for the other thirty-five percent, being three, four, five or, as in one case, as large as eight.

The variation in the number of girders is not the most significant difference between the designs. The utilization of parts of the floor system as effective material in the girder flanges, the proportioning of the area in the individual girders, the method of attaching the individual pieces, and the details are more important items of difference.

Angel Lazaro, Jr., Malabon, Rizal, Republic of the Philippines, utilized portions of his steel floor system as effective material for the top flanges of his two girders. Plate 2 of his design is shown here as Figure 1. The method of fabricating the floor system assemblies in the shop in order to decrease the amount of field welding will be shown and discussed in Chapter III.

Mr. Lazaro concerned himself with the appearance, the functionality, the ease of field erection, as well as the structural adequacy and cost of his design. Concerning appearance he states, "At the sacrifice of heavier girder web metal to satisfy specification requirements, the vertical web stiffeners have been eliminated, thus giving a clean and sweeping line to the bridge. This is going to be money well-spent since it increases the strength and rigidity of the main girders and also balances the weld of web to flange plates. If good appearance is not to be essential, a much thinner web plate can be used, say ½ inch, with welded vertical stiffeners at regular intervals." Also, as to ease of erection considering the use of shop assemblies, he states, "Simplicity is the principal criterion considered in the design of this bridge. It could be fabricated and built from Plate 2 of the plans *alone*. The bridge consists of only 18 principal parts, 6 expansion plates, 4 bearings, and 396 erection and anchor bolts—nothing else. A single 35-ton derrick, one electric welding machine, and a small crew can erect it in a few days."

Mr. Lazaro's design has one web splice located just off the centerline of the span. It has bottom flange splices about 34 ft. from each end, using the same plate thickness of 2 in. for these end flange plates, but tapers them from the 27 in. width at the splice point to an 18 in. width at the end.

Kiser E. Dumbauld, Columbus, Ohio, used two girders 25 ft.-6 in. apart. The girders are 5 ft.-4 in. deep with ⅜ in. webs and 20x6 TF sections as flanges. This new section is shown in Chapter IV. Figures 2 and 3 are Plates II and III respectively of Mr. Dumbauld's design.

The choice of depth and web thickness was based on a comparative study with a 79.5 in. depth and a ⁷⁄₁₆ in. web. The shallower depth permitted a thinner web and resulted in overall saving of weight.

After checking four types of deck construction as to the total cost of the bridge, Mr. Dumbauld used a 5 in. open grid floor to decrease the dead load and says, "The minimum dead load of the floor slab makes possible a girder of minimum weight. This makes it possible to completely shop weld a girder, curb and railing into one single unit for delivery to the job, and to transport the entire superstructure in one load by truck and trailer without overloading the highway or vehicle. The prefabrication of this bridge and delivery of all in one load eliminates delays in waiting for various shipments, reduces field marking of parts, reduces storage space and handling. The unpainted surfaces to be left for field welding are so few and well-defined that these surfaces could be protected by masking tape, and all three coats of paint sprayed on in the shop under ideal conditions."

About the welding he states, "This structure has a maximum amount of shop welding and minimum amount of field welding. All the shop welding can be positioned for maximum speed by use of rollers, cradles, cranes and blocking. Most of the field welding is flat. 344 shop pieces are welded in 24 pieces to assemble in the field. 42 lbs. of welding rod are required for field welding and 493 lbs. for shop welding when using a beveled butt joint for flange to web welding. This indicates 92% of the welding is completed in the shop."

Hans H. Bleich, New York, New York and John R. Schwarting, Long Island, New York designed the two girders of their bridge to carry all of the dead load but utilized a two-way concrete slab acting with the girders to form composite beams (or girders) to carry the live load and impact.

In describing their bridge they state, "The floor is formed by a two-way concrete slab cast integrally with a ¼ in. wearing surface. Slab thickness including wearing surface is 9½ in. at the crown, 8 in. at the gutter. The end panel of the slab is 1 in. thicker.

"The floor slab is supported by floorbeams at 20 ft. centers, and by the two main girders at 22 ft.-6 in. centers. The slab and concrete curb cantilever over the main girders to obtain the 26 ft. width of roadway without requiring steel brackets.

"Composite action is utilized in the design of the floorbeams. These beams are rolled sections with spiral shear connectors. Brackets from the

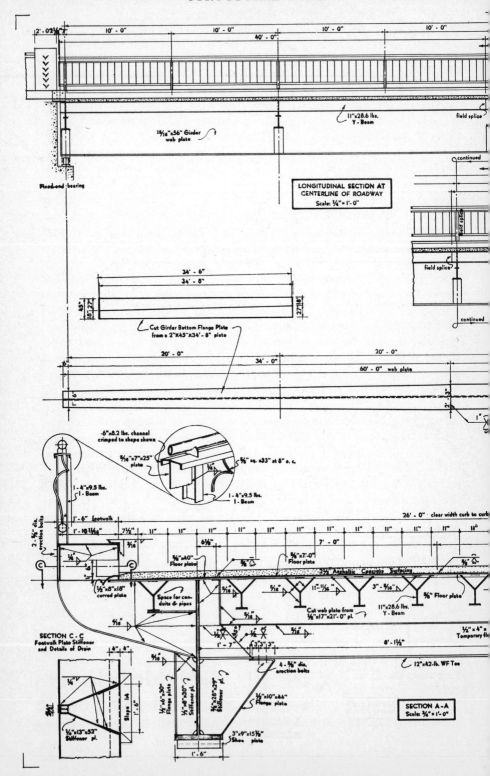

LONGITUDINAL SECTION AT
CENTERLINE OF ROADWAY
Scale: 1/4" = 1'-0"

Figure 1

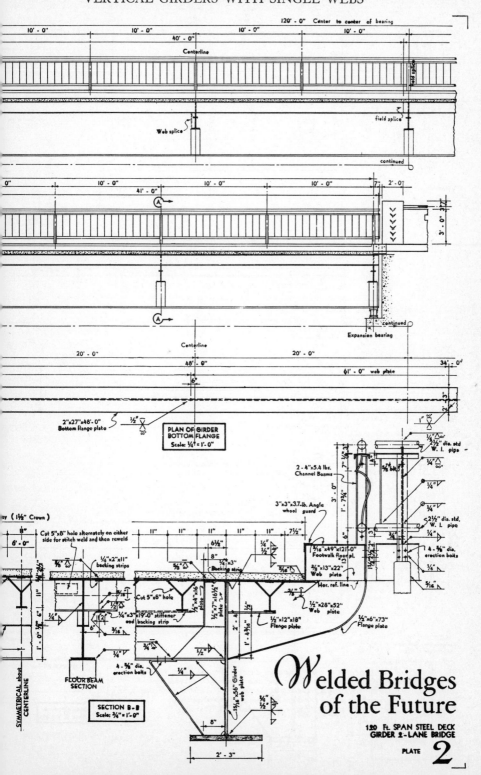

PLAN OF GIRDER
BOTTOM FLANGE
Scale: 1/4" = 1'-0"

FLOOR BEAM
SECTION

SECTION B-B
Scale: 3/4" = 1'-0"

*Welded Bridges
of the Future*

120 Ft. SPAN STEEL DECK
GIRDER 2-LANE BRIDGE

PLATE 2

Figure 1 (Concluded)

11

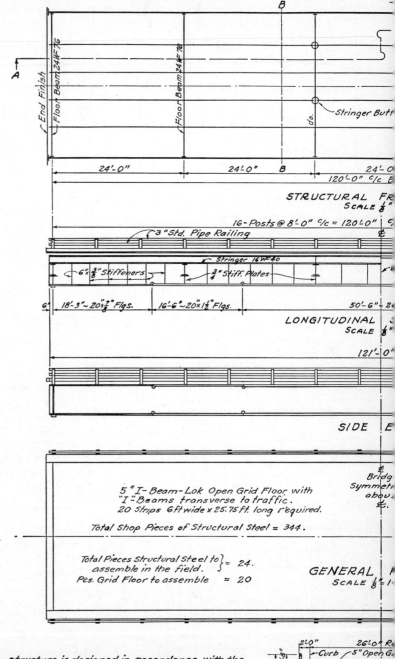

STRUCTURAL FR
SCALE ⅛"

A

End Finish

Floor Beam 24W76

Floor Beam 24W76

do.

Stringer Butt

B

24'-0"   24'-0" B   24'-0
120'-0" c/c B

16~Posts @ 8'-0" c/c = 120'-0"
3" Std. Pipe Railing

Stringer 16W40

6"x ⅜" Stiffeners   ¾" Stiff. Plates

6'   18'-3"~20x⅞" Flgs.   16'-6"~20x1½" Flgs.   50'-6"~2

LONGITUDINAL
SCALE ⅛"

121'-0"

SIDE E

5" I-Beam-Lok Open Grid Floor with
"I"-Beams transverse to traffic.
20 Strips 6ft wide x 25.75 ft. long required.

Total Shop Pieces of Structural Steel = 344.

Total Pieces Structural Steel to⎰
  assemble in the field. ⎱ = 24.
Pcs. Grid Floor to assemble = 20

GENERAL
SCALE ⅛"=1

Bridg
Symmetr
abou.

This structure is designed in accordance with the
Fifth Edition 1949 Specifications of the AASHO Standard
Specifications for Highway Bridges and 1947 Edition of the
Standard Specifications for Welded Highway and Railway
Bridges of the American Welding Society.

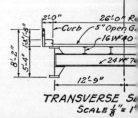

2'-0"   26'-0" R
Curb 5" Open G
16W40

24W76

8'-2" 13'-3"
5'-4"

12'-9"

TRANSVERSE S.
SCALE ⅛"=1'

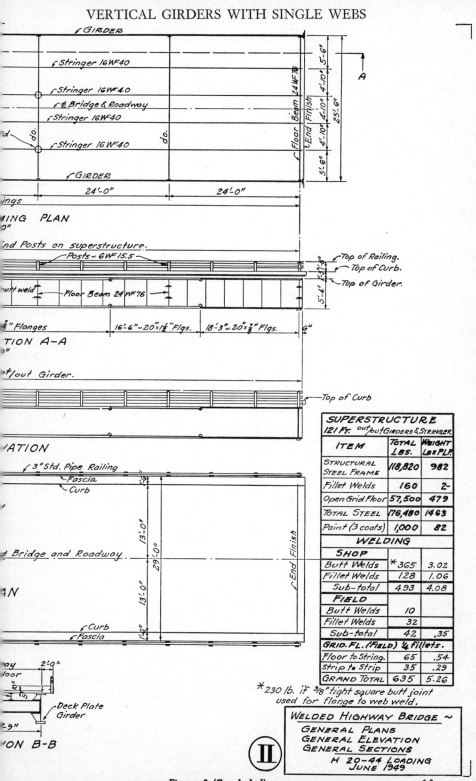

SUPERSTRUCTURE
121 FT. ᵒᵘᵗ/ₒᵤₜ GIRDERS & STRINGER

ITEM	TOTAL LBS.	WEIGHT LBS PLF.
STRUCTURAL STEEL FRAME	118,820	982
Fillet Welds	160	2~
Open Grid Floor	57,500	479
TOTAL STEEL	176,480	1463
Paint (3 coats)	1,000	82
WELDING		
SHOP		
Butt Welds	*365	3.02
Fillet Welds	128	1.06
Sub-total	493	4.08
FIELD		
Butt Welds	10	
Fillet Welds	32	
Sub-total	42	.35
GRID. FL. (FIELD) ¼ fillets.		
Floor to String.	65	.54
Strip to Strip	35	.29
GRAND TOTAL	635	5.26

*230 lb. if ³⁄₈" tight square butt joint used for flange to web weld.

WELDED HIGHWAY BRIDGE ~
GENERAL PLANS
GENERAL ELEVATION
GENERAL SECTIONS
H 20-44 LOADING
JUNE 1949

Ⅱ

Figure 2 (Concluded)   13

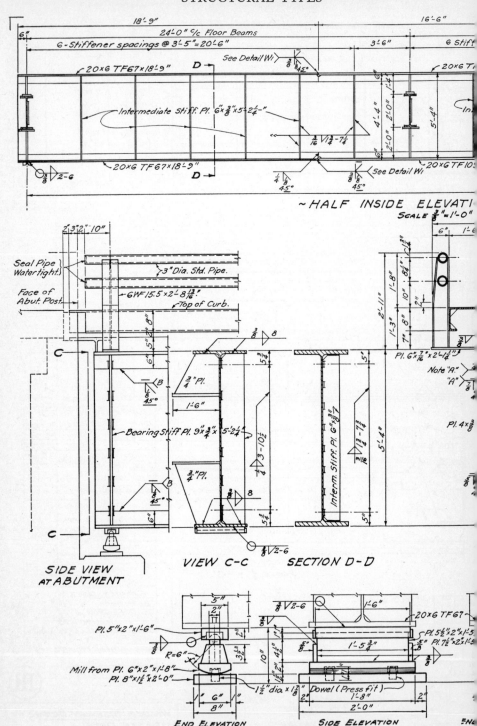

~HALF INSIDE ELEVATION
SCALE ¾"=1'-0"

SIDE VIEW AT ABUTMENT

VIEW C-C   SECTION D-D

ROCKER DETAILS
SCALE 1½"=1'-0"

END ELEVATION   SIDE ELEVATION

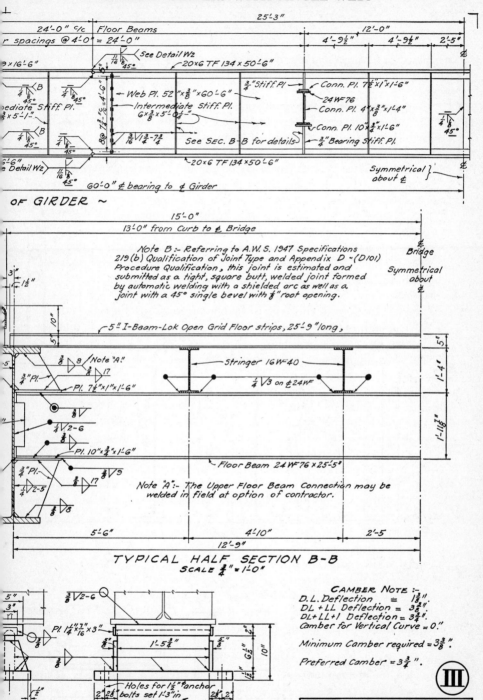

TYPICAL HALF SECTION B-B
SCALE ¾" = 1'-0"

Note B :- Referring to A.W.S. 1947 Specifications 219(b) Qualification of Joint Type and Appendix D -(D101) Procedure Qualification, this joint is estimated and submitted as a tight, square butt, welded joint formed by automatic welding with a shielded arc as well as a joint with a 45° single bevel with ⅛" root opening.

Note "A":- The Upper Floor Beam Connection may be welded in field at option of contractor.

CAMBER NOTE :-
D.L. Deflection = 1⅞".
DL + LL Deflection = 3¾".
DL + LL + I Deflection = 3¾".
Camber for Vertical Curve = 0."

Minimum Camber required = 3⅜".

Preferred Camber = 3¾".

BOLSTER DETAILS
SCALE 1½" = 1'-0"

WELDED HIGHWAY BRIDGE ~
GIRDER DETAILS
HALF SECTION B-B
ROCKER AND BOLSTER DETAILS
H20 - 44 LOADING
JUNE 1949

Figure 3 (Concluded)   15

floorbeams to the lower flanges of the plate girders provide effective cross frames at 20 ft. intervals. Intermediate floorbeams act as simple beams, while the end floorbeams together with their brackets act as two-hinged rigid frames.

"Composite action, using spiral connectors, is also utilized for the design of the main plate girders of 8 ft. depth. Top and bottom chords of the plate girders are structural tees cut from wide flange beams. Horizontal stiffeners are used to reduce the web thickness. For reasons of appearance the intermediate vertical stiffeners are on the inside of the girders only. It is assumed that the plate girder can be shipped in one piece, and no field splice is provided."

Their Exhibit C is shown in Figure 4. Field connections for the floorbeams are arranged for easy location of the beams, and to obtain down-hand welding where possible. Structural tees are used for the chords of the plate girders in order to avoid "any difficulties in welding a thin web to a substantially thicker flange plate."

More than one exhibit used very thin web plates, as well as thin material elsewhere. A design of this type is the one presented by Boris Bresler and T. Y. Lin, both of Berkeley, California. In discussing the use of thin material, they say:

"The use of light gages in the proposed design introduces several unusual problems in structural design. These problems consist in the evaluation of buckling loads and the effect of shear deformations. Much experience in dealing with these problems has been accumulated in recent years in the aircraft and light construction industries. The methods used in the proposed design make use of this experience. Also, Specifications for the Design of Light Gage Steel Structural Members, issued by the American Iron and Steel Institute in April, 1946, are adhered to where applicable. As shown below, the refinements introduced in this analysis in no way reduce the factor of safety as obtained with the conventional calculations of the strength of the structure.

"The floor deck panel is designed according to the AISI Specifications. The width-to-thickness ratio of the most highly stressed elements is such that the full cross-sectional area of the corrugation can be considered effective. The values of the width-to-thickness ratio for elements carrying low stresses is not critical as the actual stresses are well below buckling.

"The specifications included in the Rules and Conditions for the Award Program did not state specific requirements for the minimum thickness and the allowable shear stress for web plates stiffened longitudinally. For the purpose of this design it is assumed that any web thickness is satisfactory, provided the maximum shear stress does not exceed two thirds of the theoretical shear buckling stress. . . ."

Both of the two main girders have webs which are stiffened by longitudinal angles (turned so that both angle legs are welded to the web) and the girder webs are considered fully effective in resisting bending. It was found that the web plates would not buckle under the combined action of compression and shear stress. About the webs of the floorbeams, though, they state:

"The webs of the floorbeams, however, would not be stable if subjected to both shear and normal stresses. Therefore, the web sheet and web stiffeners are entirely neglected in calculating the section modulus of the floorbeam. This practice is common in design of aircraft structures, wherein the web is assumed to resist shear stresses without buckling and not to resist any normal stresses due to bending. This results in an entirely satisfactory design, and is considered to be slightly conservative, as the portion of the web effective in resisting tensile stresses due to bending is neglected in the calculation."

Some of the design features listed by Messrs. Bresler and Lin are the following. The floor system serves simultaneously as: the roadway, the compression flange of main girders, the stringers, the top lateral bracing, and the concrete form for the road surface. The resultant of the lateral forces passes very near the shear center of the bridge cross section, and thus minimizes the stresses due to torsion. The ideas of prefabrication and of automatic shop welding are incorporated in the design. The entire bridge is made up of only six prefabricated sections, obtained by dividing the bridge along the longitudinal centerline splice, and along the two transverse splices. Figure 5 shows some details of their design.

W. P. Dumbleton, London, England, designed a very thin ribbed plate for the webs of his two girders. The web has horizontal ribs ⅛ in. thick on both sides. The vertical spacing for the ribs is 10 in. The web is 10 ft. deep and has a thickness of ⅛ in. between ribs. A "Bobbin Section" with an area of 24 sq. in. serves as the bottom flange. This "Bobbin Plate" is 24 in. wide and at the edges has a thickness of 2 in., but this thickness decreases toward the center so that the center 6 in. of width has a thickness of only ¼ in. Mr. Dumbleton explains, "The merit of the Bobbin Plate is in that it provides the area required in 24 in. width, and allows a gradual change over from the thin web plate; thus giving a smooth stress flow and eliminating the common difficulty of welding thin plates to thick due to unequal heat capacity." Part of a 6 ft. width of the floor is assumed to be effective material for the top flange. The floor is composed of reinforced concrete, 6 in. thick, on top of a ribbed deck plate. The ribbed plate is ⅛ in. thick with ribs 2 in. high on only the top side. These ribs are spaced at 4 in. centers and are completely embedded in the concrete.

Francis W. Cox and Lawrence W. Cox, Omaha, Nebraska, designed their bridge with three girders. The spacing of the girders and some of their details are shown in Figure 6. In discussing their design, they made the following comments:

A three girder type was selected for economy of steel and because it

STRUCTURAL TYPES

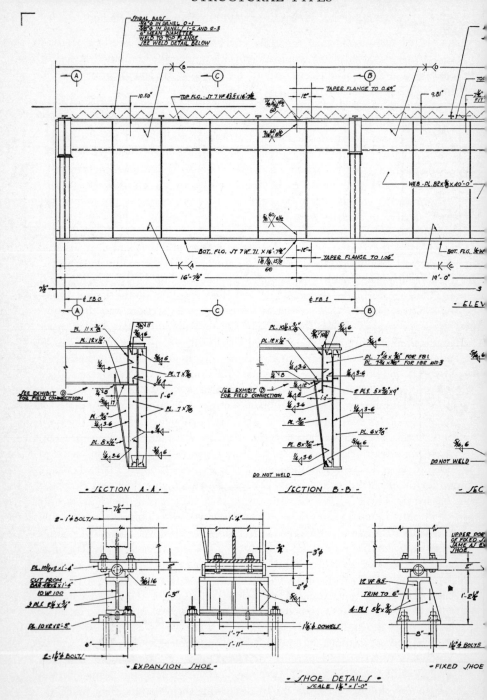

Figure 4

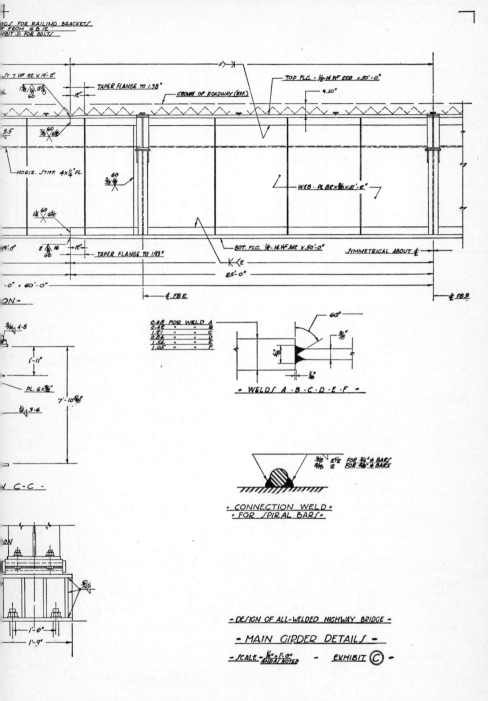

- DESIGN OF ALL-WELDED HIGHWAY BRIDGE -

- MAIN GIRDER DETAILS -

- SCALE - ¼"=1'-0" ANDAS NOTED - EXHIBIT Ⓒ -

Figure 4 (Concluded)

19

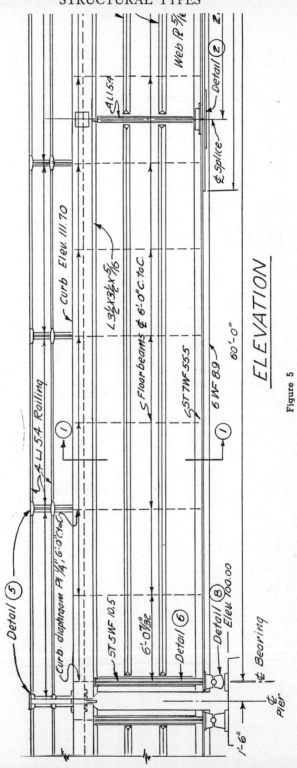

ELEVATION

Figure 5

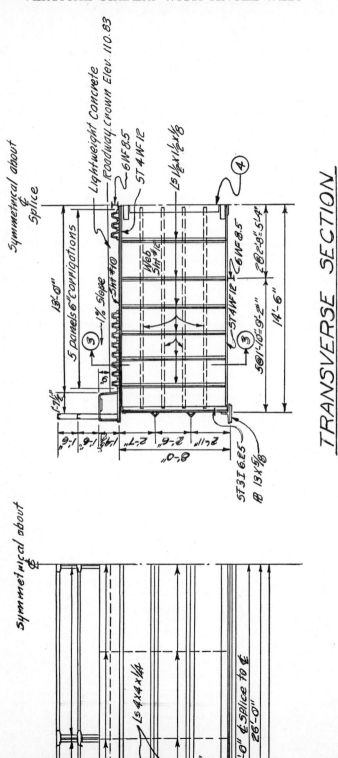

TRANSVERSE SECTION

Figure 5 (Continued)

21

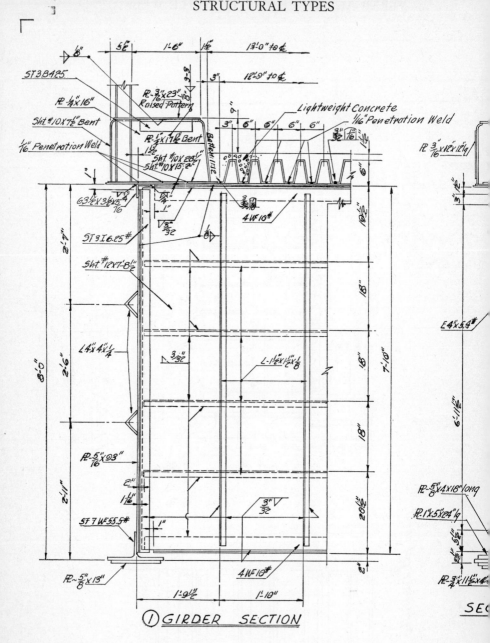

① GIRDER SECTION

Figure 5 (Continued)

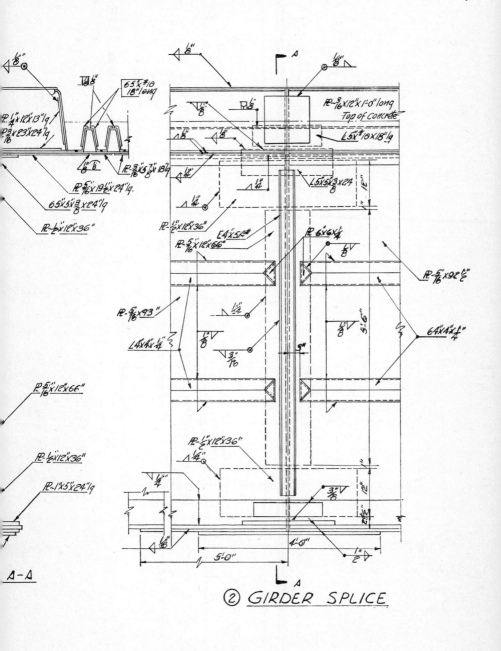

A-A

② *GIRDER SPLICE*

Figure 5 (Concluded)   23

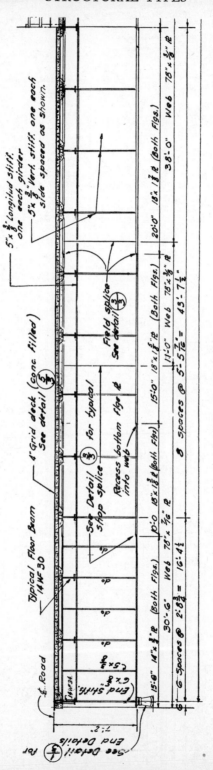

HALF; ELEVATION OF INTERIOR GIRDER

Figure 6

LONGITUDINAL

SCALE: ½ INC.

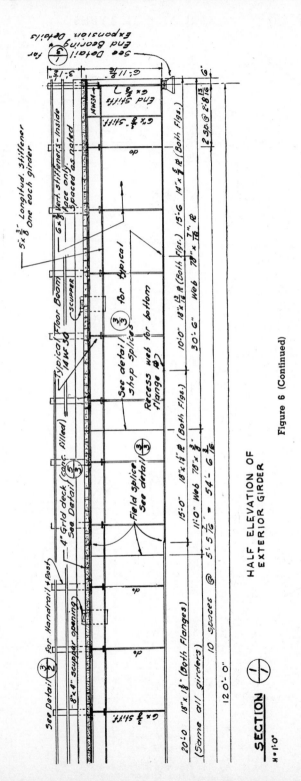

HALF ELEVATION OF
EXTERIOR GIRDER

SECTION ①

Figure 6 (Continued)

25

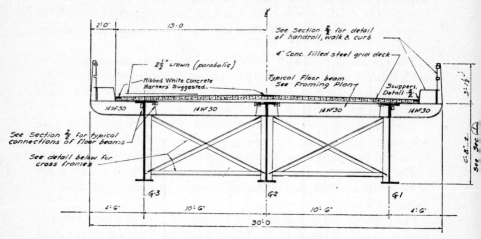

Cross Frames at Panel Points 0, 3, 6, 9, 13, 16, 19 & 22.
For concrete encasement see Sec. Detail ³⁄₅.

CROSS SECTION ①⁄₂

SCALE: ³⁄₄" = 1'-0"

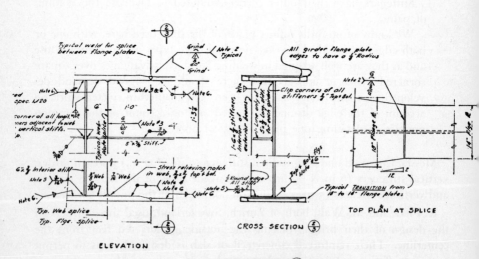

ELEVATION

CROSS SECTION ²⁄₃

DETAIL ³⁄₃

TYPICAL GIRDER DETAILS

SCALE 1¹⁄₂" = 1'-0"

Figure 6 (Concluded)

requires less overall depth than a two girder type or a truss type. We consider the depth important because in a large percent of cases it becomes an important or controlling feature in the design of a highway bridge.

The outside girders with no stiffeners exposed to the outside view, lends to better artistic treatment than the typical girder job or a truss type.

In this structure field erection work has been simplified. This speeds up erection work, saves time and lowers costs.

Steel handrails, steel curb and concrete filled steel grid floor were selected as against concrete, mainly to hold down the dead weight. An open steel deck type is not considered to be suitable for some locations.

The cross frames were detailed to utilize most of the available depth of the girders to give them great effectiveness in distributing loads between girders.

Floor beams were cantilevered to balance the loadings between girders, to make a suitable and economical support for posts and to add to the attractiveness of appearance. They were spaced close to accommodate a steel grid floor of moderate depth and without the use of additional stringers.

Main girders have flange plates with the corners rounded for three purposes. Sharp corners are not effective in transmitting stresses and can properly be eliminated. However each plate is so designed that it has the full required net area.

Rounded corners hold paint more efficiently than square ones, therefore cost of maintenance is lessened.

Rounded corners add to the esthetic appearance of the structure.

Stiffeners have their outer corners rounded to facilitate the holding of paint.

We know of no mills rolling plates of the sizes used here, with one or both edges rounded. However rounded edge types are in common use and as they are well adapted to welding and have advantages over square cornered plates, it appears that there should be a good demand developed for them. They have not been well adapted to riveted work on account of the edge distances required and on account of the common practice of detailing one plate on top of another.

Messrs. Cox used one longitudinal stiffener (5 in. x $\frac{3}{8}$ in.) on each girder, vertical stiffeners (6 in. x $\frac{3}{8}$ in.) on the inside faces of the outside girders, and vertical stiffeners (5 in. x $\frac{3}{8}$ in.) on both sides of the middle girder.

R. Fietz and M. Walt, both of Zurich, Switzerland, used three girders in the design of their bridge, placing the outside girders ten feet from the centerline. Their reinforced concrete floor slab is designed so as to permit composite action between it and the girders by utilizing shear connectors which are welded to the top flange plates of the girders. The slab is 10 in.

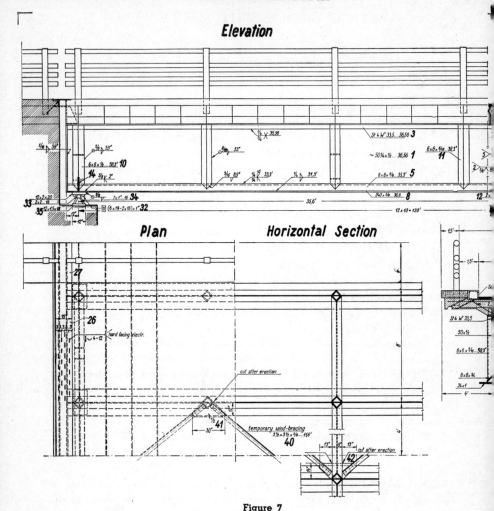

Figure 7

thick and reinforced so as to span the distance between the girders, canti-levering beyond the outside girders to the curbs. The spacing between girders is such that each girder has an equal width of floor slab for composite action. No stringers or floorbeams are used; however, transverse stiffening girders are placed at the ends and at the third points. These transverse members frame into the main girders and are the same depth as the main girders, a little over nine feet deep. No wind bracing is used and the authors state that no wind bracing is necessary during erection. Structurally the bridge is composed of a floor slab, three longitudinal girders and transverse girders at four points (ends and third points). The webs of the main girders are plates ⅝ in. thick and the flange plates are special T-shape

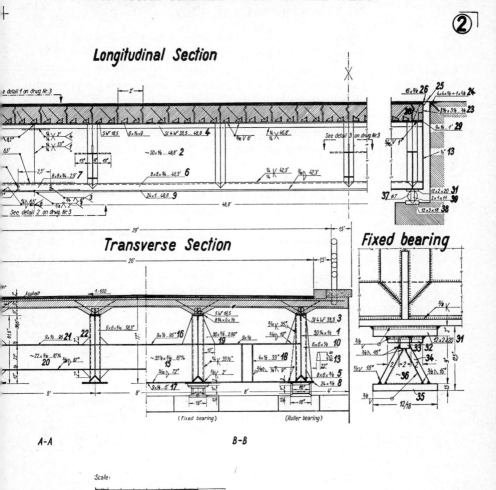

Figure 7 (Concluded)

members, having webs 4 in. high and ⅝ in. thick with the edge beveled for butt welding to the girder web plates. The main girders have vertical stiffeners every 20 feet. Between transverse girders, these stiffeners are composed of tees on each side, with the webs of the tees welded to the girder web. The floor slab is shown in Figure 64 of Chapter III and the new flange shape in Chapter IV.

Frantisek Faltus, Praha II, Czechoslovakia, employed four main girders in his design. The distance between girders is 8 ft. and his floor system consists of 2 ft. widths of precast reinforced concrete strips placed directly on the four girders and extending from the railing on one side to the railing on the other side. Shear connectors embedded in the strips are welded to the girders in order to have composite action between the concrete and the top flanges of the girders, thus permitting the top flanges of the girders to have less area than the bottom flanges. There are no stringers or floorbeams; however, Mr. Faltus used cross girders every 20 ft. which with the four main girders form what he termed an "elastic grid" which effectively distributes the load between the main girders. These cross girders are attached to the lower part of the main girders and no lateral bracing or cross bracing is necessary, except that during erection before the concrete strips are placed, temporary wind bracing is bolted between the two middle girders.

Figure 7 shows how Mr. Faltus combines one angle and one plate for a bottom flange by rotating the angle. He also rotates his vertical stiffener angles so that with the web they form a tubular section. These angles differ from normal angles in that edges are beveled for ease of welding. They are discussed further in Chapter IV.

For erection purposes and in order to have the concrete strips participate with the girders in resisting dead load as well as live load and impact, temporary erection trestles at the third points should be provided. While the concrete strips are being placed, the girders are supported only at the trestles (third points) and with no end supports, the top flange is in tension. After all strips have been placed and the shear connectors welded to the girders, the temporary trestles would be removed and the concrete would be in compression due to the dead load. Mr. Faltus suggests that after the faces of the strips are provided with a layer of cement mortar, the strips could be pressed together with some mechanical means and then the shear connectors welded to the girder before the pressure is released.

Inclined Girders

Inclined webs were employed in some of the box girders, but designs of this type are discussed under box girders. This section is restricted to designs utilizing inclined webs with common flanges at their lines of intersection which actually form a series of cells or boxes. These boxes could be termed triangulated plate girders or Vee-girders and differ from box girders in that adjacent boxes have no space between them and floorbeams are not necessary.

L. E. Grinter, Chicago, Illinois, designed a bridge composed of a reinforced concrete slab and four Vee-girders of trapezoidal cross section. The slab is made to participate with the girder as effective top flange material by the use of shear developers welded to the top flange angles. Mr. Grinter's Plate No. 1 is shown here as Figure 8.

In discussing the advantages of the Vee-girder design, Mr. Grinter lists the following items:

1. A saving in weight of structural steel of 22% as compared to a typical

30

deepened-beam design was achieved.

2. Elimination of lateral bracing and sway bracing. The Vee-girder has exceptional resistance to lateral forces.

3. Simplicity of field erection which consists merely of cantilever projection until the far end can be picked up by a crane. One temporary bent would suffice. If the erection stresses are severe, the cross struts might need to be attached to the flange angles to prevent spreading of the Vee in which case the alternate longitudinal stiffeners shown on Plate No. 1 would be preferred.

4. The structural simplicity of the Vee-girder gives it a unique architectural effect which should prove attractive. It is in harmony with the concept of modern architecture that function alone shall govern all design.

5. The fact that only three pieces need be shipped to the field (per girder unit), and that the only small pieces are the 6 in. shear-developing channels (which may all be duplicates) simplifies shipment and construction.

6. It is noted that the Vee-girder fits admirably the overpass structure where the saving of headroom is a very significant economy. The design chosen has a depth of $L \div 25$ which is exceptionally shallow.

7. The Vee-girder fabrication would be further simplified by the availability of angles rolled at some standard slope between legs (such as 60 degrees) which would eliminate the expense of rerolling a standard angle to close it to the desired shape of cross-section.

8. Maintenance of the Vee-girder bridge would be small because of its simple form and flat surfaces. Entrance to the girders should be provided at one end for painting the inside surfaces. Simplicity of maintenance should give the structure a probability of long life. A life in excess of 50 years with normal exposure is to be anticipated.

John A. Derrington, Middlesex, England, used fourteen inclined web plates, each $\frac{3}{8}$ in. thick, and top and bottom flange plates of $\frac{1}{2}$ in. thickness which form a series of triangular shaped cells or units. The roadway surface is obtained by placing pressed steel troughing on the top flange plates, filling the troughing with concrete, and applying a wearing surface of tarmac. The troughs are perpendicular to the span of the bridge and the thickness of the concrete filling varies in order to provide 2 in. of crown at the roadway centerline. This troughing and concrete filling transmit the live load transversely across the bridge and eliminate the need of stringers and floorbeams but is not assumed to be at all effective as girder flange material.

Figure 9 shows some details of Mr. Derrington's design. Some advantages which he gives for his structural arrangement are:

1. The bulk of the welding which takes stresses imposed by loading is carried out in the fabrication shop by welding machine ensuring an

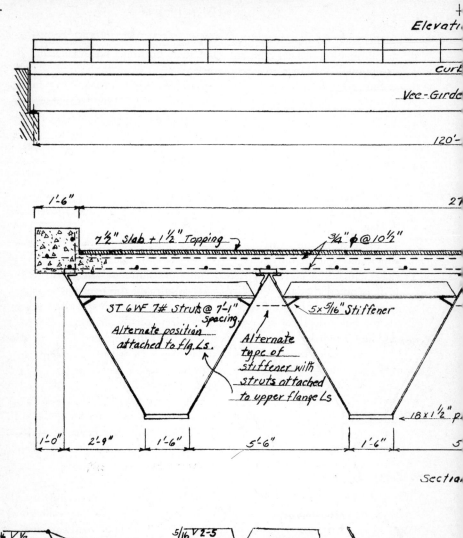

7½" Slab + 1½" Topping

¾" φ @ 10½"

ST 6WF 7# Struts @ 7'-1" Spacing.
Alternate position attached to flg. Ls.

Alternate type of stiffener with struts attached to upper flange Ls

5 x ⁵⁄₁₆" Stiffener

18 x 1½" p.

1'-6"

1'-0"   2'-9"   1'-6"   5'-6"   1'-6"

Sectia

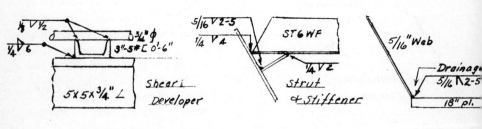

⅛ V½
¼ V 6
¾" φ
3"-5#C 0'-6"
5x5x¾" L
Shear i Developer

⁵⁄₁₆ V 2-5
¼ V 4
ST 6WF
¼ V 2
Strut & Stiffener

⁵⁄₁₆" Web
Drainage
⁵⁄₁₆ 2-5
18" pl.

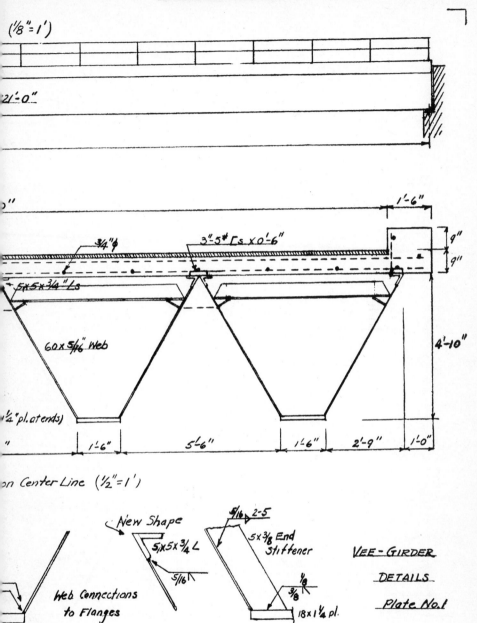

(⅛"=1')

21'-0"

1'-6"

¾"∮

3"-5# ⌐s x 0'-6"

9"

9"

5x5x¾"∟s

6.0x 5/16" Web

4'-10"

½"pl. at ends)

1'-6"   5'-6"   1'-6"   2'-9"   1'-0"

on Center Line (½"=1')

New Shape

5x5x¾ L

5/16

Web Connections
to Flanges

5/16 2-5

5x⅜ End
Stiffener

⅛
⅜

18x1¼ pl.

VEE-GIRDER

DETAILS

Plate No.1

Figure 8 (Concluded)   33

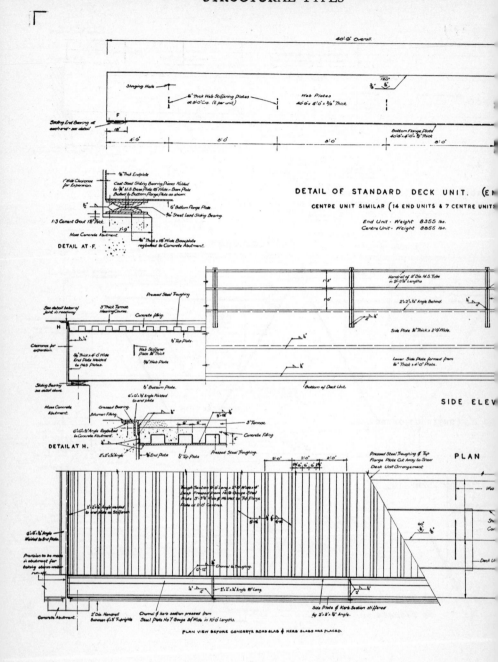

DETAIL OF STANDARD DECK UNIT.

CENTRE UNIT SIMILAR (14 END UNITS & 7 CENTRE UNITS)

End Unit - Weight 8355 lbs.
Centre Unit - Weight 8855 lbs.

DETAIL AT F.

DETAIL AT H.

SIDE ELEV

PLAN

PLAN VIEW BEFORE CONCRETE ROAD SLAB & KERB SLABS ARE PLACED.

INCLINED GIRDERS

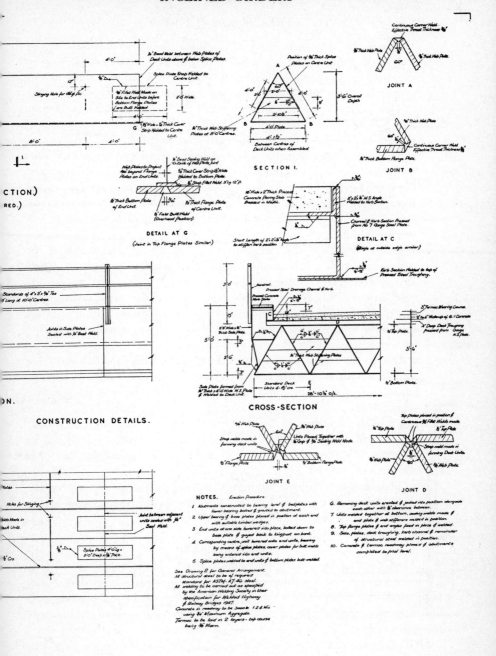

CROSS-SECTION

CONSTRUCTION DETAILS.

JOINT A

JOINT B

SECTION I.

DETAIL AT G
(Joint in Top Flange Plates Similar.)

DETAIL AT C

JOINT E

JOINT D

NOTES. Erection Procedure.

1. Abutments constructed to bearing level of bedplates with lower bearing bolts grouted to abutment.
2. Upper bearing of base plates placed in position at each end with suitable timber wedges.
3. End units at one side lowered into place, bolted down to base plate & guyed back to kingpost on bank.
4. Corresponding centre unit lowered onto end units, bearing by means of splice plates, cover plates for butt welds being entered into end units.
5. Splice plates welded to end units & bottom plates butt-welded.
6. Remaining deck units erected & jacked into position alongside each other with 8" clearance between.
7. Units welded together at bottom, sealing welds made & plates & web stiffeners welded in position.
8. Top flange plates & end angles fixed in place & welded.
9. Side plates, deck troughing, kerb channel & remainder of structural steel welded in position.
10. Concrete & tarmac roadway placed & abutments completed to final level.

See Drawing 2 for General Arrangement.
All structural steel to be of required standard for ASTM- A7 60 steel.
All welding to be carried out as specified by the American Welding Society in their specification for Welded Highway & Railway Bridges 1947.
Concrete in roadway to be 3000 b. 1-2 & Mix using ¾" Maximum Aggregate.
Tarmac to be laid in 2 layers - top course being ¾" Mesm.

Figure 9 (Concluded)   35

automatically deposited weld of highest quality at lowest cost.

2. A very simple erection procedure results, as the bulk of the work is shop fabricated, the individual units being despatched to the site in convenient size and shape for handling (weight approximately 4 tons).

3. Due to the cellular manner in which the bridge is built up, load on any point is transmitted right through the structure and consequently every member of the bridge will tend to act together. This gives a very stiff structure in particular when resisting wind pressures and other lateral forces. There will be no tendency for differential settlements between different parts of the structure at any one cross section, and as there will be no cases of reversal of stress in any member by a combination of live load, each member may be stressed to the full value of 18 kips per square inch.

4. As the flanges of the bridge in each case are the full width of the structure, a very much smaller depth is required to provide a specific area of steel and consequently the finished bridge is of striking slenderness, an outstanding architectural feature. Another great saving from this feature would be in the construction of abutments and approaches should the bridge be used for a rail or road overpass, where every saving in overall height will affect its total cost.

5. Due to the totally enclosed nature of the bridge construction its life should be virtually unaffected by corrosion of the steel and any possible damage to the structure could be repaired by replacement of the standard units affected.

6. From the maintenance point of view there is a minimum of surface area for the width and span specified so that painting costs would be reduced. The presence of re-entrant corners and inaccessible points has also been eliminated.

7. The standard type decking units could also be employed for a variety of conditions of spans, widths and loadings so that the net cost of the units should be assessed on a mass production basis.

Box Girders

Eleven percent of the exhibits employed two or more box girders as the main structural members for the bridge. Seven of the eleven percent used only two box girders. One design had eleven vertical webs which formed ten cells or boxes.

H. T. Borton and J. L. Borton, Cleveland, Ohio, spaced two box girders of varying depth transversely so that each girder would essentially support one lane of traffic. They gave the following reasons for selecting a box girder instead of a conventional truss or girder with a single web plate:

1. It permits use of lighter web plates with resultant smaller welds and

less secondary or locked up stress concentrations.

2. It provides good distribution of stress to flange plates, and allows wide plates to be used with a comparatively small projection.

3. It furnishes a clean section with a minimum of surface to maintain and few pockets and joints where corrosion may start.

4. It adapts itself well to participation in the deck framing and reduces the design span of the floor beams.

5. It gives good lateral strength and torsion resistance.

6. It simplifies future widening. Additional lanes can be added by erecting one new girder per lane and moving the curb and railing outward to the new location.

7. It has been generally used for heavy crane bridges, for strength and economy.

Figure 10a includes the detail dimensions of a deck channel which Messrs. Borton used not only as part of the slab between floorbeams but also, for the two sections above each girder, as the top flange of the box girder. They proposed "that each girder be entirely shop fabricated and shipped to the site as a unit. A member of this size is well within the handling range of the larger structural shops and the efficiency and economy of the shop assembly is greatly to be desired."

The web plates for the middle 60 ft. 6 in. are each 84 in. x ½ in. and the end plates are ½ in. in thickness and taper from an 84 in. depth at about the quarter points to a 48 in. depth at the ends. The bottom flange plates are 36 in. x ⅞ in. for the constant depth part and 36 in. x ¾ in. where the depth varies. The shop splices for the webs and bottom flange plates are located at approximately the quarter points as shown in Figure 10b; however, the shop splices for the deck channels which are used as top flange material are located at the third points directly at the centerline of the floorbeams. The deck channels not used as girder flange material are field spliced every 30 ft.

Homer M. Hadley and Harvey H. Johnson, both of Seattle, Washington, designed two box girders with a reinforced concrete slab to act structurally with the girders through welded shear connectors. Two types of shear connectors and other details of their design are shown in Figure 11.

They described their design in this manner: "Briefly, the box girder consists of a pair of ¼ in. web plates, a ⅜ in. top flange plate and a bottom flange plate varying in thickness from $1\frac{3}{16}$ in. to ½ in. The web plates have $\frac{5}{16}$ in. x 5 in. interior stiffeners with $\frac{5}{16}$ in. transverse diaphragms at 20 ft. intervals throughout the length of the girder. These are conventional means of bracing. The additional and novel feature of this design is the trussing of the four interior corners of the section. This is accomplished by means of long round bars, bent into uniform zig-zag pattern, which are introduced into the corners at desired inclinations, with their bend points

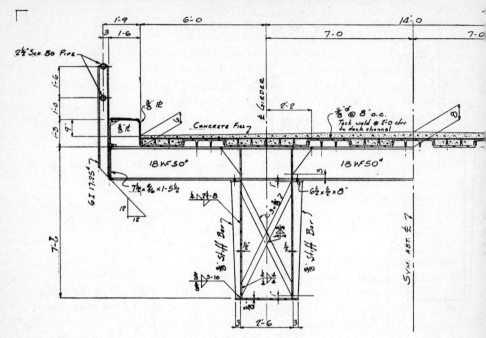

HALF SECTION AT FLOORBEAM
$\frac{1}{2}" = 1'-0$

HALF

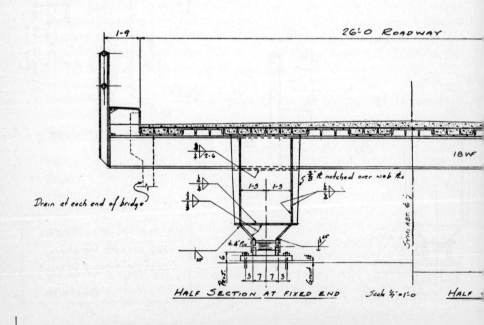

HALF SECTION AT FIXED END   Scale $\frac{1}{4}" = 1'-0$ HALF

Figure 10a

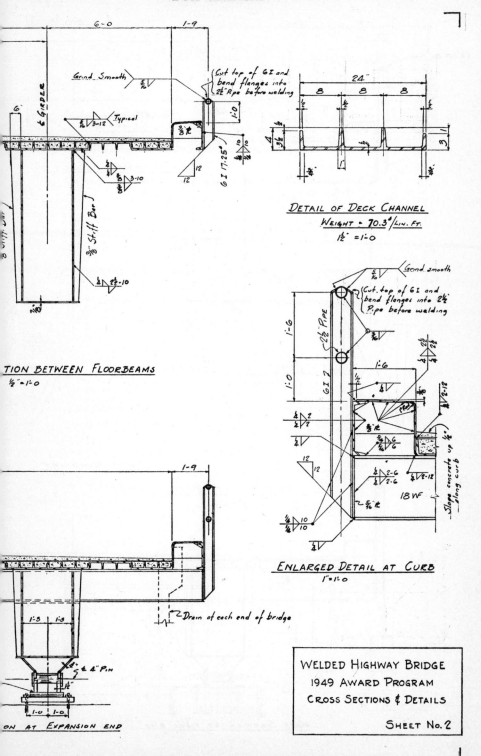

DETAIL OF DECK CHANNEL
WEIGHT = 70.3ᵇ/LIN. FT.
1½" = 1'-0

SECTION BETWEEN FLOORBEAMS
½" = 1'-0

ENLARGED DETAIL AT CURB
1" = 1'-0

WELDED HIGHWAY BRIDGE
1949 AWARD PROGRAM
CROSS SECTIONS & DETAILS
SHEET No. 2

Figure 10a (Concluded)   39

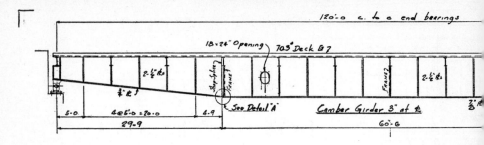

LONGITUDINAL SECTION
⅛" = 1'-0

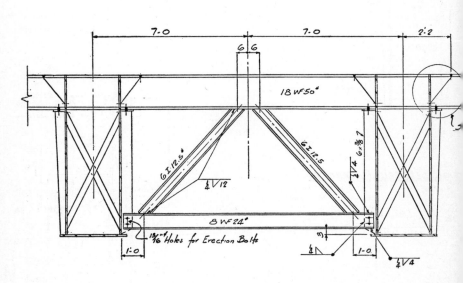

SECTION AT BRACING FRAME
½" = 1'-0

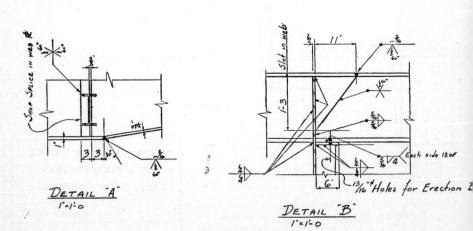

DETAIL "A"
1" = 1'-0

DETAIL "B"
1" = 1'-0

Figure 10b

BOX GIRDERS

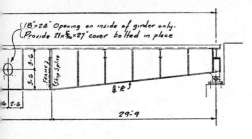

(18"×24" Opening on inside of girder only.
Provide 21×⁵⁄₁₆×27" cover bolted in place

3-6 3-6 Frame ½ Ship Splice

6 2-6

29-9

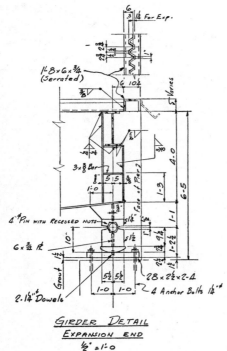

1 L 8×6×¾
(Serrated)

3×⅜ Bar

6×¾ Pt

2-1¼" Dowels

4" Pin with Recessed nuts

28 × 2½ × 2-1

4 Anchor Bolts 1¼"ø

GIRDER DETAIL
EXPANSION END
½"=1-0

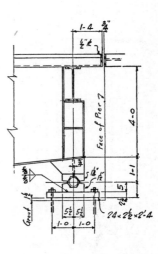

Face of Pier 7

24 × 2½ × 2-4

GIRDER DETAIL
FIXED END
Welding and shoe detail not shown
to be the same as for Expansion end
½"=1-0

WELDED HIGHWAY BRIDGE
1949 AWARD PROGRAM
LONGITUDINAL SECTION
& DETAILS
SHEET No. 3

Figure 10b (Concluded)

STRUCTURAL TYPES

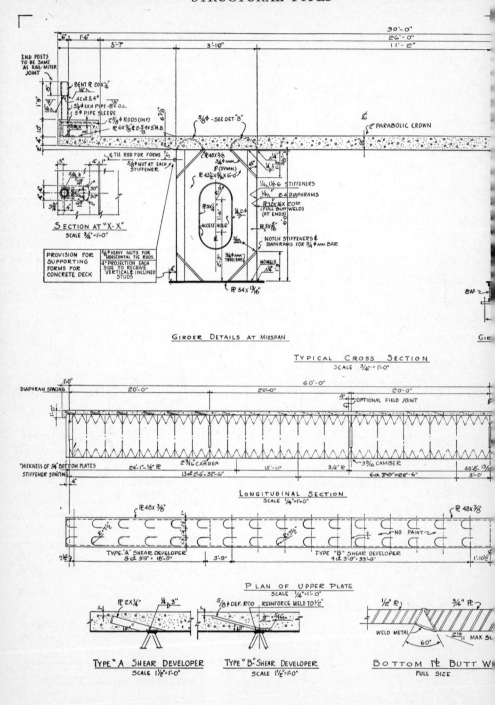

GIRDER DETAILS AT MIDSPAN

TYPICAL CROSS SECTION
SCALE 3/4"=1'-0"

LONGITUDINAL SECTION
SCALE 1/4"=1'-0"

PLAN OF UPPER PLATE
SCALE 1/4"=1'-0"

TYPE "A" SHEAR DEVELOPER
SCALE 1 1/2"=1'-0"

TYPE "B" SHEAR DEVELOPER
SCALE 1 1/2"=1'-0"

BOTTOM ₤ BUTT W
FULL SIZE

BOX GIRDERS

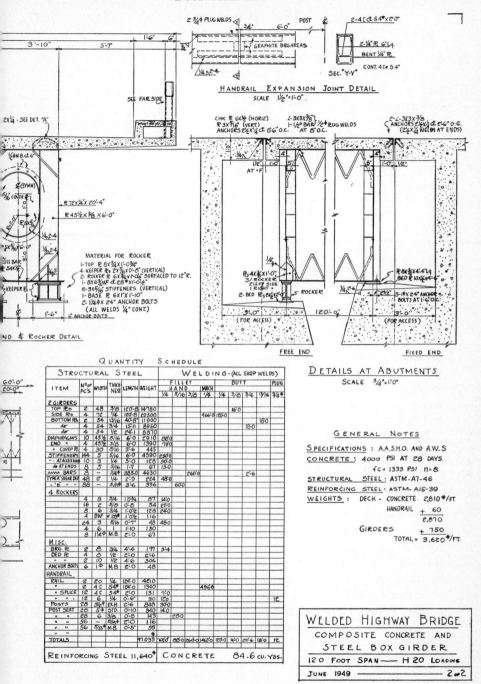

Figure 11 (Concluded)

contacting both web and flange plates. All these contact points are then welded, creating out of the bars and the main plates a set of inclined continuous trusses which find their supports at the transverse diaphragms. The vertical stiffeners on the web plates and the semi-circular shear connectors on the top flange are placed in registry with the contact points of the zig-zag truss bars. These constitute the stiffening and bracing means during erection of the girders themselves and the subsequent pouring of the reinforced roadway slab. When this slab has gained its strength, the compression flange of the girder is relieved of all but minor increase in stress and is held in close contact with the slab by the shear connectors. The slab also acts to transfer load from girder to girder, eliminating cross-bracing between them. Its weight gives stability to the bridge. Its cost is estimated locally to be about 40% of the cost of an open-grid steel deck. The two web plates, although of minimum—¼ in.—thickness are subjected to very low unit shearing stresses—about 40% of the value permitted by standard specifications. This girder readily adapts to special cases where minimum depth is important.

"Because, except for the corner trussing bars, it is made wholly of flat plates, all of minimum thickness and therefore minimum weight, because of the machine welding of the main longitudinal joints, because of its great stiffness when erected, because of the facility with which it can be made to support forms and because of the adaptability of its flat surfaces to the application of paint, this girder is inherently one of low cost and great economy. It employs nothing but common and readily available sections and can be fabricated in any existing shop."

Bert T. Wake, Pittsburgh, Pennsylvania, designed his two girders to have a trapezoidal or tee shape. His description is: "My design consists primarily of two T-shaped box girders, the top flange of which serves as battledeck bridge floor, supporting between them an 8' -o section of deck, the whole assembly being welded in such a manner as to achieve full continuity of structure, both longitudinally and transversely. The supported center section might be termed a 'sandwich' deck section, with top and bottom cover plates which act as flanges with the interior web plates to replace both the conventional floor beams and stringers. The 8'-o deck sections would be fabricated in the shop in 12'-o lengths, with the exception of the top cover plates which are field welded.

"The T-shaped box girders, with an 8'-o width of top flange plate, would be completely shop fabricated, permitting positioning of the section for downhand welding. This would reduce the field erection and welding to a minimum.

"The field erection would consist merely of erecting the two box girders, weighing about 42 tons each, erecting and welding in place the center deck sections (weight of 12'-o section 1950#) and top cover plates, followed by the erection of the curb or wing sections and guard rails.

"The bridge would be constructed entirely of plates except for the 6″ x 3½″ x ¼″ angles used in fabricating the guard rails, and a new section incorporated in the deck sections, a modified 'T' section, with a long stem and a narrow flange, which permits butt or plug welding of the deck plates to this section."

Drawing number 2 of Mr. Wake's design is shown here as Figure 12.

Helio Braga Soares da Cunha and Hugo Braga Soares da Cunha, Rio de Janeiro, Brazil, submitted a design which involves the use of two large cylindrical girders. Each cylinder is about 88 in. in outside diameter and 1 in. thick. The longitudinal seams are shop welded and the circumferential seams are field welded. Stiffening rings around the outside of the cylinders are spaced at 12 ft. intervals. These rings consist of a pair of 8 in. x ⅜ in. plates. At each ring two legs, or columns, per girder support the floorbeams. The floorbeams do not connect the two girders; that is, each girder has eleven floorbeams, or there are a total of twenty-two floorbeams, each with a length equal to one-half the roadway width. An 8 in. reinforced concrete slab spans the 12 ft. between floorbeams. The floorbeams are 12 in. wide flange sections (190 lb. per ft.) rotated so that the webs are horizontal. Figure 13 shows the manner in which the cylindrical girders are stiffened and supported at the roller end.

Single Longitudinal Members

The designs of this type which are submitted in this program consist of single longitudinal members with a number of bracket or floorbeam cantilevers. The longitudinal members are box girders of rectangular or trapezoidal section, except in one design where the main member is a single vertical truss. In this last case, in order to have resistance to overturning, a transverse truss in a horizontal position is provided just below the bottom chord of the main vertical truss.

Earle M. Cassidy, Phoenix, Arizona, and Carl W. Otto, Norfolk, Virginia, designed a rectangular box girder for their main member. It is 5 ft. in width and varies in depth from 8 ft. at the ends to about 5 ft. in the middle of the span. The top and bottom flange plates are ⅞ in. thick and the webs are ⅜ in. plates. Diaphragm plates, ½ in. thick, are placed inside the box at each floorbeam cantilever. There are eight of these diaphragms including those at the ends. Each web of the box is stiffened at two places between each diaphragm by 6 in. x ½ in. stiffener plates welded to the web on the inside. These details, as well as those of the stringer and concrete filled (I-Beam-Lok) floor, are shown in Figures 14 and 15 which are drawings number 2 and 3, respectively, of this design. Figure 14 indicates how Messrs. Cassidy and Otto obtain a tapered floorbeam by flame cutting the web of a 24 in. wide flange beam along a diagonal line; also how they are able to decrease the required number of longitudinal stringers by having

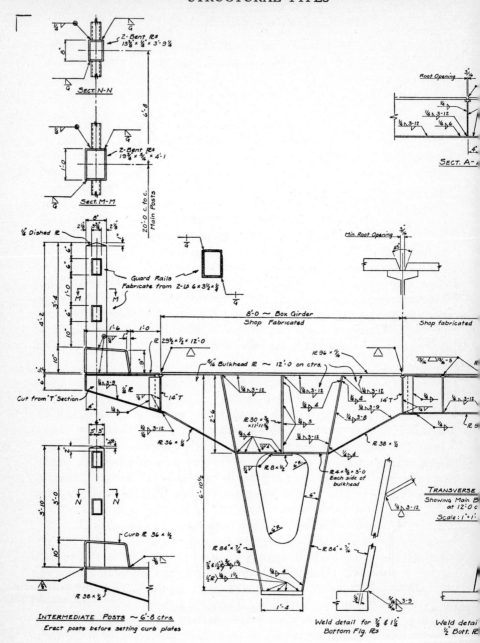

Figure 12

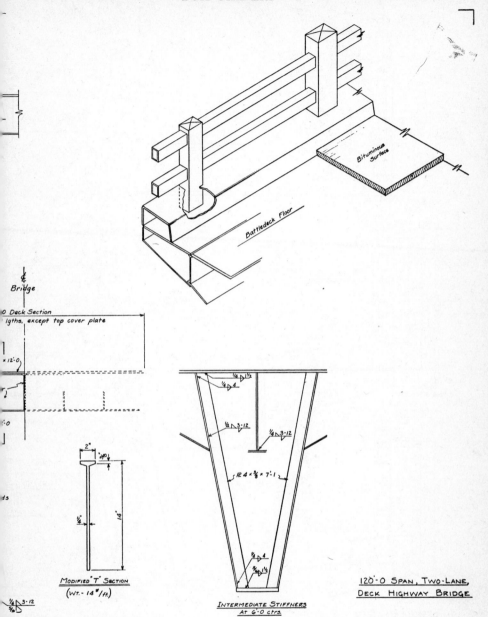

Battledeck Floor

Bituminous Surface

₵ Bridge

O Deck Section
lgths, except top cover plate

× 12'-0

2"

14"

¼"

MODIFIED "T" SECTION
(WT.- 14#/ft.)

¼ ▷ 3·12
5/16

¼ ▷ 1½
¼ ▷ 4

⅛ ▷ 3·12   ¼ ▷ 3·12

R 4 × ⅜ × 7'-1

¼ ▷ 4
5/16 ▷ 1½

INTERMEDIATE STIFFNERS
At 6'-0 ctrs.

120'-0 SPAN, TWO-LANE,
DECK HIGHWAY BRIDGE

DWG #2

Figure 12 (Concluded)

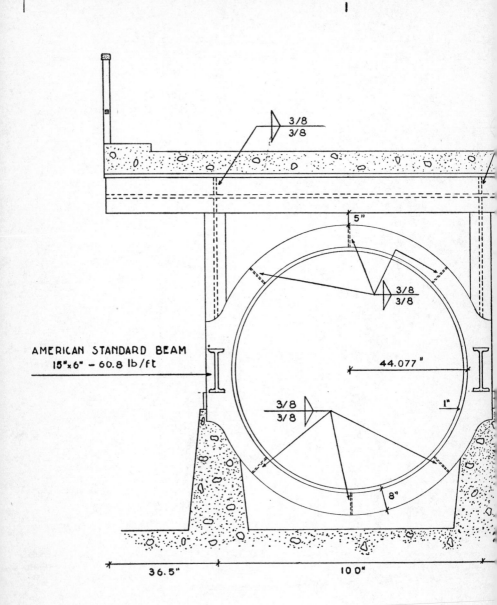

3/8
3/8

5"

3/8
3/8

AMERICAN STANDARD BEAM
15"x6" – 60.8 lb/ft

44.077"

1"

3/8
3/8

8"

36.5"

100"

DRAWING VIII
STIFFENING RINGS AT SUPPORTS

Figure 13

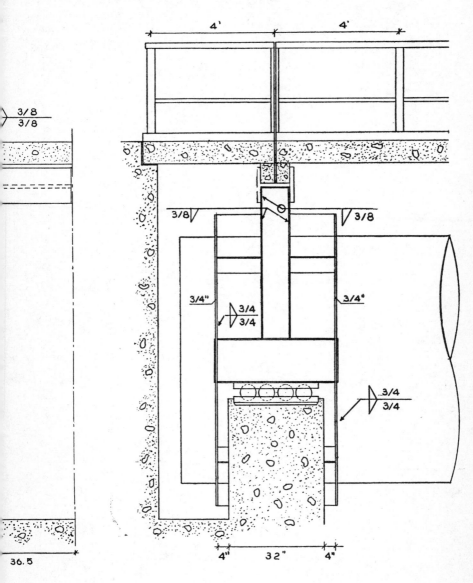

Figure 13 (Concluded)

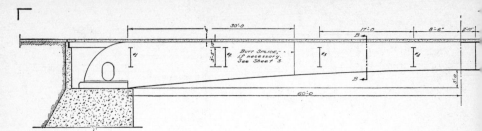

LONGITUDINAL
Scale:

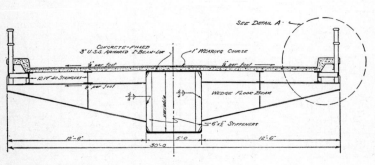

TYPICAL TRANSVERSE SECTION at B-B
Scale: ⅜"=1'-0

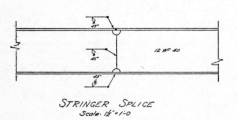

STRINGER SPLICE
Scale: 1½"=1'-0

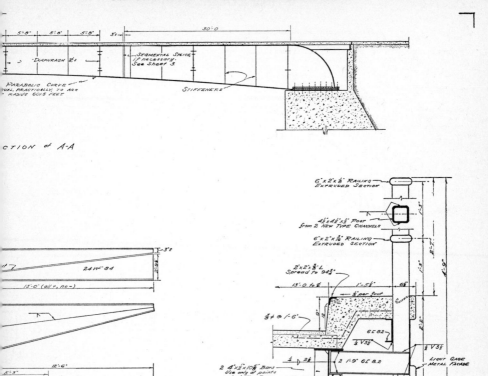

SECTION of A-A

DETAIL A
Scale: 1½" = 1'-0

LICATION of FLOOR BEAM
Scale: ½" = 1'-0

TWO-LANE, 120' SPAN, DECK TYPE

HIGHWAY BRIDGE

SECTIONS & DETAILS

DESIGNED BY:

JUNE 1949

SHEET 2 of 4

Figure 14 (Concluded)

51

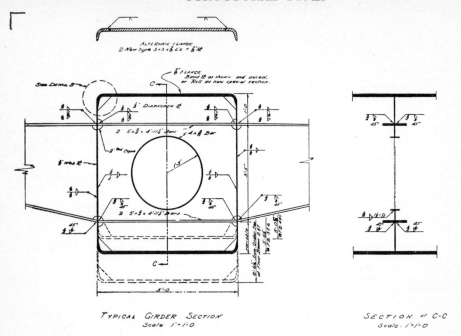

TYPICAL GIRDER SECTION
Scale: 1"=1'-0

SECTION of C-C
Scale: 1"=1'-0

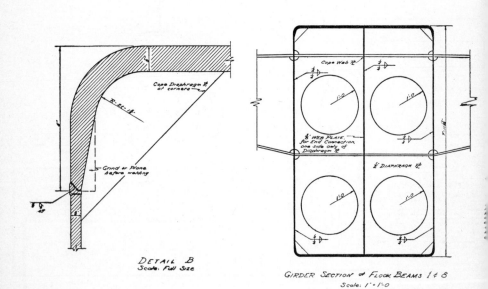

DETAIL B
Scale: Full Size

GIRDER SECTION of FLOOR BEAMS 1 & 8
Scale: 1"=1'-0

Figure 15

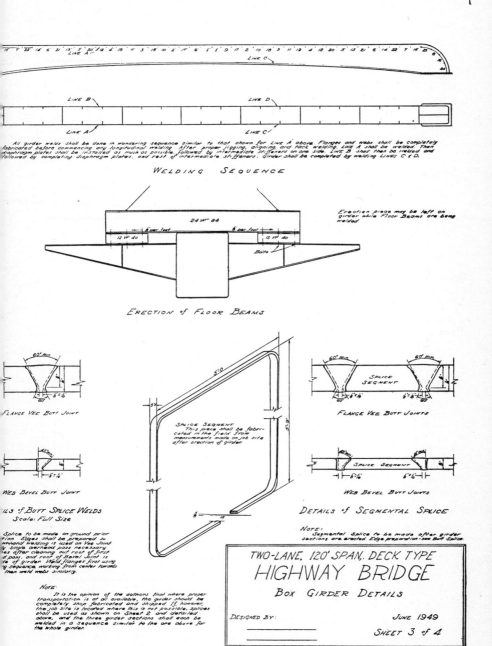

Figure 15 (Concluded)

the main box girder support the floor directly in the middle of the roadway.

Some of the points brought up by Messrs. Cassidy and Otto in their discussion of the design are:

"In the design of the supporting girder, the girder section was first chosen to resist bending. This condition required heavy flanges and light webs for an economical solution. The design stresses were kept a little low to allow for the additional shear caused by the torsion. After all stresses had been determined, they were combined by principal stresses to check the adequacy of the flanges and webs.

"Rounded corners were used in the girder cross section for two purposes. First, these corners, made with adequate radii, eliminate any concentration of the torsional stress as it flows around the cross section. These concentrations when caused by square corners are not properly investigated, and leading authorities disagree on the increase to be allowed. Most assume a 150 to 200 per cent increase. Second, rounded corners moved the flange-web welds away from what would have been square corner stress concentration areas.

"The dimensions of the parabolic curve of the lower flange were chosen to allow the flange and web thicknesses to remain constant throughout the span.

"For examination of the torsional problem the formulas of Timoshenko were adapted to the girder. With both ends of the girder fixed it was necessary to make some assumptions as to the distribution of torque to each of the two supports as caused by a torque-producing load anywhere in the span. This assumption was that the induced torque at the supports was inversely proportional to the distance from that support to the center of gravity of the loads inducing the torque. Of course this is approximate for the girder with its varying depth from support to mid-span. However, the torsional shear stresses in the girder cross section were small (2225 psi in the webs and 950 psi in the flanges at the supports) and further investigation could not have refined the design sizes appreciably. A more general use of torsional members in large structures would warrant considerable study of the whole field of torsion and its structural applications in order to supplement the academic discussions now present in texts.

"Some indication of the stiffness of the box girder is given by the following figures. Assuming that the girder was of a constant depth of 5 ft. throughout its length, the deflection of the outer edge of the roadway at mid-span under the maximum torsion-producing loading was computed as only 0.55 in. Considering the added stiffness contributed by the deepened haunches, the actual torsional deflection is even less than this one-half inch. Again, the vertical deflection of the girder when solved using the actual girder dimensions, fixed supports, and the design loading was 1.02 in., well within the desirable maximum of 1.8 in. for a bridge of this span.

"In order to resist the bending moment and the applied torque and at the same time allow some horizontal movement, it was decided to use a three plate assembly for the end connection which would allow some sliding. The middle plate is the sliding plate and is an enlarged continuation of the bottom flange of the girder. The girder top flange is bent in an arc of 8 ft. radius and welded to the sliding plate. This tranfers the top flange fibre stress from the horizontal to the vertical where it may be resisted by a downward thrust. Three web plates are used in the end connection to transfer the shear.

"Attention is called to the ease of erection of this span. The girder is erected first, either as one 42 ton assembly if the site is suitable or in three sections that require one splice on the ground and a finishing splice in place. The ground splice would join one end section and the center section. With the two ends on their supports the final splice would be made using a small splice piece indicated on the drawings. The floor beams are erected by use of a wide flange erection piece that is bolted to each pair of opposite-framing beams on the ground. The whole unit is then lifted onto the girder, with the erection piece resting on the girder top flange and supporting the beams for welding. Floor stringers are quickly set on the beams and fillet welded flange to flange. The floor grid is delivered to the site already cut to the proper roadway width and is dropped on the stringers and tack welded. No skilled or time-consuming welding jobs exist on the job site. The welds are fast and simple to make."

The ends of the box were fixed against rotation by supporting the ends of the end floorbeam cantilevers at the outside edges of the abutments, thus preventing these end floorbeams from deflecting downward.

Ralph L. Hants, Sacramento, California, designed a box girder composed of two girders, 6 ft.-1 in. apart, connected at both the top and the bottom by plates, 84 in. x ⅝ in., to form a single box, 6 ft. x 7 ft. The seven feet of depth for the girders is obtained by making each girder from two special tees which have webs 42 in. deep. Cantilever frames, or brackets, are spaced at 10 ft. centers and the stiffeners for the webs and plates of the box are spaced at 5 ft. centers. A typical section of this design is shown in Figure 16. Mr. Hants used a reinforced concrete floor which is ribbed in order to decrease the weight and yet have sufficient strength to span the ten feet between floorbeams. Figure 16 shows how an ⅛ in. steel bed plate is used as a form for the concrete floor.

The design of E. Scheyer, Brooklyn, New York, employs a single vertical truss as the longitudinal member. It has a depth of 9 ft.-5 in. with special tees used as both top and bottom chords. Immediately below this main truss is a horizontal (or transverse) truss, 11 ft.-2 in. wide. This transverse truss and the reinforced concrete floor slab act together in resisting lateral forces and torsion due to unbalanced vertical loads by providing outrigger frames attached to the floorbeams and the transverse truss. These floorbeams and outrigger frames occur every 10 ft. The chords of the transverse truss

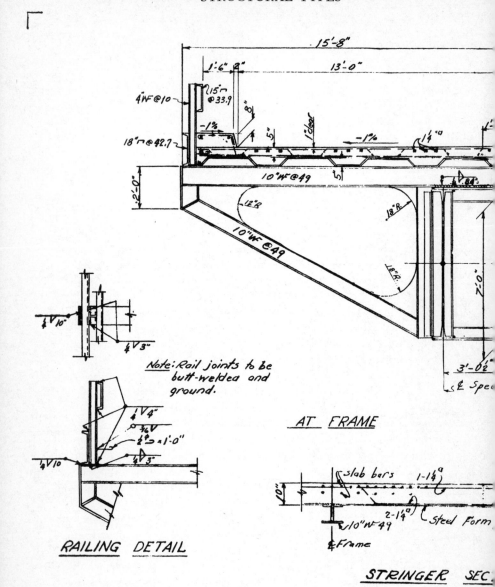

Note: Rail joints to be
butt-welded and
ground.

AT FRAME

RAILING DETAIL

STRINGER SEC.

Figure 16

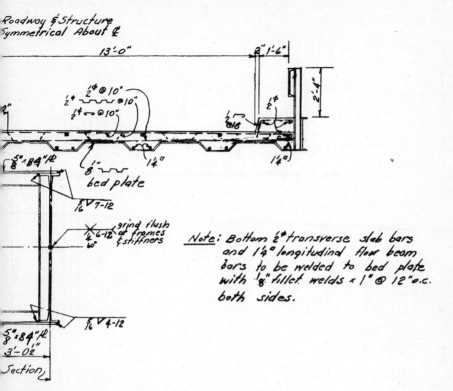

Roadway & Structure
Symmetrical About ℄

bed plate

grind flush
of frames
& stiffners

Note: Bottom $\frac{1}{2}$" transverse slab bars and $1\frac{1}{4}$" longitudinal floor beam bars to be welded to bed plate with $\frac{1}{8}$" fillet welds × 1" @ 12" o.c. both sides.

Section

AT. INTERMEDIATE DIAPHRAGM

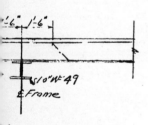

TYPICAL   SECTION
Scale: $\frac{3}{8}$" = 1'-0"   sheet D-3 of 8

Figure 16 (Concluded)   57

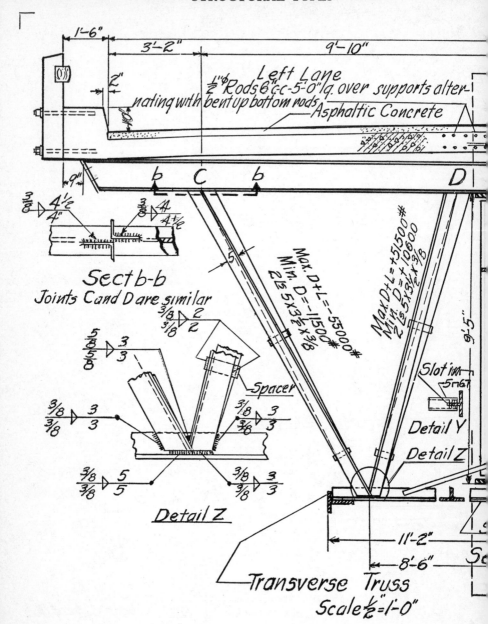

1'-6"

3'-2"

9'-10"

2"

1"ϕ
½" Rods 6" c.c.-5'-0" lg. over supports alternating with bent up bottom rods

Left Lane

Asphaltic Concrete

9"

b   C   b   D

3/8 4½"
     4"

3/8 4"
     4½"

5

Sect b-b
Joints C and D are similar

Max. D+L=-55000#
Min. D=-11500#
2 Ls 5x3½x3/8

Max. D+L=+51500#
Min. D=+10600
2 Ls 5x3½x3/8

9'-5"

Slot in
5"x6"
Detail Y

Detail Z

3/8 2
3/8 2

5/8 3
5/8 3

Spacer

3/8 3
3/8 3

3/8 3
3/16 3

3/8 5
3/8 5

3/8 3
3/8 3

Detail Z

11'-2"

8'-6"

Transverse Truss
Scale ½"=1'-0"

Figure 17

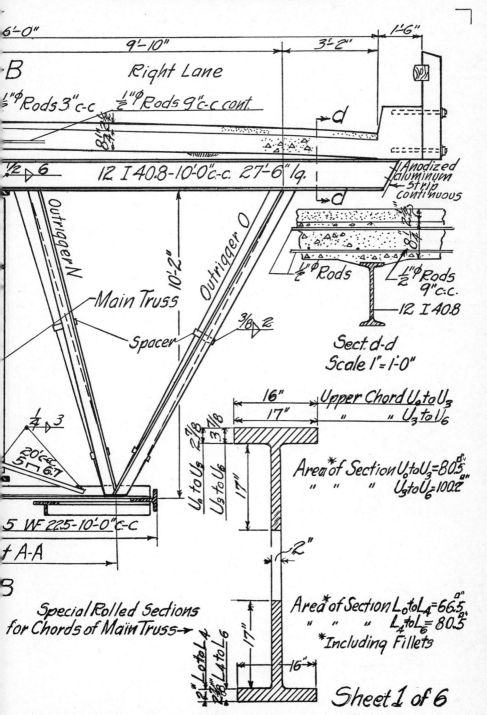

B

Right Lane

$\frac{1}{2}"\phi$ Rods 3"c-c $\frac{1}{2}"\phi$ Rods 9"c-c cont.

12 I 40.8-10'-0"c-c. 27'-6" lg.

Anodized aluminum strip continuous

$\frac{1}{2}"\phi$ Rods $\frac{1}{2}"\phi$ Rods 9"c.c.

12 I 40.8

Sect. d-d
Scale 1"=1'-0"

Outrigger N

Outrigger O

Main Truss

Spacer

10'-2"

$\frac{3}{8}$ 2

Upper Chord U_0 to U_3
"   " U_3 to U_6

Area of Section U_0 to U_3 = 80.5$^{a"}$
"   "   " U_3 to U_6 = 100.2$^{a"}$

Area of Section L_0 to L_4 = 66.5$^{a"}$
"   "   " L_4 to L_6 = 80.5
*Including Fillets

16"
17"

U_0 to U_3 2 $\frac{1}{8}$
U_3 to U_6 3 $\frac{1}{8}$

17"

2"

L_0 to L_4
L_4 to L_6

17"

16"

$\frac{1}{4}$ 3

20' c.c.
5 ⌷ 6.7

5 WF 22.5-10'-0"C-C

A-A

B

Special Rolled Sections
for Chords of Main Truss→

Sheet 1 of 6

6'-0"
9'-10"
3'-2"
1'-6"

$\frac{1}{2}$ 6

Figure 17 (Continued)   59

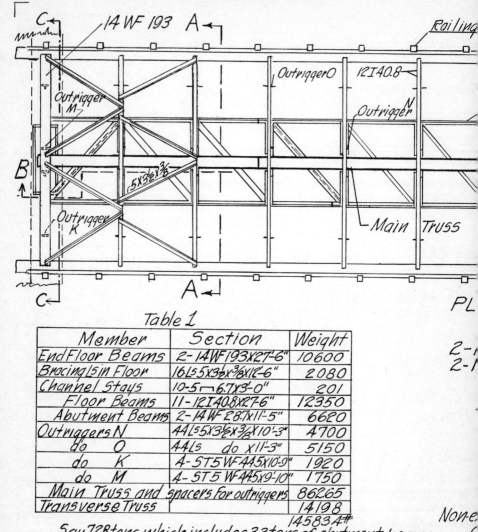

14 WF 193 A

Railing

Outrigger O 12 I 40.8

Outrigger M

Outrigger N

5x3½x⅜

Main Truss

Outrigger K

C

A

PL

Table 1

Member	Section	Weight
End Floor Beams	2-14WF193x27'-6"	10600
Bracing Ls in Floor	16 L 5x3½x⅜x12'-6"	2080
Channel Stays	10-5 ⌐ 6.7x3'-0"	201
Floor Beams	11-12 I 40.8x27'-6"	12350
Abutment Beams	2-14 WF 28.7x11'-5"	6620
Outriggers N	4 4 Ls 5x3½x⅜x10'-3"	4700
do O	4 4 Ls do x11'-3"	5150
do K	4-5T5WF44.5x10'-9"	1920
do M	4-5T5WF44.5x9'-10"	1750
Main Truss and spacers for outriggers		86265
Transverse Truss		14198

14583 A#

2-1
2-1

Say, 72.8 tons, which includes 3.3 tons of abutment beams
Weight per lineal ft. including abutment beams = 0.606 Tons
" " " " of steel superstructure = 0.578 Tons
" " " " " " exclusive of
abutment steel and end floor beams = 1071 # This
figure is the Dead Load of the steel in the design.
Weight per ft. length of roadway = 4175 #

Non-e
C
c
f

*Exclusive of abutment beams

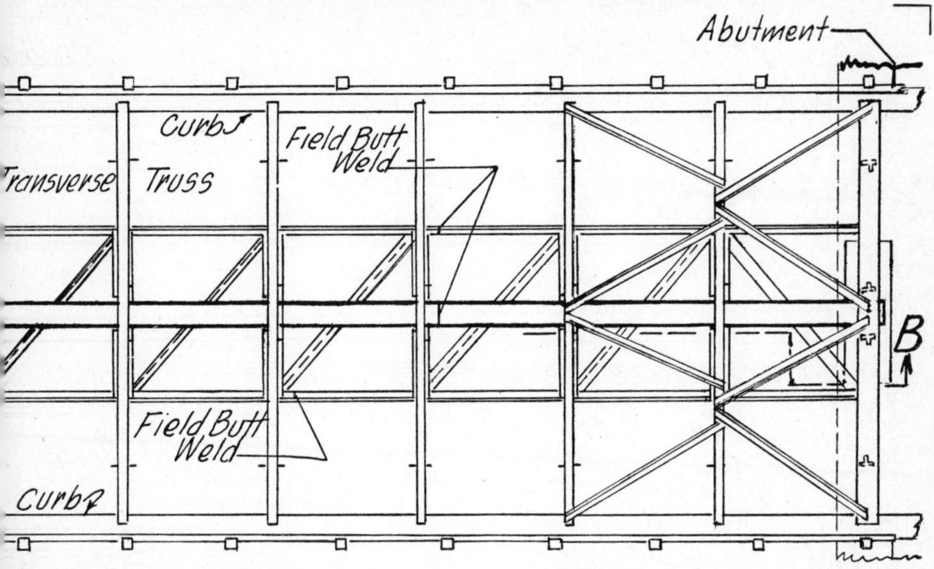

" OF MONO-TRUSS WELDED BRIDGE
Scale ⅛"=1'-0"

eel RockerPlates   4660#
eel Forgings   7420
al Ni. Steel   12080#
el Castings   9000#
Rollers   2200#
oncrete   106 cu.yds.
haltic Concrete   24 cu.yds.
inforcing Rods   7.2 tons
ood Handrail   720 bd.ft.
ding expansion joint filler 60"□
ete floor designed for 1000#□"
te compression, and 18000#□"
inforcing rods

Table 2
Shop Fillet Welds

Weld size	3/4"	5/8"	1/2"	3/8	1/4
Main Truss	744	484	784	6	
TransverseTruss	19	282	138	69	
Outriggers N&O		198		1100	
" M&F	160				
Abut. beam to forging		144			
Totals	923	1108	922	1175	

Table 3
Field Fillet Welds

Weld size	3/4"	5/8"	1/2"	3/8"	1/4"
Main Truss		112"			
Main Truss to abutment beams		96			
TransverseTruss		26		°98"	
Outriggers N&O				615	
" M&F	160				
5 ⌐ 6.7					80
Floor Beams				156	
Totals	160	234		809	80

°Welds to abutment

Total area of 8 field butt welds = 333□"

Figure 17 (Continued)   61

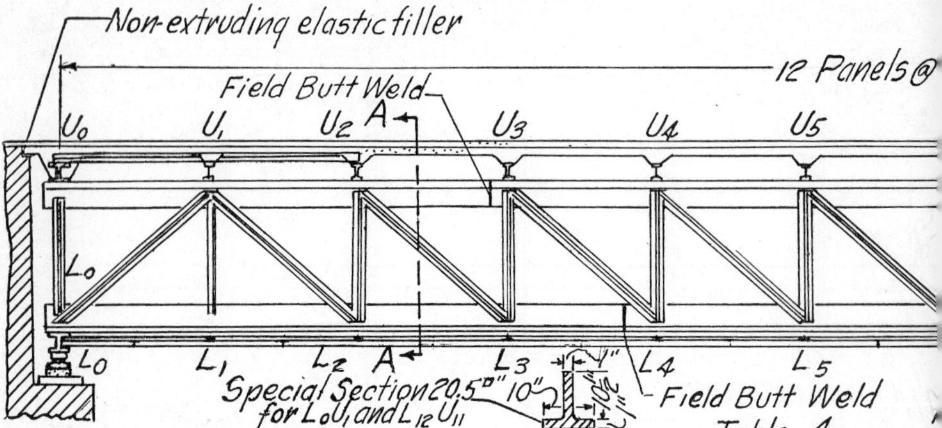

Non-extruding elastic filler

Field Butt Weld

12 Panels @

U_0 U_1 U_2 A U_3 U_4 U_5

L_0

L_0 L_1 L_2 A L_3 L_4 L_5

Special Section 20.5" 10" for L_0U_1 and $L_{12}U_{11}$

Field Butt Weld

Table 4

Mark	Max.	Min.	Counter Stress	Dead Load	O.T.D.L.
$L_0U_1 - L_{12}U_{11}$	-589800#				
$U_1L_1 - U_{11}L_{11}$	Nominal				
$U_1L_2 - U_{11}L_{10}$	+499800				
$U_2L_2 - U_{10}L_{10}$	-325300				
$U_2L_3 - U_{10}L_9$	+414900	+283300	-5100	+290400	
$U_3L_3 - U_9L_9$	-258000	-173800	+3300	-177100	
$U_3L_4 - U_9L_8$	+295100	+177400	-16200	+193600	
$U_4L_4 - U_8L_8$	-192500	-116000	+10500	-126500	
$U_4L_5 - U_8L_7$	+197200	+87400	-29200	+116600	
$U_5L_5 - U_7L_7$	-128200	-56900	+19000	-75900	
$U_5L_6 - U_7L_6$	+100400	-17100	-44300	+38900	+27200
U_6L_6	-115900				
*$U_0U_2 - U_{12}U_{10}$	816000				
$U_2U_3 - U_{10}U_9$	1103000				
$U_3U_4 - U_9U_8$	1305000				
$U_4U_5 - U_8U_7$	1430000				
$U_5U_6 - U_7U_6$	1470000				
$L_0L_1 - L_{12}L_{11}$	517000				
$L_1L_2 - L_{11}L_{10}$	517000				
$L_2L_3 - L_{10}L_9$	816000				
$L_3L_4 - L_9L_8$	1108000				
$L_4L_5 - L_8L_7$	1305000				
$L_5L_6 - L_7L_6$	1430000				
$U_0L_0 - U_{12}L_{12}$	105000				
Spacers for outriggers					

*The stress is in U_0U_2 and $U_{11}U_{10}$. Only nominal stress in U_0U_1 and $U_{12}U_{11}$
** Area of L_0U_1 plus area of $L_{12}U_{11}$

   Figure 17 (Continued)

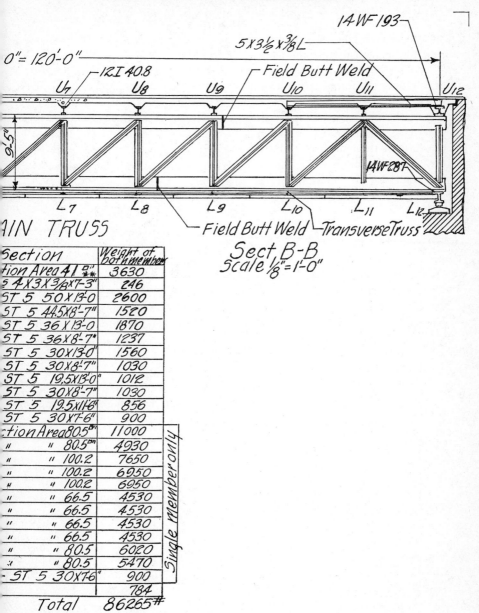

0"= 120'-0"

14 WF 193

5 X 3½ X ⅜ L

Field Butt Weld

12 I 40.8

U_7 U_8 U_9 U_{10} U_{11} U_{12}

9'-5"

14 WF 287

L_7 L_8 L_9 L_{10} L_{11} L_{12}

Field Butt Weld Transverse Truss

AIN TRUSS

Sect. B-B
Scale ⅛"=1'-0"

Section	Weight of both members
tion Area 4.1 ☐☐**	3630
5 4 X 3 X ⅜ X 7'-3"	246
ST 5 50 X 13'-0	2600
ST 5 44.5 X 8'-7"	1520
ST 5 36 X 13'-0	1870
ST 5 36 X 8'-7"	1237
ST 5 30 X 13'-0	1560
ST 5 30 X 8'-7"	1030
ST 5 19.5 X 13'-0"	1012
ST 5 30 X 8'-7"	1030
ST 5 19.5 X 11'6"	856
ST 5 30 X 7'-6"	900
ction Area 80.5 ☐"	11000
" " 80.5 ☐"	4930
" " 100.2	7650
" " 100.2	6950
" " 100.2	6950
" " 66.5	4530
" " 66.5	4530
" " 66.5	4530
" " 66.5	4530
" " 80.5	6020
" " 80.5	5470
- ST 5 30 X 7-6"	900
	784
Total	86265 #

Single member only

Sheet 3 of 6

Figure 17 (Concluded)   63

are special tees, and regular tees are used for most of the web members of both the main truss and the transverse truss.

Mr. Scheyer provided channel braces as shown in Section A-A of Figure 17 to reduce the unsupported length of the tension flange of the main truss. These braces are made light and flexible (5 in. channels) to prevent deflection of the main truss from producing appreciable vertical bending in the transverse truss. Figure 17 shows a typical section, a plan view, and an elevation of the main truss which are drawings 1, 2, and 3, respectively, of Mr. Scheyer's design. The end bearings are 7 ft.-6 in. wide, located below end frames at an elevation beneath that of the transverse truss.

Vertical Trusses

Twenty-two percent of the designs utilized vertical trusses as the main structural members. Fourteen percent used two trusses, but in the other eight percent, the number of trusses was from three to seven.

The size, shape, and make-up of the individual truss members varied considerably in the different designs. Some designs employed fabricated sections, others selected rolled shapes, rectangular tubes, or circular pipe. In a few cases, parts of the floor slab were designed to participate as effective material for the top chords. Many other differences can be noted in the following discussion of some of these designs.

Fred Miller, Toledo, Ohio, spaced his two Warren trusses 18 ft. apart. The trusses are 15 ft. deep, do not have verticals, and have both chords and diagonals made of either 12 in. or 10 in. pipe. The deck is $\frac{7}{16}$ in. plate stiffened with 4 in. x 3 in. x $\frac{5}{16}$ in. angles every 15 in. These angles are perpendicular to the roadway with the top of the vertical leg welded to the underneath side of the floor plate. The bottom leg of the angles is horizontal. Stringers (14 WF 34) are 20 ft. long, spaced at 2 ft.-7 in. centers.

Figure 18 is a cross section of this bridge and Figures 19 and 20 show the member sizes and details for the trusses and bracing. These truss members are made of seamless steel pipe, sealed in the shop to preclude the possibility of internal corrosion after erection, and connected at the joints by double gusset plates $\frac{1}{2}$ in. thick. As shown in the lower center of Figure 19 (Sheet 3 of 5), a "Pipe Adapter Bar" is used on each side of a pipe at the attachment of the pipe to the gusset plates. The adapter bars are shown here, but the detail dimensions of both sizes (PAB 1 for 12 in. pipe and PAB 2 for 10 in. pipe) are shown later in Chapter IV. This new shape is to be rolled to fit the external diameter of the pipe and the necessary lengths are to be shop welded to the pipe prior to assembly of the trusses.

In discussing the advantages of tubular members and pipe adapter bars, Mr. Miller made the following statements:

For trusses and certain other structural framing the tubular section is superior to other available and usable sections particularly as a compression member. It is the designer's opinion that if an adapter bar such as that proposed in the subject design were available, the use of pipe for heavily loaded trusses would be practical and economical. It is believed, moreover, that designers and fabricators would prefer this type construction for lighter trusses and frames, rather than the customary pipe-to-pipe or single gusset plate arrangements. Some factors substantiating these opinions are:

(a) All shop and field welding is either straight fillet or fillet-in-slot type. This is advantageous both to the designer and fabricator.

(b) Double gusset plates are employed. This is considered structurally essential in heavily loaded trusses, particularly those subjected to repeated live loadings.

(c) Cutting of the pipe is limited to 90° end cuts. For welded pipe trusses in which a single gusset plate might be used, slotting of the pipe to receive the plate is required; in designs where direct pipe to pipe welding is employed, precise cutting to length and line is necessary to fabricate to close tolerances. Use of adapter bars and twin plates will allow the length of the pipes to vary at least one-half inch without affecting the final truss configuration and dimensions.

(d) The pipe sections are sealed in the shop using a thin rectangular plate welded to the adapter bars. This eliminates the possibility of internal corrosion.

(e) Places for the retention of moisture are substantially fewer than for conventional riveted or welded trusses which employ rolled and/or built up sections.

(f) Accessibility for painting is very good.

(g) Because of the simplified cutting and welding requirements as outlined in (a) and (c) above, the shop fabrication cost can be expected to be less for the proposed type truss than for trusses welded pipe to pipe or those employing WF shapes butt-welded to built-up I-connectors, which are types of trusses currently in use.

Mr. Miller computed the weight of an all welded truss fabricated of rolled sections and found that, exclusive of the gussets plates, the total weight was 25,865 lbs. as compared to 25,395 lbs. for the tubular sections including the special pipe adapter bars. Since these weights vary less than one-half ton for two trusses, no particular advantage for the tubular type truss was claimed as far as quantity of steel was concerned; however, to the advantages mentioned above, he added these:

"Uniformity of section makes for a more pleasing appearance.

"The number of parts to be assembled is substantially fewer than for the truss using conventional rolled sections. This will be reflected in a lower shop cost per ton.

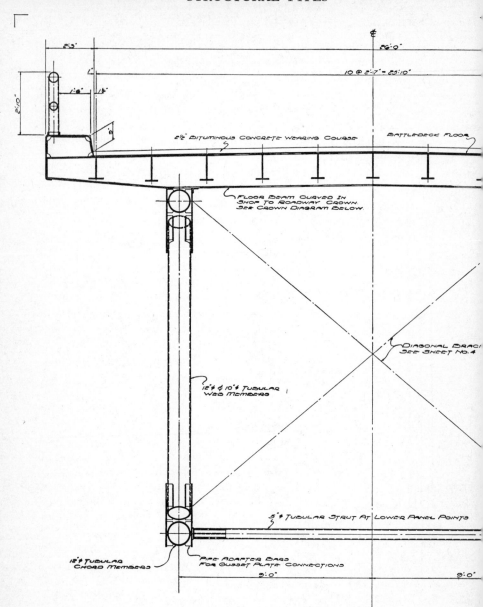

2½" BITUMINOUS CONCRETE WEARING COURSE

BATTLEDECK FLOOR

FLOOR BEAM CURVED IN
SHOP TO ROADWAY CROWN.
SEE CROWN DIAGRAM BELOW.

₵

26'-0"

10 @ 2'-7" = 25'-10"

DIAGONAL BRACI
SEE SHEET NO. 4

12"⌀ & 10"⌀ TUBULAR
WEB MEMBERS

5"⌀ TUBULAR STRUT AT LOWER PANEL POINTS

12"⌀ TUBULAR
CHORD MEMBERS

PIPE ADAPTER BARS
FOR GUSSET PLATE CONNECTIONS

9'-0"

9'-0"

BRIDGE CROSS-SECTION
SCALE: ¾" = 1'-0"

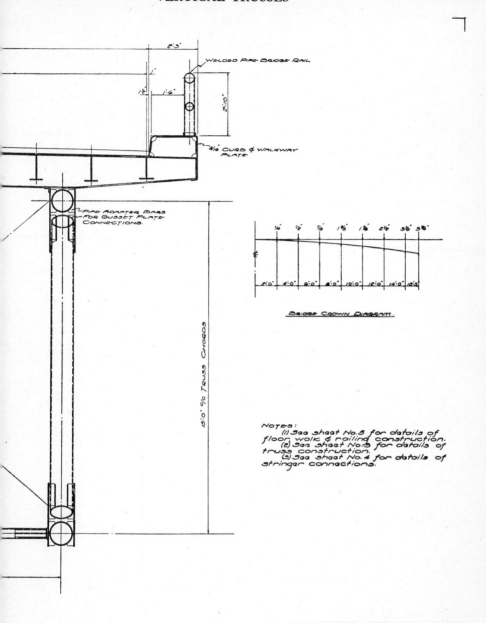

BRIDGE CROWN DIAGRAM

NOTES:
(1) See sheet No.5 for details of floor, walk & railing construction.
(2) See sheet No.3 for details of truss construction.
(3) See sheet No.4 for details of stringer connections.

WELDED BRIDGES OF THE FUTURE
1949
AWARD PROGRAM
SPONSORED BY
THE JAMES F. LINCOLN
ARC WELDING FOUNDATION

Figure 18 (Concluded)

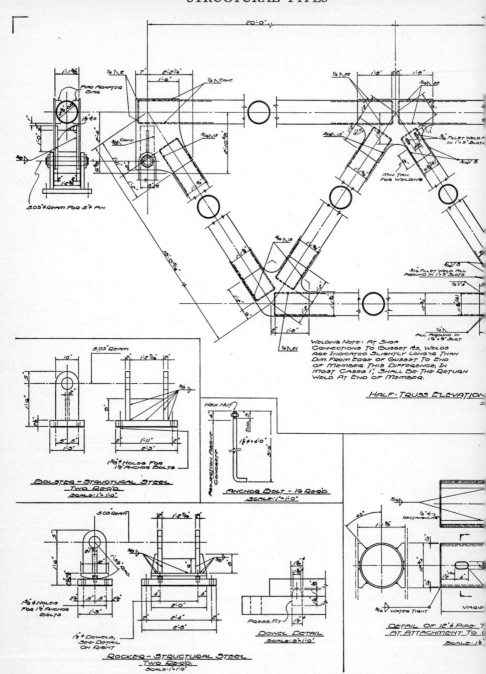

Figure 19

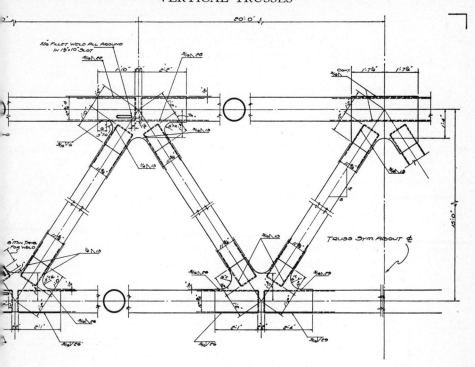

5/16 FILLET WELD ALL AROUND IN 1½"x10" SLOT

TRUSS SYM. ABOUT ₵

6" MIN. TANG. FOR WELD

...OWING CONNECTION DETAILS
...: ¾" = 1'-0"

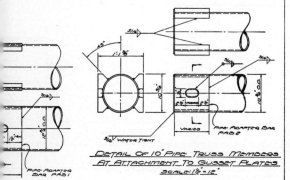

DETAIL OF 10" PIPE TRUSS MEMBERS
AT ATTACHMENT TO GUSSET PLATES
SCALE: 1½" = 1'-2"

5/16 V WATER TIGHT

PIPE ADAPTER BAR PAD 2

NOTES:
(1) See Sheet #4 for Camber Information and for size & weight of truss members.
(2) Double Gusset Plates ½" thick throughout truss welding indicated in truss elevation applies to plate both near side and far side.
(3) Shop & Field Welding shall be in accordance with all applicable portions of The Standard Specifications for Welded Highway and Railway Bridges of the American Welding Society, 1947.
(4) Care shall be taken to assure that tubular truss members are completely free of moisture before ¼" End Plates are attached in shop. Non-corrosive chemical drying agent, approved by owners engineering inspector, shall be used if necessary to eliminate moisture within pipes.
(5) Shop Paint - One coat red lead and oil except at field welded connections.
(6) See Sheet No. 4 for details of bracing brackets attaching to trusses. Fabricator shall shop weld a 12" length of 3x3x¼"L to trusses at lower panel points to support ends of 5" pipe struts during erection. Burn off Ls before completing field welds.

WELDED BRIDGES OF THE FUTURE
1949
AWARD PROGRAM
SPONSORED BY
THE JAMES F. LINCOLN
ARC WELDING FOUNDATION

Figure 19 (Concluded)

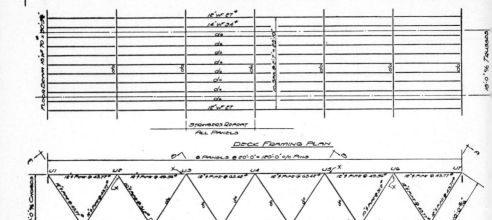

DECK FRAMING PLAN

TRUSS FRAMING

"X" INDICATES FIELD CONNECTIONS

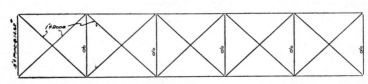

ALL 1" Φ BRACING RODS UPSET TO 1⅛" Φ
AND FITTED WITH TURNBUCKLES.

FRAMING IN PLANE OF LOWER CHORD OF TRUSSES

FRAMING DIAGRAMS — SCALE ⅛" = 1'-0"

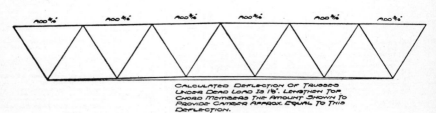

CALCULATED DEFLECTION OF TRUSSES
UNDER DEAD LOAD IS 1⅛". LENGTHEN TOP
CHORD MEMBERS THE AMOUNT SHOWN TO
PROVIDE CAMBER APPROX. EQUAL TO THIS
DEFLECTION.

CAMBER INFORMATION

Figure 20

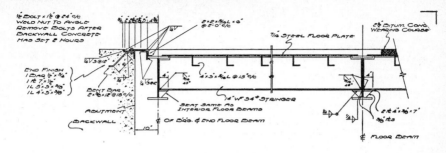

SECTION SHOWING END FINISH DETAIL AND
STRINGER TO FLOOR BEAM CONNECTIONS
SCALE: 1" = 1'-0"

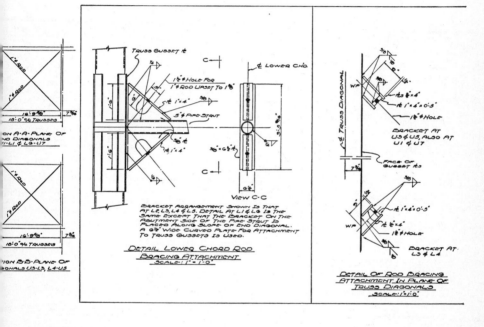

DETAIL LOWER CHORD ROD
BRACING ATTACHMENT
SCALE: 1" = 1'-0"

DETAIL OF ROD BRACING
ATTACHMENT IN PLANE OF
TRUSS DIAGONALS
SCALE: 1" = 1'-0"

NOTES:
(1) End Finish shall be curved in shop to
roadway crown. See sheet #2 for roadway
crown, ordinates.
(2) All rod bracing shall be fitted with turnbuckles and supplied with hex nut & washer
each end.
(3) Shop paint - one coat red lead and oil
except at field welded connections.

Figure 20 (Concluded)

"Although currently not recognized by design specifications, it is felt that, by reason of distribution of metal in the tubular section, a higher design unit stress in tension might be justified as compared to that permitted for bars, channels, beams, etc. Should future experimentation substantiate such increase in unit stress, the weight advantage of the tubular type truss would be improved."

James H. Jennison, Pasadena, California, curved the bottom chords of his two trusses. The trusses have ten panels of 12 ft. and a center depth of 14 ft. The reinforced concrete deck is used as the main compression member for the top chords of the trusses and is designed for the combined stresses due to bending and direct compression. Except for the center diagonal, all web members and bottom chord members are 10 in. wide flange sections. The steel top chord member is proportioned to resist the stresses occurring during the pouring of the concrete deck while the bridge is supported on temporary timber bents. Mr. Jennison stated:

"The top chord was made amply strong to carry these erection stresses produced by dead loads including forms and falsework since a little settlement of the falsework is to be expected, which would add an unknown amount stress. The top chord steel must also be capable of transferring horizontal stress components from the joints into the concrete deck through the shear-anchorage devices. The top chord steel will be prestressed during pouring of the deck; and, this erection stress was limited to 8000 lb. per sq. in. to allow for subsequent loading of 10,000 lb. per sq. in., maximum, based on $n = 10$ and $f_c = 1000$ lb. per sq. in."

A 4 in. tee serves as this chord member except in the first two panels where a 9 in. fabricated channel is used. The shear anchorage to transmit loads from the deck slab to this top chord consists of one-inch-square hooked reinforcing bars and angle shear-lugs.

Most of the truss and falsework details are shown in Figures 21, 22, and 23 which are sheets 4, 7, and 8, respectively, of Mr. Jennison's nine drawings. The Longitudinal Section A-A of Figure 21 shows a cross section of the reinforced concrete floorbeams which are designed as composite beams with the T-section (ST 6 WF 13.5) anchored into the lower face as reinforcement. In discussing the floorbeams and cross-frames, Mr. Jennison said:

"The T-section was the most suitable shape from the standpoint of welded connection details and shear and bond anchorage to the concrete. The hooks welded to the stem hold the T-section in place and provide shear reinforcement for the concrete beam, supplementing the stirrups. The lugs, made from angle sections, provide for horizontal shear, and also hold the concrete firmly against the stem of the T-section. By making the floorbeam the top member of the cross-frame, a middle support was provided for the floorbeam. The compression stress added to the bending moments in the floorbeams by truss action of the cross-frame does not add much to the required cross section. Moments were determined by treating the floorbeams as continuous over three supports, and these results were combined with the compression arising from truss action of the cross-frame.

"The cross-frames also transfer wind loads from the trusses to the deck. The deck serves as a horizontal beam or panel to resist all lateral forces."

C. J. Pimenoff, Montreal, Canada, discussed his bridge as follows:

"Warren trusses with parallel chords were adopted in prefence to other type of truss or plate girder on the grounds of economy and, to a lesser degree, pleasing appearance.

"Rolled sections were used throughout, thus greatly simplifying the detailing and fabrication, as the connecting and other detail material has been all but eliminated. The wide flange beam sections were chosen for their constant inside-to-inside-of-flange depth, which makes them suitable for flange-to-flange welded connections. To keep the secondary stresses to a minimum and for the simplicity and efficacy of connections the sections were turned with the flanges parallel to the axis of the truss.

"Most of the stress from the diagonal members is transmitted to the chords from flange-to-flange through single bevel groove welds, requiring the preparation of only the ends of the diagonals. Although the drawings call for the trusses to be shop welded in three sections, it ought to be pointed out that the design is eminently suitable for field fabrication of trusses. In fact, it might be considered as the outstanding feature of the design that, with the exception of bearings, floor expansion joints and perhaps fence posts, the structural members require so little and so simple fabrication that, if ordered to nearly correct lengths, they could be shipped from mill directly to site, resulting in very considerable economy and in saving of time.

"It would, of course, call for an improved fieldburning technique than is general today, but there is no doubt that with proper equipment the erectors could prepare satisfactory edges for the single bevel and 'V' groove welds.

"It is believed that the stresses, induced through the shrinkage of the welds, will not be serious as the truss is free to deform sufficiently to relieve them.

"Floor members and bracing are all of very straight-forward design giving the simplest of details.

"Bottom laterals were omitted being quite unnecessary in deck spans provided with adequate top lateral and sway bracing.

"Pipe handrail with fence posts outside of it was adopted for appearance—it is thought that uninterrupted horizontal lines, as seen from the roadway, would add to the clean-cut lines of the bridge.

"For the deck, concrete slab was adopted, after much thought, on account of its considerably lower cost than a steel deck or grid type of floor. In a long span bridge it would pay to go to a more expensive but lighter floor,

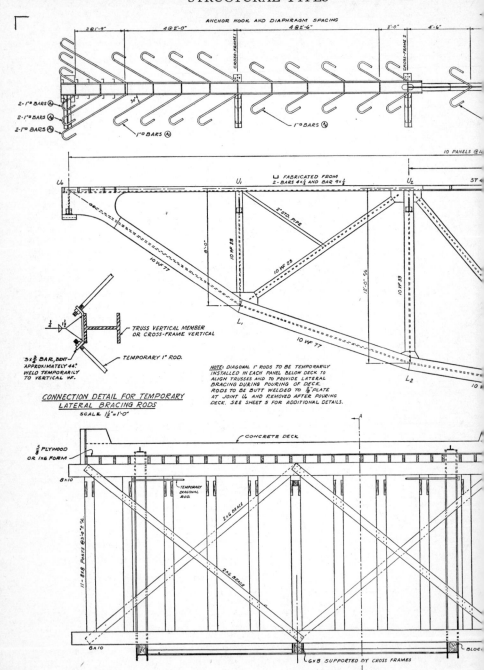

CONNECTION DETAIL FOR TEMPORARY
LATERAL BRACING RODS
SCALE 1½"=1'-0"

NOTE: DIAGONAL 1" RODS TO BE TEMPORARILY
INSTALLED IN EACH PANEL BELOW DECK TO
ALIGN TRUSSES AND TO PROVIDE LATERAL
BRACING DURING POURING OF DECK.
RODS TO BE BUTT WELDED TO ½" PLATE
AT JOINT U₆ AND REMOVED AFTER POURING
DECK. SEE SHEET 5 FOR ADDITIONAL DETAILS.

TRANSVERSE SECTION B-B SHOWING DECK FORMS AND FALSEWORK

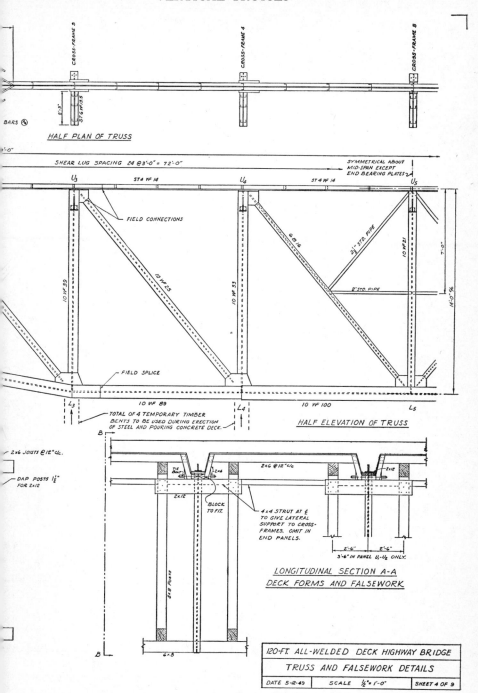

HALF PLAN OF TRUSS

HALF ELEVATION OF TRUSS

LONGITUDINAL SECTION A-A
DECK FORMS AND FALSEWORK

120-FT. ALL-WELDED DECK HIGHWAY BRIDGE		
TRUSS AND FALSEWORK DETAILS		
DATE 5-12-49	SCALE ½"= 1'-0"	SHEET 4 OF 9

Figure 21 (Concluded)

STRUCTURAL TYPES

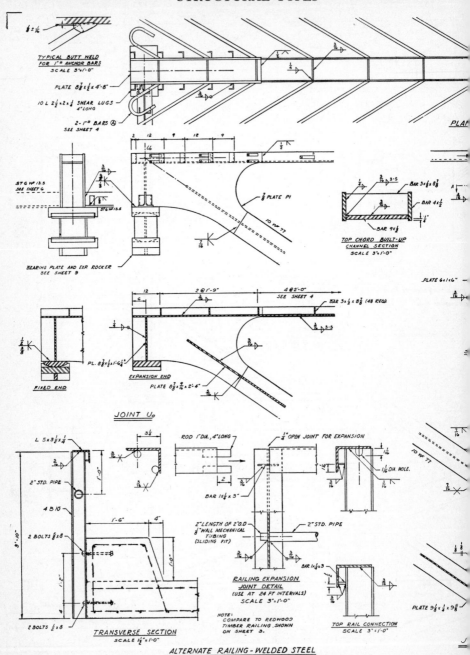

Figure 22

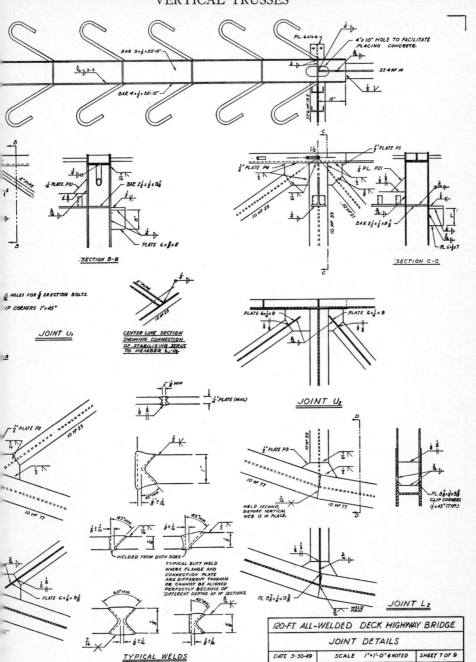

Figure 22 (Concluded)

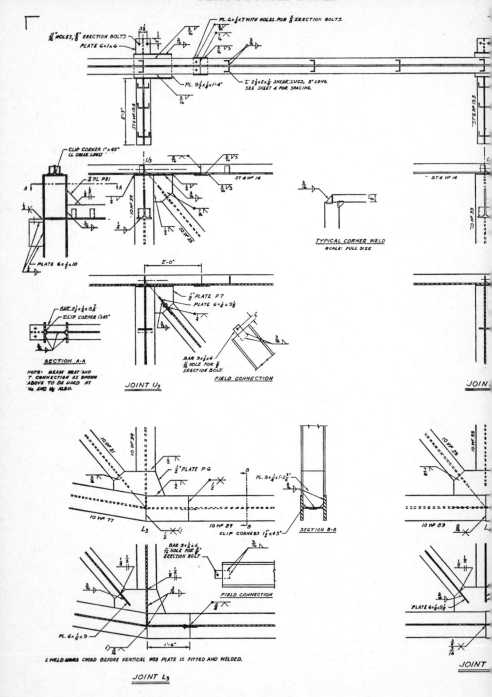

TYPICAL CORNER WELD
SCALE: FULL SIZE

SECTION A-A

NOTE: BEAM SEAT AND T CONNECTION AS SHOWN ABOVE TO BE USED AT U₂ AND U₄ ALSO.

JOINT U₃

FIELD CONNECTION

SECTION B-B

FIELD CONNECTION

L WELD LOWER CHORD BEFORE VERTICAL WEB PLATE IS FITTED AND WELDED.

JOINT L₃

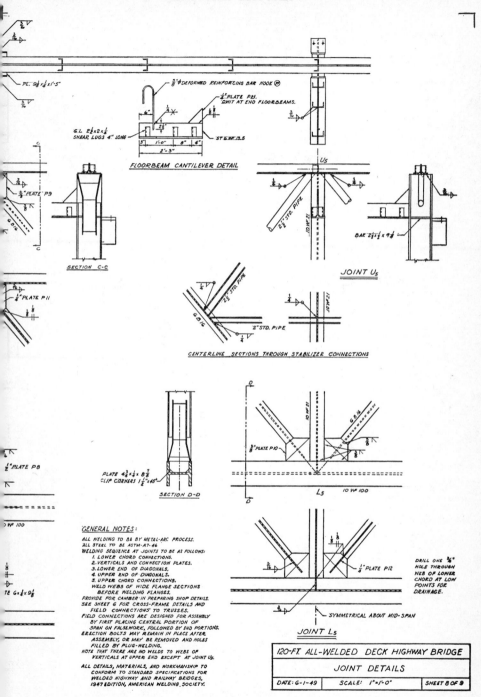

FLOORBEAM CANTILEVER DETAIL

SECTION C-C

JOINT U5

CENTERLINE SECTIONS THROUGH STABILIZER CONNECTIONS

SECTION D-D

GENERAL NOTES:

ALL WELDING TO BE BY METAL-ARC PROCESS.
ALL STEEL TO BE ASTM-A7-46
WELDING SEQUENCE AT JOINTS TO BE AS FOLLOWS:
1. LOWER CHORD CONNECTIONS.
2. VERTICALS AND CONNECTION PLATES.
3. LOWER END OF DIAGONALS.
4. UPPER END OF DIAGONALS.
5. UPPER CHORD CONNECTIONS.
WELD WEBS OF WIDE FLANGE SECTIONS
BEFORE WELDING FLANGES.
PROVIDE FOR CAMBER IN PREPARING SHOP DETAILS.
SEE SHEET 6 FOR CROSS-FRAME DETAILS AND
FIELD CONNECTIONS TO TRUSSES.
FIELD CONNECTIONS ARE DESIGNED FOR ASSEMBLY
BY FIRST PLACING CENTRAL PORTION OF
SPAN ON FALSEWORK, FOLLOWED BY END PORTIONS.
ERECTION BOLTS MAY REMAIN IN PLACE AFTER
ASSEMBLY, OR MAY BE REMOVED AND HOLES
FILLED BY PLUG-WELDING.
NOTE THAT THERE ARE NO WELDS TO WEBS OF
VERTICALS AT UPPER END EXCEPT AT JOINT U5.

ALL DETAILS, MATERIALS, AND WORKMANSHIP TO
CONFORM TO STANDARD SPECIFICATIONS FOR
WELDED HIGHWAY AND RAILWAY BRIDGES,
1947 EDITION, AMERICAN WELDING SOCIETY.

JOINT L5

DRILL ONE ⅜"
HOLE THROUGH
WEB OF LOWER
CHORD AT LOW
POINTS FOR
DRAINAGE.

SYMMETRICAL ABOUT MID-SPAN

120-FT. ALL-WELDED DECK HIGHWAY BRIDGE		
JOINT DETAILS		
DATE: 6-1-49	SCALE: 1"=1'-0"	SHEET 8 OF 9

Figure 23 (Concluded) 79

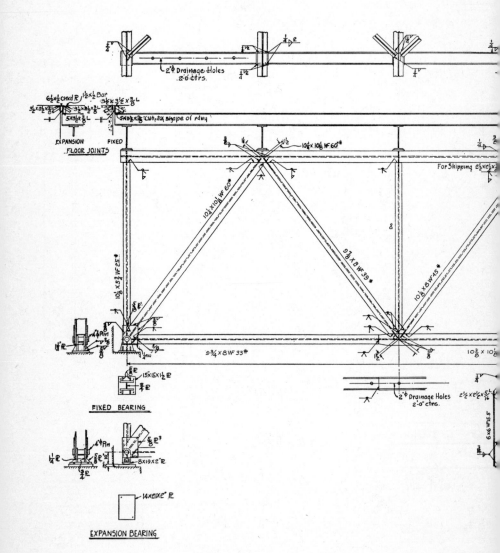

Figure 24

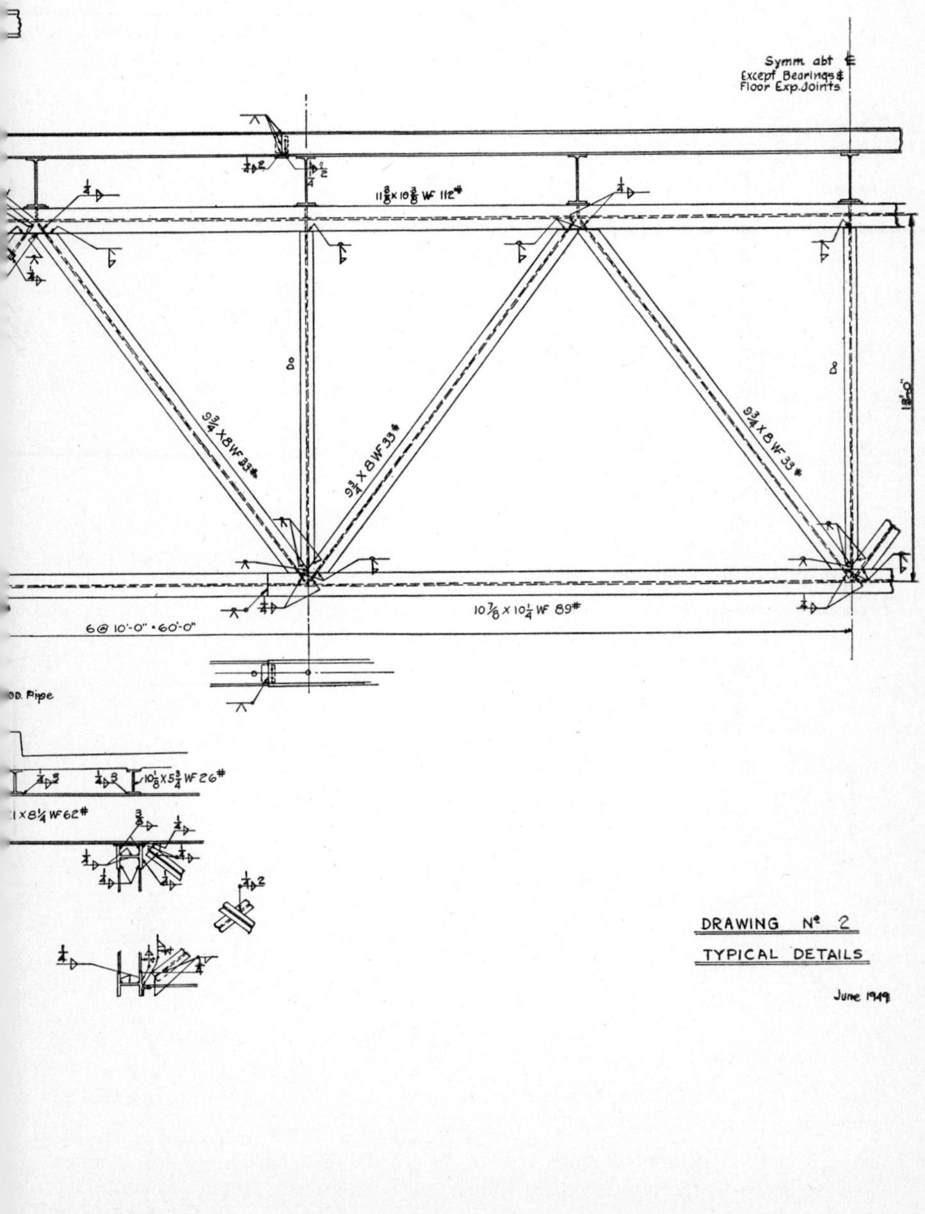
Symm. abt ℄
Except Bearings & Floor Exp. Joints
11 3/8 x 10 3/8 WF 112#
9 3/4 x 8 WF 33#
9 3/4 x 8 WF 33#
9 3/4 x 8 WF 33#
Do
Do
18'-0"
10 7/8 x 10 1/4 WF 89#
6 @ 10'-0" = 60'-0"
OD. Pipe
10 1/8 x 5 3/4 WF 26#
x 8 1/4 WF 62#
DRAWING No 2
TYPICAL DETAILS
June 1949

Figure 24 (Concluded)

but in the bridge of the specified span the saving in trusses would be small and would not nearly offset the additional cost of the floor.

"It is also considered desirable to have a deck of some weight to prevent excessive limberness of structure under live load."

Figure 24 shows drawing number 2 of Mr. Pimenoff's design. The floor-beams, all 21 WF 62, are cantilevered beyond the trusses, and are spaced 18 ft. apart. There are seven rows of stringers (10 WF 25). The stringer spacing is 4 ft.-5 in. The cross-frames occur every second panel (at the panels having the truss verticals). Each cross-frame utilizes a floorbeam for the top strut, the main truss verticals, and a T-section (ST 6 WF 13.5) for the bottom strut and both diagonals.

Ralph E. Spaulding, Los Angeles, California, curved the top chords of his two trusses, but the verticals at the panel points are continuous from the bottom chords of the trusses to the floor system which they support. The center depth of the trusses is 14 ft. and the distance from bottom chord of truss to floor system (approximate length of the verticals) is 15 ft.-5 in. Each interior panel has two crossed diagonals. Concerning these items of his design, Mr. Spaulding said, "The parabolic type of truss was taken so as to keep the maximum stresses in the chords fairly constant throughout their length.

"The designer believes the feature of running the verticals or posts from the lower chord up thru the upper chord to support the floor system has merit. It will be noted that the segments of the upper chord bear upon the web of this vertical member just the same as a column bears upon its base plate, so that a minimum of welding is required at these points. A new type of tension member is proposed for the diagonals, detail of which is shown on the drawings. Although the designer ordinarily prefers a single diagonal to crossed diagonals, in this design crossed diagonals are used so as to avoid reversal of stress in the individual diagonals."

The top chord is two, 12 in. channels turned so that when the legs are welded together, the two channels form a rectangular tube. The bottom chord is a single 15 in. channel with legs turned down. The diagonals are special "Ribbed Bulb Bars" as shown in Chapter IV. Special "cross" shaped sections (also shown in Chapter IV) are used for the web members of the transverse trusses which occur at every panel point.

In Figure 25, the end panel is shown to be 16 ft.-8 in. and the interior panels to be 21 ft.-8 in. The stringer system Mr. Spaulding used is known as the Restrained Cantilever Beam System. This system requires the end spans to be shorter than the intermediate spans so that all maximum moments will be more nearly equal. This floor system is discussed in Chapter III. The connection details are shown in Figure 26. All diagonals of the lateral wind bracing for the lower chord are 5 in. x ¼ in. "Ribbed Bars".

INCLINED TRUSSES

E. H. McBroom, Sacramento, California, used four trusses with a steel battle deck floor to serve as the top chords for the four trusses. Web members and bottom chords are rectangular tubular sections which are fastened at the joints with gusset plates welded into slotted holes pierced through the tubular sections. Concerning these items of the design, Mr. McBroom stated:

"Although previous practice has tended to make a definite separation between deck and supporting members it is the opinion of the designer that a steel deck constructed integrally with the trusses would provide the maximum stiffness and strength combined with a minimum of weight and fabrication.

"The use of four trusses instead of two was dictated by the need for fastening the deck to the trusses in several places. It has the further advantage of facilitating the distribution of dead and live loads between trusses and thus making the entire bridge an integral unit.

"With four trusses the exterior one is placed close enough to the curb to support the outside truck wheel without resorting to out-riggers or brackets. This eliminates considerable fabrication and improves the appearance of the structure.

"Dividing the loads between four trusses instead of two also makes for lighter members, and smaller less complicated joints which can be developed by single pass welds using only a single gusset plate at each joint.

"The use of single gusset plates at joints and rectangular or square tubular sections for web and bottom chord members has several advantages. The conventional type of truss using I-beam or channel members and a double system of gusset plates was designed primarily for riveting through the flanges, and occasionally through the web. For the welding process the I-beam or channel section loses much of its merit because the welded connection can be made to any exterior surface.

"For the single plate—tubular section combination all the welding is on the outside and easily accessible instead of being confined in the narrow opening between the plates as is usually the case. It does away with the drainage pocket between the plates which is usually a difficult problem to solve, if any attempt is made to solve it at all. Elimination of the second gusset plate reduces the weight and the cost of the additional fabrication."

The ⅝ in. traffic plate is attached to the trusses by means of 5/16 in. fillet welds around ¾ in. x 2½ in. slots at 12 in. centers. Between the trusses the ⅝ in. traffic plate is supported by 8 in. standard beams which are spaced at 1 ft.-8 in. centers. These stringers have a span of 10 ft. and rest on floorbeams which frame between the trusses. The details of the floor system and also the truss members are shown in Figure 27.

Inclined Trusses

Inclined trusses as described in this section could be termed space trusses,

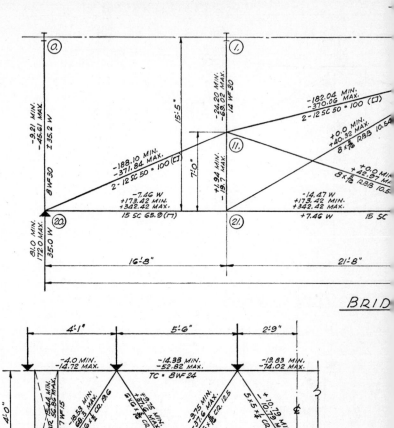

BRID...

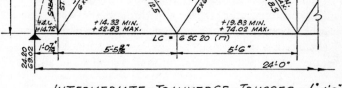

INTERMEDIATE TRANVERSE TRUSSES ~ $\frac{1}{2}$" = 1'-0"

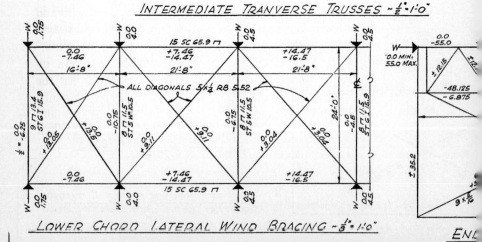

LOWER CHORD LATERAL WIND BRACING ~ $\frac{1}{8}$" = 1'-0"

EN...

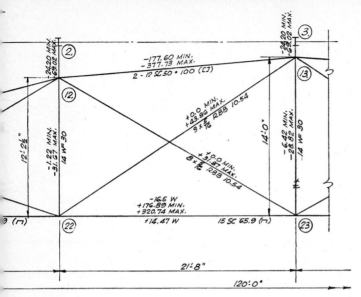

② −24.20 MIN. / 69.02 MAX.

−177.60 MIN. / −377.73 MAX. (C.I)
2 - 12 ℄ .50 • 100 (C.I)

③ −24.20 MIN. / 69.02 MAX.

⑫ ⑬

+0.0 MIN. / +43.86 MAX.
9 × 5/16 RBB 10.54

−6.42 MIN. / −28.82 MAX.
14 WF 30

12'-2½"
−1.22 MIN. / −31.67 MAX.
14 WF 30

14'-0"

+0.0 MIN. / +31.87 MAX.
8 × 5/16 RBB 10.54

−16.5 W / +176.89 MIN. / +320.74 MAX.
+14.47 W

②② ②③

9 (⊓) 15 ℄ 65.9 (⊓)

21'-8"

120'-0"

E TRUSSES − ¼"•1'-0"

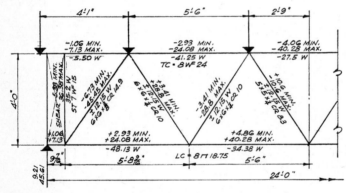

4'-1" 5'-6" 2'-9"

−1.06 MIN. / −7.13 MAX.
−5.50 W

−2.93 MIN. / −24.08 MAX.
−41.25 W
TC • 8 WF 24

−4.06 MIN. / −40.28 MAX.
−27.5 W

−5.88 MIN. / SHEAR 30.39 MAX.
35.2 W
ST 7 WF 15

−6.73 MIN. / −45.45 MAX.
6 12.15 W
6×6×⅜ CR 14.9

+3.41 MIN. / +28.8 MAX.
+ 12.15 W
6×6×⅜ CR 10

−3.41 MIN. / −28.8 MAX.
± 12.15 W
6×6×¼ CR 10

+10.6 MIN. / +10.6 MAX.
+ 12.15 W
5×5×¼ CR 8.3

4'-0"

+1.06 / +7.13

+2.93 MIN. / +24.08 MAX.
−48.13 W

LC • 8 ⊓ 18.75

+4.86 MIN. / +40.28 MAX.
−34.38 W

9½"
9.21 / 45.61

5'-8½" 5'-6"

24'-0"

END TRANVERSE TRUSSES − ½"•1'-0"

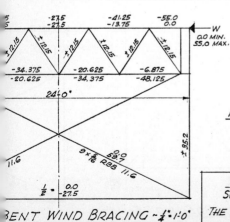

−27.5 / −27.5   −41.25 / −13.75   −55.0 / 0.0

W
0.0 MIN. / 55.0 MAX.

± 12.15   + 12.15   ± 12.15   ± 12.15   ± 12.15

−34.375 / −20.625   −20.625 / −34.375   −6.875 / −48.125

24'-0"

± 35.2

9 × 5/16 RBB 11.6   0.0 / 59.7

11.6

½ / 0.0 / −27.5

BENT WIND BRACING − ¼"•1'-0"

MAXIMUM & MINIMUM STRESSES & SIZES OF MEMBERS

②.

WELDED BRIDGE OF THE FUTURE
SUBMITTED FOR THE 1949 AWARD PROGRAM
OF
THE JAMES F. LINCOLN ARC WELDING FOUNDATION
JUNE 30, 1949

Figure 25 (Concluded)

85

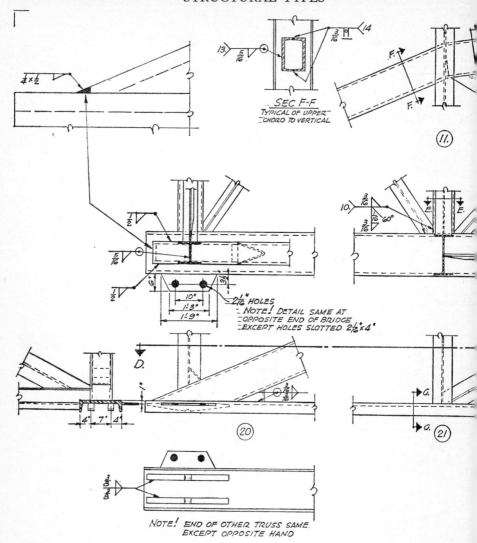

SEC F-F
TYPICAL OF UPPER
CHORD TO VERTICAL

(11.)

(10.)

NOTE! DETAIL SAME AT
OPPOSITE END OF BRIDGE
EXCEPT HOLES SLOTTED 2⅛"×4"

(20)

(21)

NOTE! END OF OTHER TRUSS SAME
EXCEPT OPPOSITE HAND

WELDING NOTES:

10. TYPICAL DETAIL FOR ENDS OF ALL DIAGONALS IN LOWER CHORD LATERAL BRACING.

11. TYPICAL FOR INTERSECTION OF ALL VERTICALS WITH LOWER CHORD.

12. TYPICAL FOR ALL ENDS OF DIAGONALS IN THE TRUSS.

13. TYPICAL WELD DETAIL OF ALL INTERSECTIONS OF UPPER CHORD SECTIONS WITH VERTICAL MEMBERS.

14. BUTT AT JUNCTION OF TOES OF SHIP CHANNELS. SHOP MADE BY AUTOMATIC SUBMERGED OR HIDDEN ARC OR BY LINCOLN "MANUAL LINCOLNWELD" HIDDEN ARC. WHEN SO MADE NO ROOT OPENING IS REQUIRED.

15. MAKE THIS FIELD WELD FIRST BEFORE ANY OTHER MAIN MEMBER IS ATTACHED, SO THAT THE CHANNEL SECTION CAN BE TURNED OVER. TO BE MADE BY THE HIDDEN ARC METHOD AS WITH THE LINCOLN "MANUAL LINCOLNWELD" MACHINE. AFTER WELDING IT IS TO BE LOW TEMPERATURE HEAT TREATED AND THEN GROUND SMOOTH.

16. A SPECIAL CONDITION WHICH PRECLUDES THE USUAL TYPE OF BUTT WELD. STRESS IN WELD METAL IS LOW, ONLY 3,000 P.S.I. MAXIMUM.

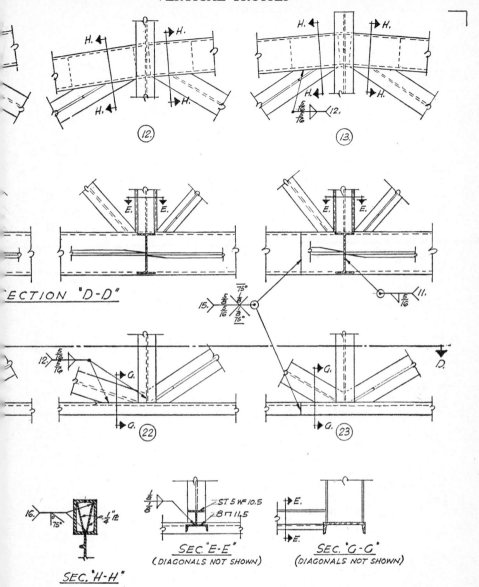

BRIDGE TRUSS
JOINTS & WELDING DETAILS

③

WELDED BRIDGE OF THE FUTURE
SUBMITTED FOR THE 1949 AWARD PROGRAM
OF
THE JAMES F. LINCOLN ARC WELDING FOUNDATION
JUNE 30, 1949

Figure 26 (Concluded)

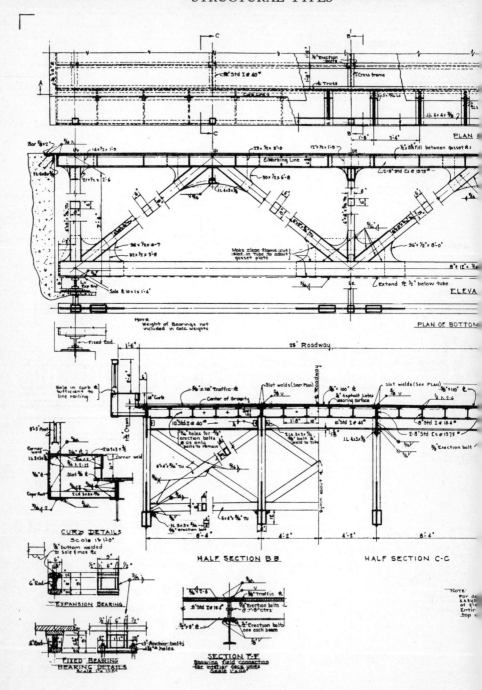

Figure 27

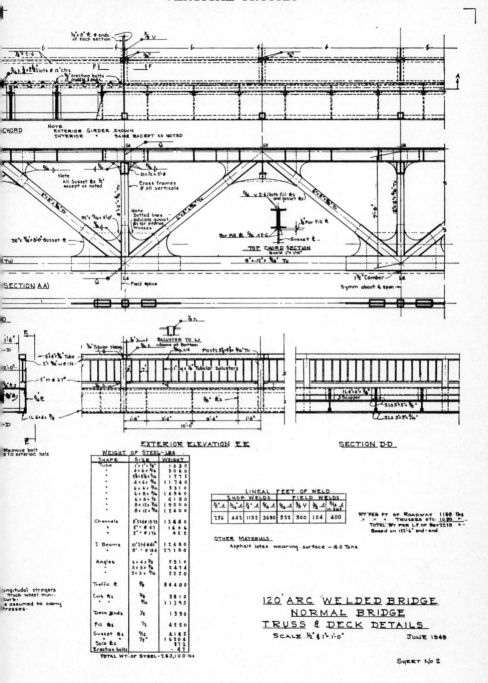

120' ARC WELDED BRIDGE
NORMAL BRIDGE
TRUSS & DECK DETAILS
SCALE ½" & 1" 1'-0"   JUNE 1948

SHEET No 2

Figure 27 (Concluded)   89

triangular trusses, or three-dimensional trusses; and in all cases the word, frames, or frameworks, could be substituted for the word, trusses. The type of structure included here is one in which the web members are inclined so that the planes of two web systems intersect in a line which is the axis of a chord; thus, a single space truss (triangular truss) would have two top chords, two inclined web systems, but only a single bottom chord. For a bridge where the main longitudinal structure is provided by a single space truss, there is no bottom lateral bracing and no cross frames or sway bracing are necessary.

Eight percent of the designs utilized this type of structure, all but one of which used a single space truss. One design had three space trusses; that is, six inclined web systems with four top chords, and three bottom chords.

Thomas C. Kavanagh, State College, Pennsylvania, in discussing his design, said, "It seems reasonable to predict that bridges of the future will achieve considerable economy due to the utilization of favorable characteristics of three-dimensional structures, in combination with welding. The aircraft field has long recognized the efficiency of three-dimensional frames and closed shell construction employing the *torsional* strength of such structures to take eccentric loads.

"The advantages of a triangular bridge, though recognized by the structural engineering profession for almost a century, have never been fully exploited because of difficulties with shapes and connections for a space structure of this type, and also because of uncertainty as to the structural behavior of such a bridge. The introduction of one or two new rolled shapes, together with the employment of welding for connections, easily overcomes the former difficulties; and the fact that the structural action of the truss as a space frame can be analyzed with certainty and without undue difficulty is attested by the few bridges of this type which have successfully withstood the test of use.

* * *

"It will be emphasized here that the attempt has been directed in this entry toward achieving the *maximum economy* with the *simplest* type of space structure. It is possible to devise more elaborate schemes involving the triangular truss cross section, but these would be at the expense of simplicity of detail and ease of analysis; further it is not felt that these more elaborate schemes would be adopted until long after the fundamental design submitted has been accepted by the profession. In like manner, while girder type structures based on the triangular principle are feasible, they will not in general prove as economical as truss types for spans over 100 ft.

"The design submitted herewith envisages a space truss of triangular cross section, which would result essentially from bringing together the two lower chords of the conventional double-plane bridge trusses. The space framework thus formed offers the advantages of great stiffness and better appearance by virtue of its unusual compactness, with economy effected by the elimination of the bracing required by AASHO Sec. 3.6.67 and 3.6.68 respectively, as above noted. Additional savings which become apparent in the detail design include lowered bending moments in the floor beams due to more favorable placement of their supports, and lowered direct stresses in truss chord members caused by extreme off-center live loads, by virtue of the space-frame action of the structure. This latter characteristic of structural action depending on torsional rigidity is illustrated in Table 1 on the drawings, and has been noted in the past by Petersen in a patent in 1899 and by Leonhardt in a design for one of the Rhine bridges [see W. Haupt, 'Die Mitteltraegerbruecke', *Die Bautechnik,* Feb.-March, 1948], in which the chords were found not more stressed for eccentric loadings than for centrally applied loads.

"Table 1 of the drawings shows the design stresses for the triangular section bridge under the assigned loadings. To illustrate the reduction in chord stresses effected by utilizing the space frame relationships, the table indicates the stresses in a conventional bridge with identical floor system and with two parallel trusses spaced 15 ft. apart and with the same vertical height as the subject truss. The reduction in chord stresses is appreciable, whereas the slight increase in bracing stresses due to greater participation is

TABLE 1. COMPARATIVE DESIGN STRESSES

TRIANGULAR SECTION TRUSS VS CONVENTIONAL 2-PLANE BRIDGE OF SAME HEIGHT

			MEMBER	TRIANGULAR SECTION BRIDGE	CONVENTIONAL 2-PLANE BR.	% REDUCTION
SIDE TRUSSES	CHORDS	UPPER	$U_0 U_2$	-132 K	-146 K	10%
			$U_2 U_4$	-262	-313	14%
		LOWER	$L_1 L_3$	$+406$	$+250$ ∮	19%
			$L_3 L_5$	$+549$	$+335$ ∮	16%
	DIAGS.		$U_0 L_1$	$+188$	$+227$	
			$L_1 U_2$	-141	-161	
			$U_2 L_3$	$+95$	$+118$	
			$L_3 U_4$	$-57 (+23)$	$-75 (+36)$	
	VERTS.		$U_1 L_1$	-68	-89	
			$U_2 L_2$	0	0	STRESSES
			$U_3 L_3$	-68	-89	ARE D+L+I
			$U_4 L_4$	0	0	(EXCEPT *)
LATERAL (TOP) TRUSS	DIAGS	END BAY		± 42	± 18 *	
		OTHERS		± 27	± 11 *	
	VERTS	END		-68	± 16 *	
		OTHERS		$+25$	± 6 *	

∮ EACH CHORD

easily absorbed by the conventional minimum sections required for slenderness ratios.

"Thus the triangular section bridge gives greater utilization of web member capacity which frequently must be placed in the bridge for minimum slenderness ratio requirements rather than stress requirements. An additional, though minor, advantage of this framework lies in the decreased wind pressures on the bridge due to the sloping exposed faces of the members.

"The earliest noteworthy triangular bridges were employed by the English engineer Brunel [see Waldo G. Bowman, 'Famous German Triangular Bridge has American G. I. Neighbor'. *Engineering News-Record,* May 10, 1945, p. 4] in the Chepstow bridge (1852) and the Saltash bridge (1859), both having tubular compression chords. The latter structure had two 455 ft. spans. An English patent for a triangular bridge was granted to John Shields in 1898. German engineers have from time to time espoused the cause of this type of structure, the best known design being the two-track railroad bridge built at Duren, Germany, with a single span of 256 ft. [see reference by Waldo G. Bowman]. Recent proposals by Haupt [see reference by W. Haupt] claim an extended utility for this type of structure in modified form.

"The design submitted incorporates a new rolled shape especially suited for the chords of bridges whose cross section is in the form of an equilateral triangle. The use of such shapes in connection with arc welding for connections, permits of simple fabrication and well-ordered joint details. It eliminates the more complex joint designs formerly required [see reference by W. Haupt] with bent plate and angle connections where rivets are employed.

* * *

"With reference to the new shapes proposed, although it is known that tubular or box cross sections offer maximum use of materials, there are certain factors which preclude the employment efficiently of closed shapes if the letter of the specifications [American Welding Society] are followed. Accepting the demonstrated superiority of butt-welded joints over fillet-welded joints for dynamic loadings involving repeated stress and impact, it will be found difficult from a practical viewpoint to achieve a satisfactory butt joint with a closed section in view of the requirements of Section 218 prohibiting one-sided butt welds. It appears that the transmission of loads through open flanges by direct butt welding will still afford the most practical joint for some time or until the present difficulties with one-sided butt-welds are overcome.

"The shapes proposed for the chords are somewhat similar to rolled sheet piling shapes, and provide for simple butt-welding of any 10″ WF section. The resulting detail is very clean and improved over the comparable section composed of shapes and angles. The web members are standard shapes presently available. The BP shapes employed for the diagonal give a slightly better column allowable than does the corresponding WF section.

"Several schemes of erection are possible, depending on the local conditions. The one contemplated here is shop assembly in plane panels comprising upper stringers, floor beams and one top chord; shop assembly of one side truss in units between chord splices; and final job assembly in a jig of these panels with remaining members into complete triangular bridge sections between the chord splices. These sections are light and can be lifted into place by crane, assuming use of falsework is possible. The cantilever flooring can be added afterwards in the form of shop welded sections, after the triangular span is in place. Grating and sills are added and field welded to the stringers after the latter are in place. Such a sequence places a maximum amount of welding in the shop, without involving panels of undue size."

The floor system used by Mr. Kavanagh is composed of steel bridge decking (15¼ lb. per sq. ft.), 7 in. sills at 18 in. centers, 16 in. stringers at 4 ft.-4 in. centers (except for exterior stringers which are 8 WF 35), and 18 in. intermediate floorbeams. The details of this floor system and an elevation, plan view, and the details of his space truss are shown in Figures 28, 29, and 30. Details of the two new shapes are shown in Figure 29.

Figure 31 illustrates a method of determining the reactions for a space truss, and concerning this, Mr. Kavanagh stated, "From an analysis standpoint, the stresses are determined for the structure as a space framework. While this may appear formidable, the problem is actually simplified by the fact that with a space frame with plane faces of the type shown, the forces may be resolved into components parallel to the planes involved, and the analysis is carried out in large measure by methods of plane truss analysis. By virtue of the minimum number of supports required from a practical standpoint, the structure is externally statically indeterminate to the second degree. The sequence of analysis by the Maxwell-Mohr method is straightforward, however, as may be gauged by the illustrative analysis shown on the drawing for a single load. It is to be noted that the use of a temporary false strut (T) simplifies the analysis by reducing it to the calculation of a series of cantilevered plane trusses. The bridge has been analyzed for two-lane live loading (H-20-44), both centrally loaded and with maximum off-center loading; also for maximum off-center loading of a single lane of live load."

R. W. Ullman, Cleveland Heights, Ohio, submitted a bridge designed with three space trusses which form a trapezoidal space structure having four top chords and three bottom chords. Mr. Ullman described it as follows:

"Three girders [trusses] of equilateral triangular cross-section are placed in a so to speak, upside down position so that the long side of the trapezoid

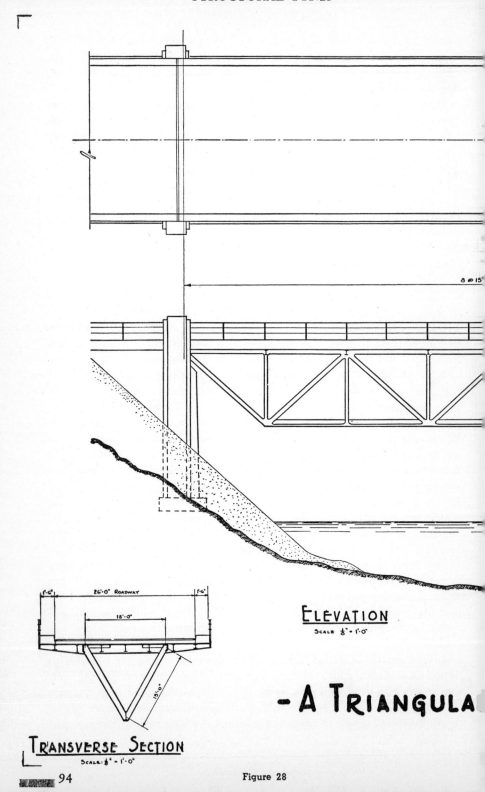

8 @ 15'

ELEVATION

SCALE ⅛" = 1'-0"

- A TRIANGULA

TRANSVERSE SECTION

SCALE: ⅜" = 1'-0"

1'-6" | 26'-0" ROADWAY | 1'-6"

18'-0"

15'-0"

Figure 28

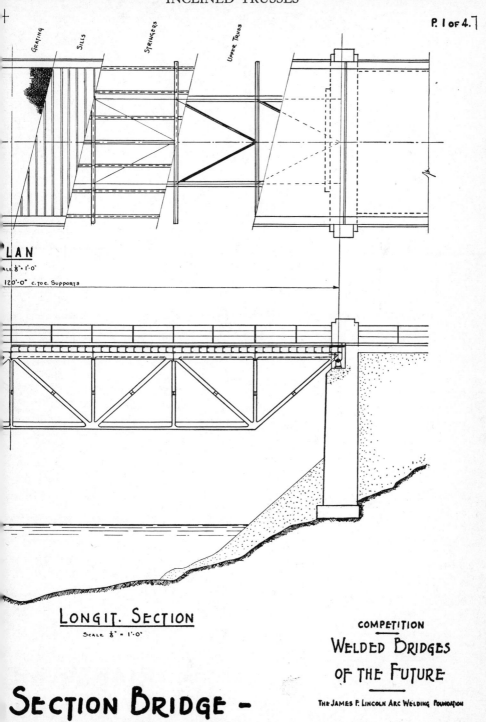

PLAN

SCALE ⅛" = 1'-0"

120'-0" c. to c. Supports

LONGIT. SECTION

Scale ⅛" = 1'-0"

SECTION BRIDGE -

COMPETITION

WELDED BRIDGES

OF THE FUTURE

THE JAMES F. LINCOLN ARC WELDING FOUNDATION

Figure 28 (Concluded)

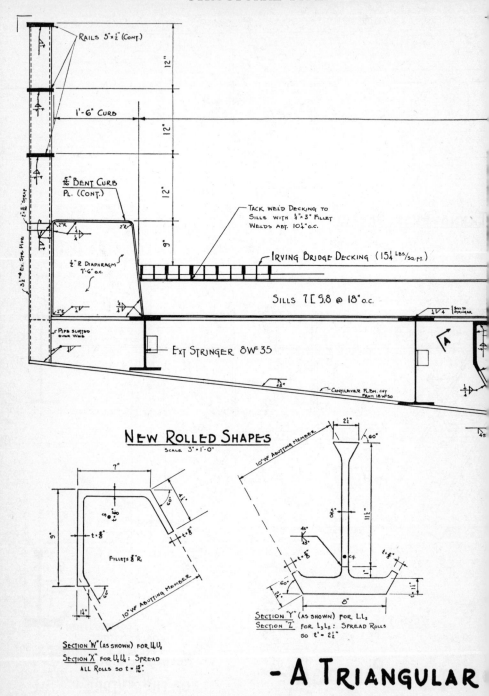

RAILS 5"x½" (CONT.)

12"

1'-6" CURB

12"

5/16" BENT CURB PL. (CONT.)

12"

2"R

2'2"

½" R DIAPHRAGM 7'-6" o.c.

9"

2"2"

PIPE SLOTTED OVER WEB

EXT STRINGER 8W 35

TACK WELD DECKING TO SILLS WITH ¼"x 3" FILLET WELDS ABT. 10½" o.c.

IRVING BRIDGE DECKING (15¼ LBS/SQ.FT.)

SILLS 7 [9.8 @ 18" o.c.

CANTILEVER FL.BM. CUT FROM 18 WF50

NEW ROLLED SHAPES
SCALE 3" = 1'-0"

7"

60°

4½"

9"

t = ⅜"

t = ⅜"

FILLETS ⅜" R.

10" WF ABUTTING MEMBER

60°

1½"

SECTION "W" (AS SHOWN) FOR U₄U₅
SECTION "X" FOR U₃U₄: SPREAD ALL ROLLS SO t = 1½".

2½"

60°

10" WF ABUTTING MEMBER

5"

45°

45°

t = ⅜"

t = ⅜"

11½"

60°

8"

SECTION "Y" (AS SHOWN) FOR L₁L₂
SECTION "Z" FOR L₃L₄: SPREAD ROLLS SO t' = 2½"

- A TRIANGULAR

DE

Figure 29

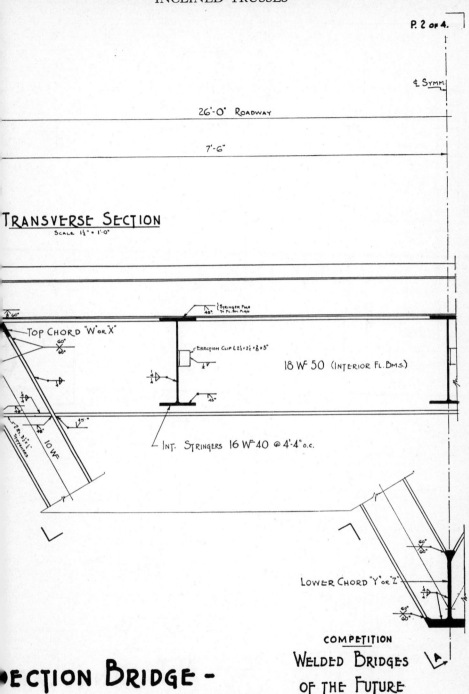

¢ SYMM

26'-0" ROADWAY

7'-6"

TRANSVERSE SECTION
SCALE 1½" = 1'-0"

STRINGER FL&
TO FL. BM. FLGE

TOP CHORD "W" OR "X"

ERECTION CLIP L 2½ × 2½ × ⅜ × 3"

18 W= 50 (INTERIOR FL. BMS.)

INT. STRINGERS 16 W= 40 @ 4'-4" O.C.

10 W=

2 BO. 5½ × ½
STRINGERS

LOWER CHORD "Y" OR "Z"

═CTION BRIDGE -

LS

COMPETITION
WELDED BRIDGES
OF THE FUTURE

THE JAMES F. LINCOLN ARC WELDING FOUNDATION

Figure 29 (Concluded)

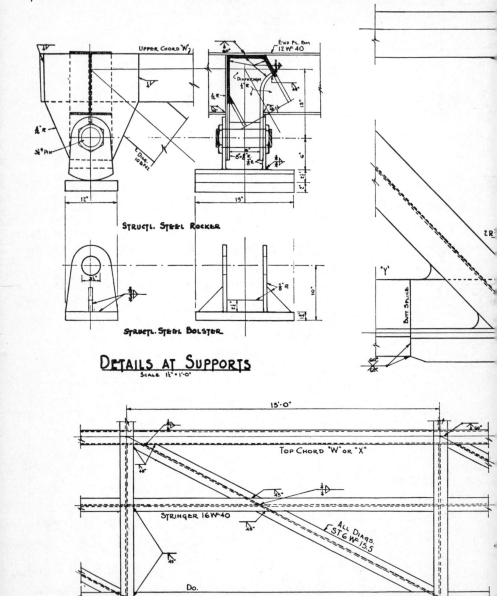

DETAILS AT SUPPORTS
Scale 1½" = 1'-0"

PLAN OF TOP BRACING
Scale 1" = 1'-0"

-A TRIANGULAR

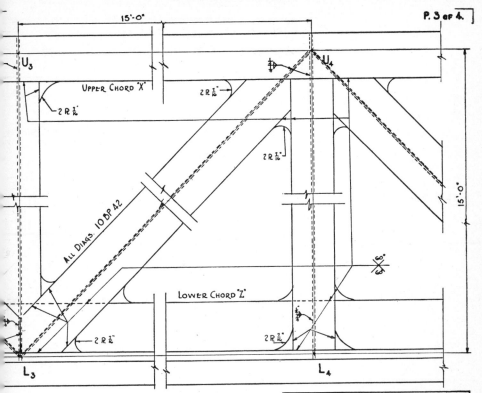

SECTION A·A

Scale 1½" = 1'-0"

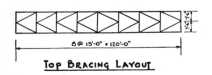

8 @ 15'-0" = 120'-0"

TOP BRACING LAYOUT

FINAL BRIDGE WEIGHT		
ITEM	KIPS	LBS. PER F.
DECKING	48.2	401.7
SILLS	20.4	170.0
STRINGERS	32.5	271.6
FLOOR BEAMS	21.6	105.5
H. RAIL & CURBS	12.7	180.3
TOTAL FLOOR SYSTEM	135.4	1,129.1
TRUSSES & BCG.	44.4	370.3
BOLSTERS, ROCKERS	1.4	12.3
GRAND TOTAL	181.2	1,511.7

COMPETITION

WELDED BRIDGES
OF THE FUTURE

The James F. Lincoln Arc Welding Foundation

SECTION BRIDGE -
TAILS

Figure 30 (Concluded)

99

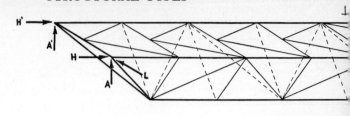

BRIDGE WITH

LOADING CONDITION

$X_B = X_R = 0$:

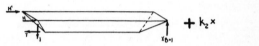

$+ k_1 \times$

$X_B = 1$:

$+ k_2 \times$ Do.

$X_R = 1$:

TABLE I. COMPARATIVE DESIGN STRESSES
Triangular Section Truss vs. Conventional 2-Plane
Bridge of Same Height

		Member	Triangular Section Bridge	Conventional 2-Plane Br.	% Reduction
Side Trusses	Chords	$U_0 U_2$	−132 K	−146 K	10%
	Lower, Upper	$U_2 U_4$	−262	−313	14%
		$L_1 L_3$	+406	+250 ✱	19%
		$L_3 L_5$	+343	+335 ✱	16%
	Diags.	$U_2 L_1$	+188	+227	
		$L_1 U_2$	−141	−161	
		$U_2 L_3$	+95	+118	
		$L_3 U_4$	−57(+23)	−73(+36)	
	Verts.	$U_2 L_2$	−68	−69	
		$U_2 L_2$	0	0	
		$U_3 L_3$	−68	−69	
		$U_4 L_4$	0	0	
Lateral (Top) Truss	Horiz. Diags.	End Bay	±42	±18 ✱	Stresses are D+L+I (except ✱)
		Others	±27	±11 ✱	
		End	−68	±16 ✱	
		Others	+25	±6 ✱	

✱ Each Chord.

MAXWELL-MO

$0 = \delta_{bo} + X_b \delta_{bb}$

$0 = \delta_{ro} + X_b \delta_{rb}$

Where, in general, $\delta_{mn} =$

− A TRIANGULAR

STRESS

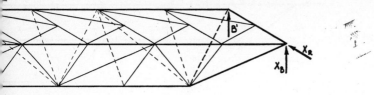

REACTIONS

SUBSCRIPT

(o)

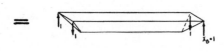

(b)

(r)

EQUATIONS

$$X_r \, \delta_{br} \Big\} \quad \text{SOLVE FOR}$$
$$X_r \, \delta_{rr} \quad \quad X_b \, \& \, X_r$$

$$S_m \, S_n \frac{L}{AE}.$$

SECTION BRIDGE -

ANALYSIS

COMPETITION
WELDED BRIDGES
OF THE FUTURE

THE JAMES F. LINCOLN ARC WELDING FOUNDATION

Figure 31 (Concluded)

101

forms the girder [truss] top to which a reinforced concrete deck slab is anchored. The three girders [trusses], together with the bottom laterals, form five equilateral triangles each having side lengths of 8'-8". (See typical cross-section, Figure 32.) The inclined 6 sides of these triangles are the load carrying members of the bridge; they are designed as trusses of the Warren type. Top and bottom chords of these trusses consist of special 60°, 12" x 6" angles; diagonals and posts are wide flange T-sections welded to the long leg of the chord angles.

"A reinforced concrete slab for the deck construcion will provide ample thickness, weight and rigidity for heavy load concentrations. The concrete deck is attached to the top chord by means of welded-on lugs and longitudinal bars designed to transmit the horizontal shear. This device assures a composite action of the two materials; the deck slab and top chord will represent the compressive members of the span, and the bottom chord the tensile member of the span.

"Top laterals have been placed at right angles to the bridge axis in order to gain maximum effective depth for the deck reinforcement. No special stresses have been assigned to the top laterals because of their imbedment in the concrete slab. The function of these laterals is to tie two inclined trusses together into a triangular girder and to resist horizontal shear.

"Bottom laterals, field welded in, tie the three girders together to form a trapezoid. They are designed for compressive stresses resulting from D.L. & L.L. overhang."

Advantages of this design as compared with more conventional designs were listed as follows:

1. Great Economy—A triangular truss type girder will require approximately 50% less steel than a plate girder bridge.

2. Increased Lateral Stiffness—Because of the triangular breakdown, no cross frames are required.

3. Load Concentrations on interior panel points are taken by two trusses instead of one.

4. The triangular truss girder is particularly suitable for fabrication using the arc welding process. The trusses are welded in a flat position (see section P-P, Figure 33). By welding together the bottom angles of two trusses and then welding on the top laterals, the truss girder is easily assembled into one piece and is ready for transport and erection. To complete the trapezoid only little field welding is required such as attaching interior shear lugs to adjacent girders, welding in 2" x ½" bar stiffeners between interior top angles and the welding of bottom laterals.

5. Deflections because of composite action are very low. The maximum L.L. deflection is approximately 0.76 in. which is $\frac{1}{1900}$ of the span. Dead load deflection is approximately 1.17 in. and it is recom-

mended that the truss be cambered 2 in.

The top chords of the trusses were designed for the D.L. stresses only. The reinforced concrete deck and the top chords act together in resisting the L.L. stresses.

The top and bottom chords are butt-welded at splices and the diagonals and posts are fillet welded to the chords. If fillet welding to the angle faces is not favored, Mr. Ullman suggests that instead of fillet welding the posts and diagonals to the chord angles, it would be possible to butt-weld the flanges of the members to the outer edge of the top and bottom chord angles, and then fillet weld the web to the angle faces. However, this would make more accurate and complicated cutting of the T-sections necessary.

Harry Gottfeldt, Wembley, Middlesex, England, incorporated two new shapes in the design of his space truss. The sections are referred to as the Y-shape and the cruciform or X-shape. These shapes are described in Chapter IV. The space truss has two top chords 20 ft. apart and one bottom chord. The depth of the structure is about 10 ft. The span of the floorbeams is reduced to 10 ft. by having center vertical members at each panel point. The floor is composed of a $1\frac{3}{16}$ in. traffic plate supported on stringers spaced at about 2 ft.-10 in. centers.

Figure 34 shows a cross section and a plan of this structure and Figures 35 and 36 show longitudinal views and details.

Mr. Gottfeldt summarized the advantages of his structure as: rigidity, especially with regard to torsion; reduction in weight, mainly due to omission of all secondary bracing; reduction in labor costs, due to smaller number of members; and reduction in maintenance costs, due to smaller surface area and, in the case of deck bridges, to the protection afforded the V-shaped lower part by the deck. He also stated:

"The calculation of a three-chord girder [truss] may, at first, offer some unusual features, but there is no real difficulty. It is easily shown that the chord forces are independent of the position of the loads in a transverse direction (this is not the case with two ordinary girders, where each would have to be calculated for more than half the total load, and this implies a further saving in weight). This statement is, however, only true if the top chords form also the chords of the horizontal bracing (here supplied by the battledeck floor), and in order to prevent the outer stringers from taking up this function, sliding joints have been provided in the outer parts of the floor."

D. M. Armitstead, P. R. Brown, P. J. Henegan, J. H. Minnich, and W. Wheeler, all of Hanover, New Hampshire, designed a space frame, triangular in section, composed of two 18 panel K trusses with a common lower chord. The section is an equilateral triangle, 16 ft. on a side with the roadway overhanging 5 ft. The lower chord, webs, and verticals are steel pipe, while the upper chord is made up of bulb angles integral with the steel grid floor.

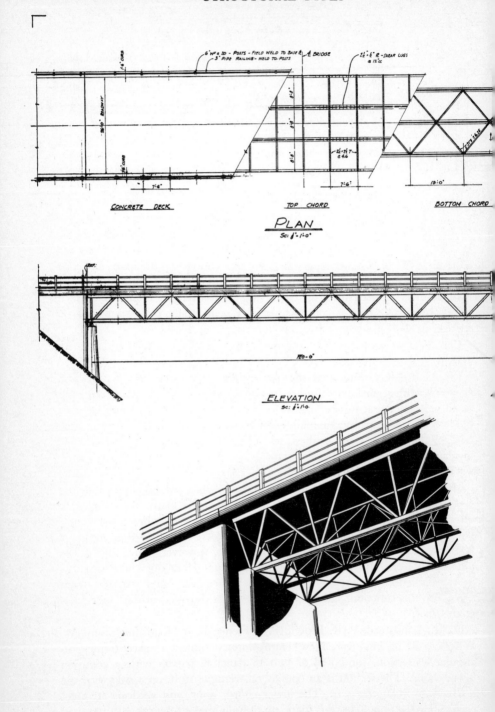

CONCRETE DECK   TOP CHORD   BOTTOM CHORD

PLAN
Sc: ⅛" = 1'-0"

ELEVATION
Sc: ⅛" = 1'-0"

Figure 32

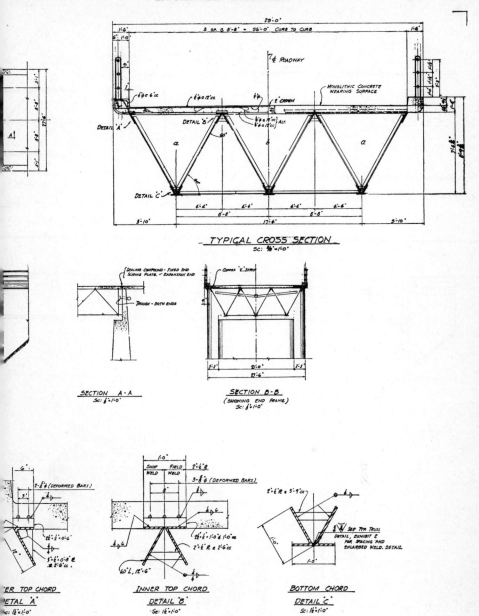

TYPICAL CROSS SECTION
Sc: 3/8" = 1'-0"

SECTION A-A
Sc: 1"=1'-0"

SECTION B-B
(SHOWING END FRAME)
Sc: 1"=1'-0"

ER TOP CHORD
DETAIL "A"
Sc: 1½"=1'-0"

INNER TOP CHORD
DETAIL "B"
Sc: 1½"=1'-0"

BOTTOM CHORD
DETAIL "C"
Sc: 1½"=1'-0"

EXHIBIT 1

Figure 32 (Concluded)   105

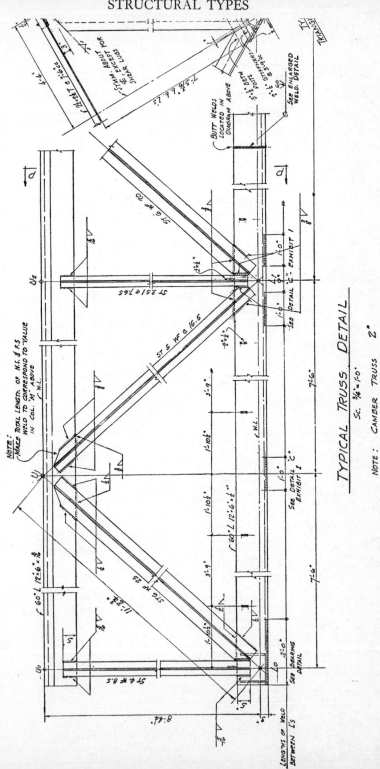

TYPICAL TRUSS DETAIL

Sc. 3/4" = 1'-0"

NOTE : CAMBER TRUSS 2"

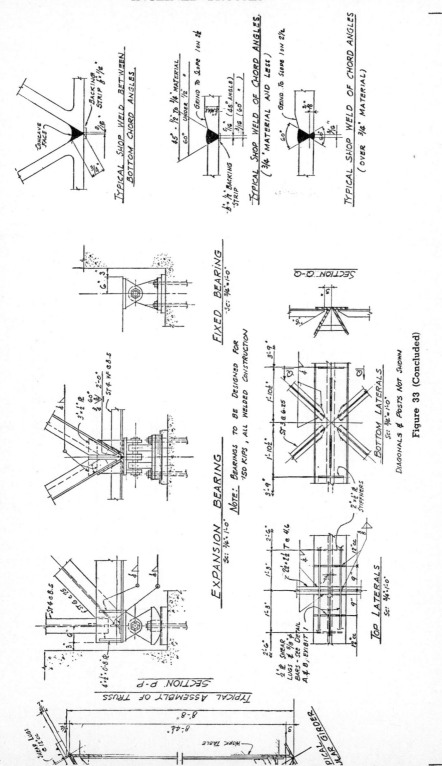

Figure 33 (Concluded)

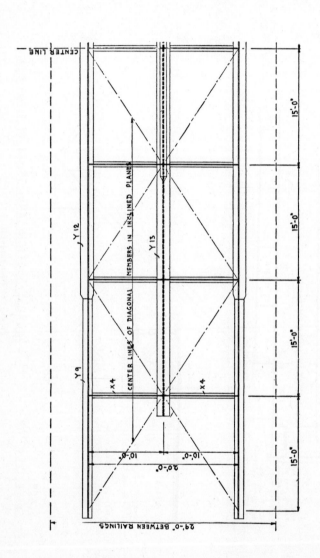

½ PLAN OF THREE-CHORD TRUSS (DECK OMITTED)

SCALE : ³⁄₁₆" = 1'-0"

Figure 34

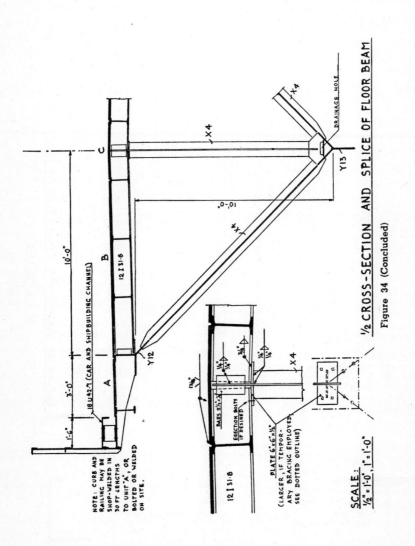

½ CROSS-SECTION AND SPLICE OF FLOOR BEAM

Figure 34 (Concluded)

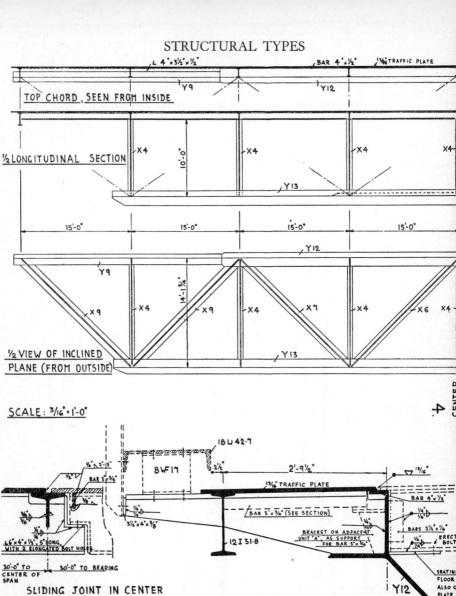

SCALE: 3/16"=1'-0"

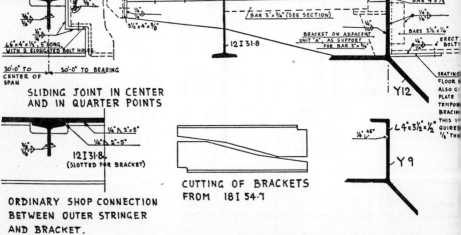

SLIDING JOINT IN CENTER
AND IN QUARTER POINTS

ORDINARY SHOP CONNECTION
BETWEEN OUTER STRINGER
AND BRACKET.

CUTTING OF BRACKETS
FROM 18 I 54·7

DETAILS OF CANTILEVERED PART OF ROADWAY (UNITS "A")
SCALE: 1½"=1'-0", ¾"=1'-0"

Figure 35

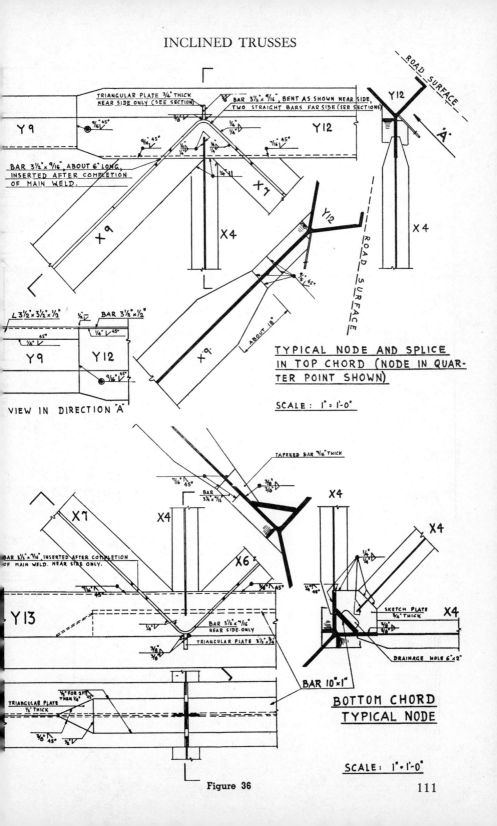

TYPICAL NODE AND SPLICE IN TOP CHORD (NODE IN QUARTER POINT SHOWN)

SCALE: 1" = 1'-0"

VIEW IN DIRECTION "A"

BOTTOM CHORD TYPICAL NODE

SCALE: 1" = 1'-0"

Figure 36

111

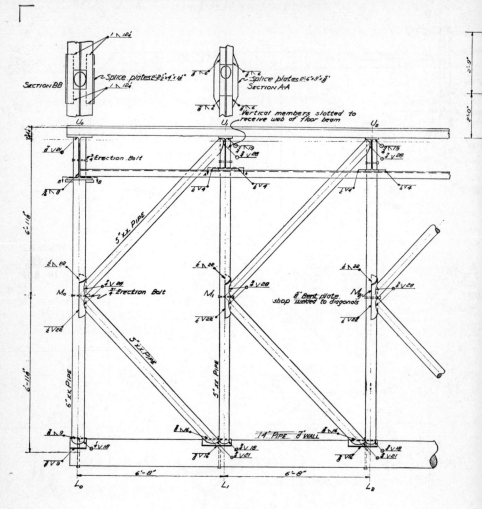

TYPICAL LONGITUDINAL SECTION C-C

Figure 37

A plan was presented that would complete much of the welding in the shop and still furnish easily handled units for field erection. The plan was to shop weld three panels of verticals and webs together with the saddle plates. These could then be erected by lifting them into place on the lower chord, fastening them with bolts through the saddle plates to the preceding vertical truss member and the lower chord. These joints would be welded, followed by placing the floorbeam in the slotted ends of the truss verticals and welding as specified. Then the upper chord, grid floor, etc. would be placed and welded.

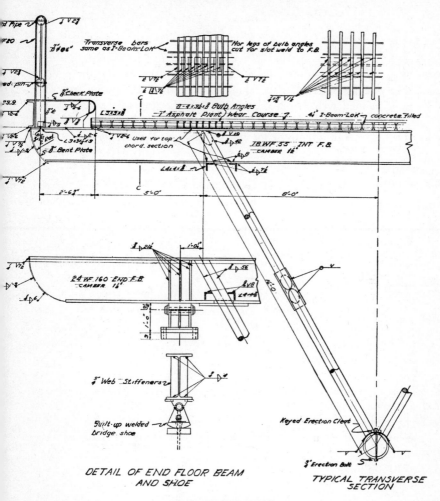

DETAIL OF END FLOOR BEAM
AND SHOE

TYPICAL TRANSVERSE
SECTION

Figure 37 (Concluded)

A typical longitudinal section and a typical transverse section are shown in Figure 37. As seen in this figure, each of the upper chords consists of 8 bulb angles above the floorbeams, integral with the grid floor, and 2 angles below the floorbeams. The web members are 5 in. pipe, except for the end verticals which are 6 in. pipe. The lower chord is a 14 in. pipe. The intermediate floorbeams are 18 in. wide flange beams at 55 lb. per ft. but the end floorbeams are 24 WF 160. The end floorbeams were larger due to the bending resulting from the transverse eccentricity of the end reactions. All floorbeams are designed for the bending due to floor loads and the axial load caused by the fact that they are members of the space frame.

Vierendeel Trusses

The basic geometric figure in a Vierendeel truss is a quadrangle, and this type of structure has appropriately been described as a truss without diagonals. The flexural stresses in the chords and verticals, resulting from the absence of inclined web members, require that the joints be made capable of resisting moment which can be done rather easily if welding is the means of fabrication. About a tenth of the entries submitted in this program were designs for Vierendeel trusses. Most of the designers had two trusses, but others had more, either three, four, or six.

Engineers of the United States, as a group, have considered Vierendeel bridge construction with riveted fabrication too costly for practical use; however, for welded bridges, some have taken the opposite view consistent with the many European engineers who believe they are economical.

A. W. Fischer, Washington, D. C., presented the following discussion:

"Since the 120 ft. Vierendeel truss has few wide flange rolled sections, I believe the cost of handling and fabrication will be less than the cost of a plate girder or a truss with diagonal and vertical members of the same span. The Vierendeel truss as designed has no eccentricities at any of the joints and I believe that the calculated stresses are more representative of the true stresses than those calculated for a plate girder or a truss with diagonals and vertical members.

"It is my belief that the maintenance of the Vierendeel truss is less costly than that of a plate girder or a truss with diagonal and vertical members as there are fewer members to maintain.

"I believe that the probable life of the Vierendeel truss is longer than that of a plate girder or a truss with diagonal and vertical members as the webs of the rolled sections in the Vierendeel truss are generally thicker and will resist corrosion longer.

"It is my opinion that the Vierendeel truss is more pleasing in appearance than a plate girder or a truss with diagonal and vertical members, as the rectangular openings help to beautify the elevation. The ratio of panel length to height is greater than unity thereby giving the bridge horizontality."

Figure 38 shows the drawing for Mr. Fischer's design. The top and bottom chords are 36 in. wide flange beams, 170 lb. per ft. sections for the middle 60 ft. and 150 lb. per ft. sections at the ends. The five middle verticals are 33 WF 108 and the other four (at and nearest the ends) are 33 WF 130. The vertical distance between centerlines of the chords is 12 ft.-6 in. The 8 in. reinforced concrete slab is supported on four stringers (18 WF 50). The stringers rest on floorbeams (30 WF 108) which frame into the top chords. The details for the connection of these members and of the bracing members are given in this figure; however, the details of the shoes are shown in Chapter V.

VIERENDEEL TRUSSES

D. T. Brigham, Coatesville, Pennsylvania, and F. D. Steiner, Baldwin, New York, used three longitudinal Vierendeel trusses, seven Vierendeel type cross frames, and a reinforced concrete floor slab in the design of their bridge. Consistent with keeping a small number of members, there are no stringers or floorbeams. The transverse spacing of the main trusses is 11 ft. and their overall depth is 14 ft.-9 in. Each truss has nine panels of 13 ft.-4 in.; however, the cross frames are 20 ft. apart. The reinforced concrete slab which spans the distance between trusses is anchored to the top chords in order to have composite action for live load and impact stresses.

Three new wide flange shapes were introduced for this design so that all truss members, including the brackets, would have the same width (14 in.). Thus, all webs are in the same plane and there are no eccentricities and no protruding parts. All members of the truss are new shapes, 21 x 14 WF, and weigh either 86 lbs., 106 lbs. or 138 lbs. per ft. of length. The brackets are made from 24 x 14 WF 130. As mentioned by Messrs. Brigham and Steiner, these new sections are not indispensable for this type and size of bridge, but "were mainly chosen for better adaptation as to cross-sectional areas, and for greater lateral rigidity which cannot be overemphasized in bridge design."

Details of the main truss members, the brackets and connections, and the reinforced concrete floor slab are shown in Figures 39, 40, and 41. All of the important connections are butt welded and most of the fillet welds can be made in one pass. Each chord has the same cross section throughout its length; however, two field butt welds are indicated to permit each truss to be shop welded in three parts. As can be seen in these figures, the number of members in the bridge is small and those for the trusses, including the brackets, can be flame cut without wastage.

S. P. Asrow, Chicago, Illinois, obtained torsional stiffness for the chords and verticals of his two Vierendeel trusses by fabricating channels into rectangular shapes. By a similar means, the rectangular struts between the bottom chords are made, but the box shape floorbeams are formed by welding channels to the steel floor plate. All of these channels are new sections, varying in size and weight compared with currently available channels, but they all have wide flanges and thick webs. Mr. Asrow made the following comments in discussing his design and the advantages of Vierendeel trusses:

"The design of a bridge suitable for fabrication by welding should embody certain fundamental characteristics, namely, rigidity and simplicity. The open web truss best utilizes these characteristics. The members of the welded truss must be of a shape such that rigid direct connection is possible. The thick web channel has this advantage.

"The open web truss or Vierendeel truss, as it is often referred to, has been used extensively in the European Lowlands and its acceptance in the United States is growing steadily. This type of truss will no doubt gain

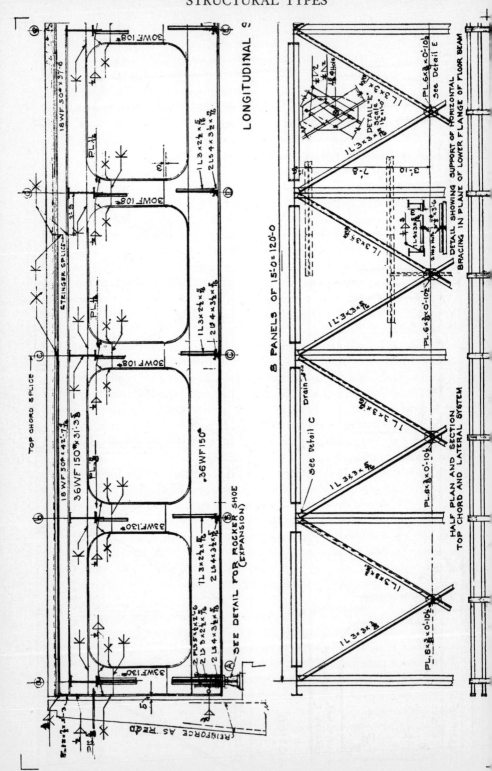

LONGITUDINAL

8 PANELS OF 15'-0 = 120'-0

HALF PLAN AND SECTION
TOP CHORD AND LATERAL SYSTEM

DETAIL SHOWING SUPPORT OF HORIZONTAL
BRACING IN PLANE OF LOWER FLANGE OF FLOOR BEAM

Figure 38

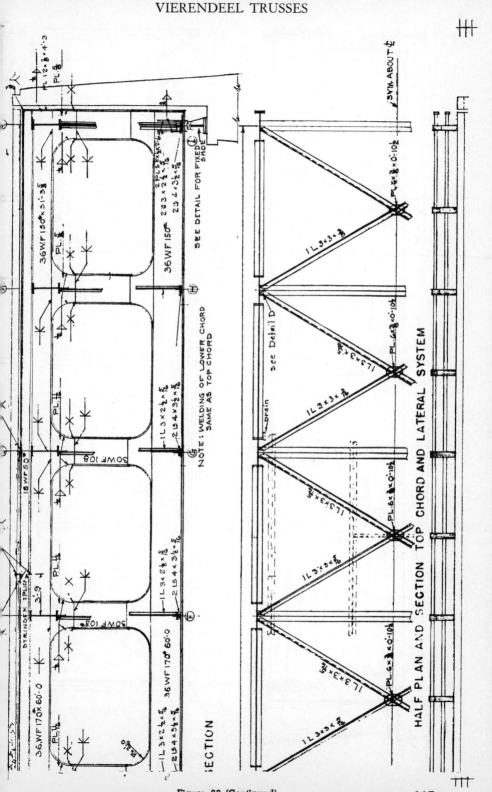

HALF PLAN AND SECTION TOP CHORD AND LATERAL SYSTEM

SECTION

NOTE: WELDING OF LOWER CHORD
SAME AS TOP CHORD

Figure 38 (Continued)

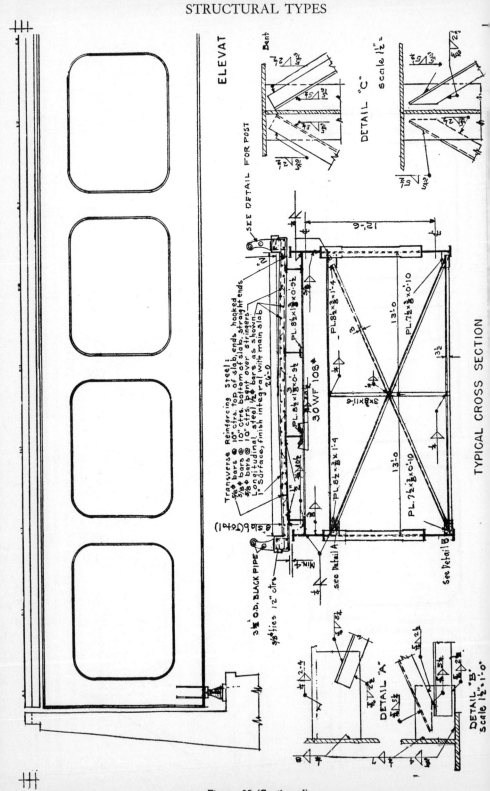

Figure 38 (Continued)

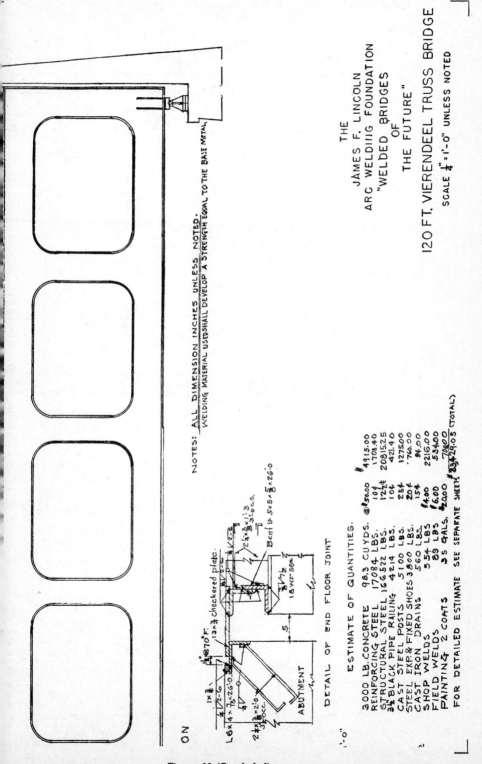

NOTES: ALL DIMENSION INCHES UNLESS NOTED.
WELDING MATERIAL USED SHALL DEVELOP A STRENGTH EQUAL TO THE BASE METAL.

THE
JAMES F. LINCOLN
ARC WELDING FOUNDATION
"WELDED BRIDGES
OF
THE FUTURE"

120 FT. VIERENDEEL TRUSS BRIDGE

SCALE $\frac{1}{4}$"=1'-0" UNLESS NOTED

DETAIL OF END FLOOR JOINT

ESTIMATE OF QUANTITIES.

3000 LB. CONCRETE	98.3 CU.YDS.	@$50.00	$	4915.00
REINFORCING STEEL	17084 LBS.	10¢		1708.40
STRUCTURAL STEEL	166522 LBS.	12½¢		20815.25
3½ BLACK PIPE RAILING	4214 LBS.	10¢		421.40
CAST STEEL POSTS	5100 LBS.	25¢		1275.00
STEEL EXP. & FIXED SHOES	3800 LBS.	20¢		760.00
CAST IRON DRAINS	560 LBS.	15¢		84.00
SHOP WELDS	554 LBS	$4.00		2216.00
FIELD WELDS	89 LBS	$6.00		534.00
PAINTING 2 COATS	35 GALS.	$20.00		700.00

$23,429.05 (TOTAL)

FOR DETAILED ESTIMATE SEE SEPARATE SHEETS

Figure 38 (Concluded)   119

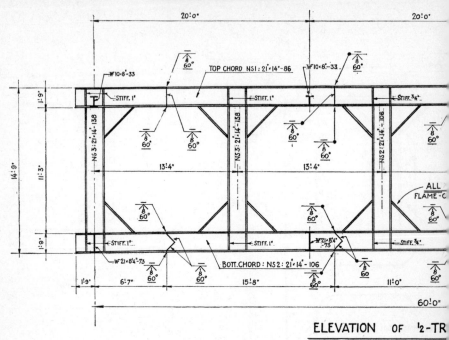

ELEVATION OF ½-TR

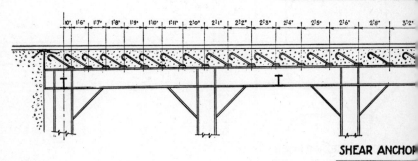

SHEAR ANCHOR

45 SHEA

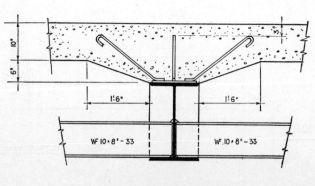

SECTION D-D

DETA

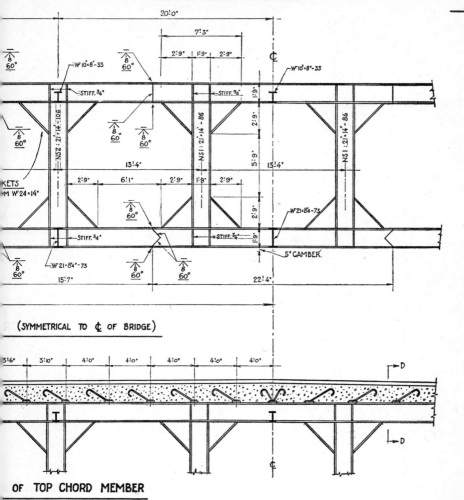

(SYMMETRICAL TO ℄ OF BRIDGE)

OF TOP CHORD MEMBER

HORS PER 1 TRUSS

" = 1'-0"

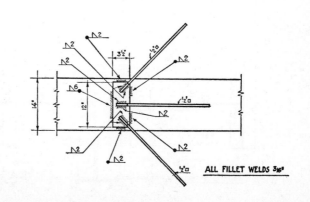

SHEAR ANCHOR

" = 1'-0"

ALL FILLET WELDS 3/16"

PLAN

SHEET 2

Figure 39 (Concluded)

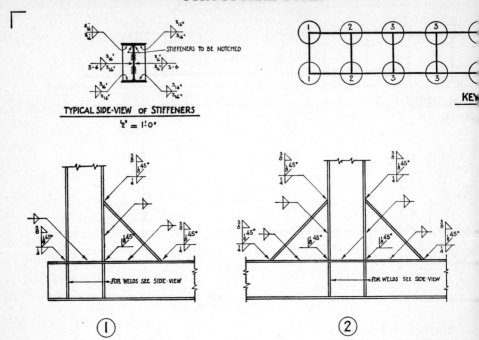

TYPICAL SIDE-VIEW OF STIFFENERS
½" = 1'-0"

KEY

FOR WELDS SEE SIDE-VIEW

① ②

ALL FILLET WELDS

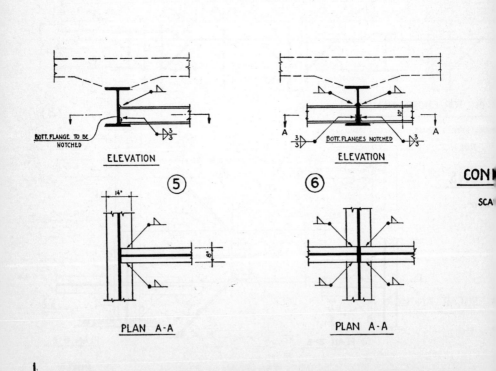

ELEVATION ⑤

BOTT. FLANGE TO BE NOTCHED

ELEVATION ⑥

BOTT. FLANGES NOTCHED

CON

SCA

PLAN A-A PLAN A-A

Figure 40

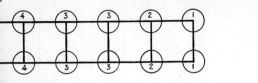

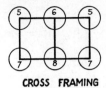

PLAN OF TRUSS

ELEVATION

CROSS FRAMING

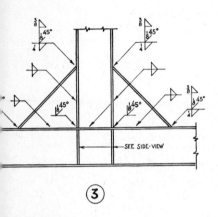

③

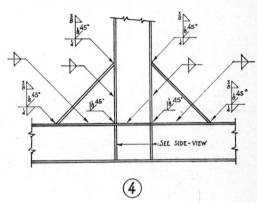

④

UNLESS OTHERWISE NOTED

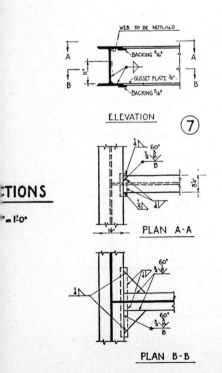

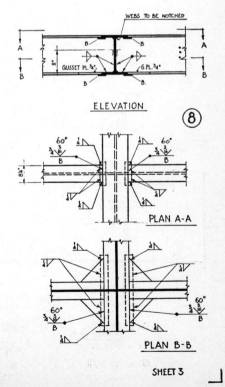

SECTIONS

1" = 1'-0"

SHEET 3

Figure 40 (Concluded)   123

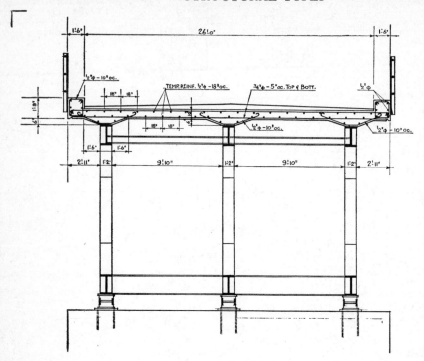

CROSS - SECTION

SHOWING REINFORCING OF FLOOR SLAB

Allowable Unit Stresses for Concrete Floor

Flexure $f'_c = 3000$ #/□"
Shear 90 #/□"
$n = 10$

$\tfrac{1}{4}" = 1!0"$

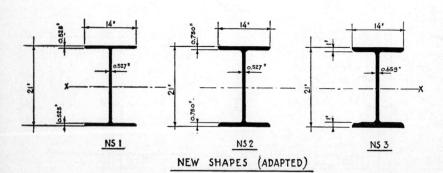

NS 1   NS 2   NS 3

NEW SHAPES (ADAPTED)

$A_s = 25.25$ sq.in. $A_s = 31.3$ sq.in. $A_s = 40.5$ sq.in.

$I_x = 1900$ in.⁴ $I_x = 2490$ in.⁴ $I_x = 3177$ in.⁴

$W = 86$ lb./ft. $W = 106$ lb./ft. $W = 138$ lb./ft.

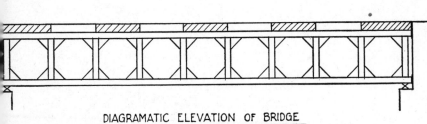

DIAGRAMATIC ELEVATION OF BRIDGE

SHOWING SEQUENCE OF POURING OF FLOOR SLAB

FIRST POURING

SECOND POURING

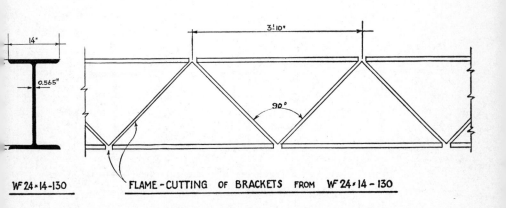

W 24×14-130

FLAME-CUTTING OF BRACKETS FROM W 24×14-130

wider acceptance and shows promise of becoming the bridge truss of the future. Its fabrication by means other than welding is difficult, however, and the curved fillets at the vertical-to-chord joints which are used to satisfy moment requirements are not esthetically appealing.

"The analyses of the open web truss that are to be found in the literature vary from simple and short to extremely complicated and very long. It is agreed by many prominent engineers that under certain conditions, an assumption can be made to simplify the problem. By assuming the point of contraflexure at the midpoint of the members of the truss, the open web truss is converted from an indeterminate structure to an easily analysed determinate one. The conditions under which this assumption is possible are: 1) that the top and bottom chords are of about the same moments of inertia or stiffness, and 2) that the chords are not sloping. Any design that is to attain a wide acceptance must be simple and rapid.

"The application of the specifications to the design of the open web truss requires considerable judgment. The interior vertical members of the open web truss are subject to combined compressive and bending stresses. Since they primarily resist bending, their design based on the permissible compressive stress is unduly severe. This condition also applies to other members. However, for lack of a better criteria, strict conformance to the specifications is warranted.

"The concentrated load to be used for the design of various members of the open web truss is questionable. Since the chords of a truss ordinarily resist axial load, their design using an 18,000 lb. concentrated load seems reasonable. The verticals of an open web truss however, primarily resist the shear that would be considered in the design of a plate girder, therefore a 26,000 lbs. concentrated load is used in the determination of the stresses.

"The recommendation to be found in the Welded Bridge Specifications regarding participation of the floor system in chord stresses is not clear. Welded construction using a thick web channel makes practicable the use of the top chords of the open web truss to decidedly reduce the floor beam stresses. The chords, therefore, participate in the floor beam stresses and not vice-versa. Nevertheless, a small torsional stress in the chord results and consideration of this stress has been made.

"The bridge specifications have heretofore discouraged the use of closed sections. The prevention of rust and corrosion on the inaccessible surfaces through painting was the reason. Welding makes possible the use of *sealed* closed sections of a high torsional resistance. These sections do not need painting on the interior surfaces since rusting is limited to that caused by the trapped moisture and oxygen. Thus, the member having high torsional stiffness can be used to facilitate a direct connection joint, increase the rigidity, and improve the appearance of a bridge.

"Regard for the appearance of a highway bridge has lagged far behind that given to other structures. This bridge design presented for consideration is a modern one. By welding, connections are direct and therefore unsightly gusset plates have been eliminated. The usual shape of the open web truss is modified to improve its appearance; that is, there is no curved fillet at the juncture of the verticals and the chords. To emphasize a low horizontal effect, the depth of the truss is as small as economy will permit and the railing, though sturdy, appears as a horizontal line. In general the bridge has clean, simple and sharp lines that are found in other modern structures.

"The trusses, designed using the assumption described in the introductory paragraphs, have many unique features. The top chord is utilized as the curb, making possible a reduction in the span of the floor beams and the use of narrower abutments. It is made up of two thick web channels and a centrally located plate to form a sealed, torsion-resistant closed section. The centrally located plate is extended out for rigid connection of the floor plate. By using a centrally located plate, area requirements for compression are met without causing a great difference in the moments of inertia of the top and bottom chords. This is essential to the use of an approximate analysis for the truss. The chords are designed so that they may be fabricated in the shop by means of long continuous machine-made welds.

"The truss verticals are fabricated from two thick web channels even though a reduction in the amount of steel used is possible. This reduction could be made by adding fillets at the joints and also by making them up from six short lengths of channel welded together. The resulting lighter member is not esthetically appealing, however, and the increased cost of fabrication would no doubt more than offset the saving in steel. Notice should be made of the way that the end vertical carries the end shear directly down onto the rocker."

Figure 42 shows an elevation of the main truss, both bearings, a typical detail of floorbeam and floor plate attachment, and the expansion detail at the approach. As shown in the latter, bolting the floor plate directly to the abutment eliminates the necessity for transferring the horizontal loads to the abutment through the use of a rigid end portal. A transverse section and the connection details for the floorbeams and the bottom chord ties are shown in Figure 43. The details at the panel points of the truss are shown in Figure 44.

Other Types

About one-eighth of the designs entered in this program could not be properly classified as any one of the seven types previously considered, and although they are not similar, they have been collectively given this classification. They include such structures as a tied arch, a two-hinged arch, a stiffened arch, an inverted arch, a modified Vierendeel truss, a girder with large holes, a truss and girder combination, a tensed cable, a rigid frame, a forked frame, and a cellular box. Some of these types will be discussed in the following paragraphs.

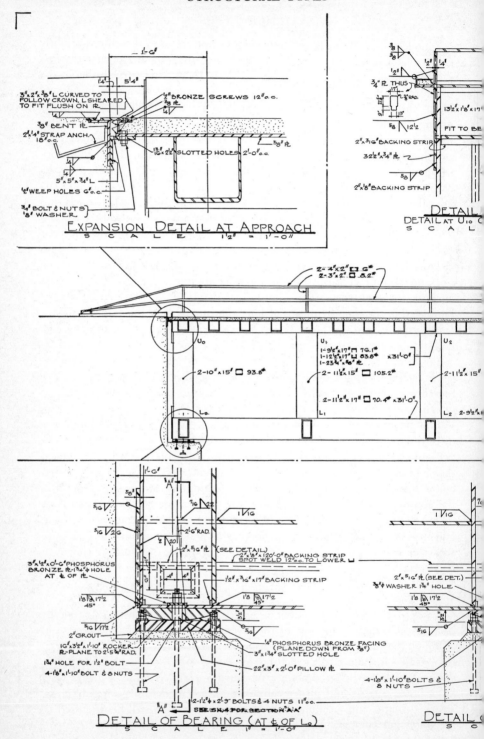

EXPANSION DETAIL AT APPROACH
SCALE 1½" = 1'-0"

DETAIL AT U₁₀
SCALE

DETAIL OF BEARING (AT ℄ OF L₀)
SCALE 1" = 1'-0"

DETAIL
S C

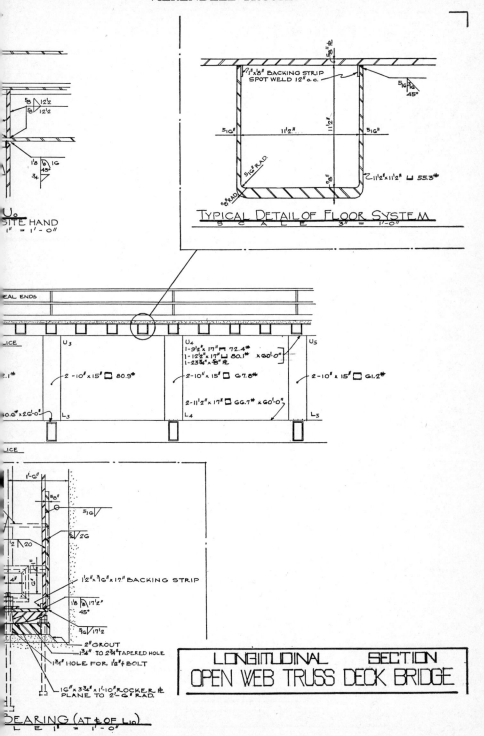

TYPICAL DETAIL OF FLOOR SYSTEM
SCALE 3" = 1'-0"

LONGITUDINAL SECTION
OPEN WEB TRUSS DECK BRIDGE

Figure 42 (Concluded)   129

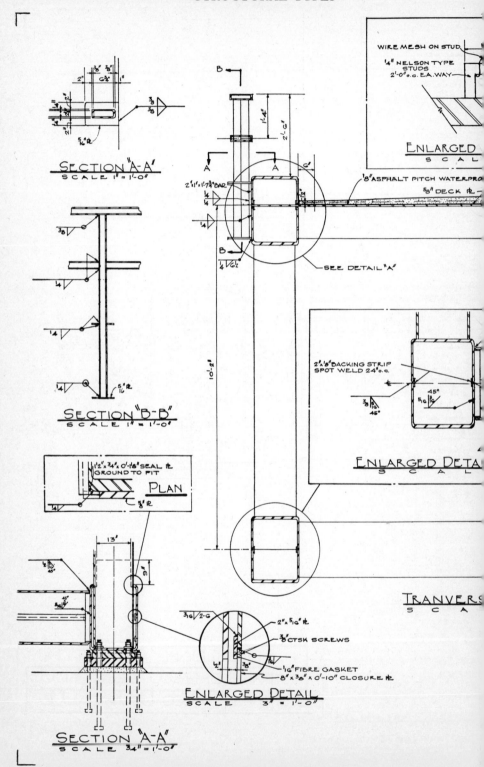

SECTION "A-A"
SCALE 1" = 1'-0"

SECTION "B-B"
SCALE 1" = 1'-0"

PLAN

ENLARGED
SCALE

ENLARGED DETAIL
SCALE

TRANVERS
SCALE

ENLARGED DETAIL
SCALE 3" = 1'-0"

SECTION "A-A"
SCALE 3/4" = 1'-0"

Figure 43

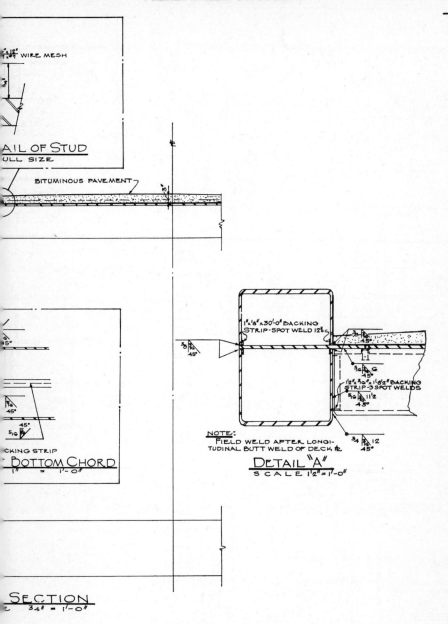

Figure 43 (Concluded)   131

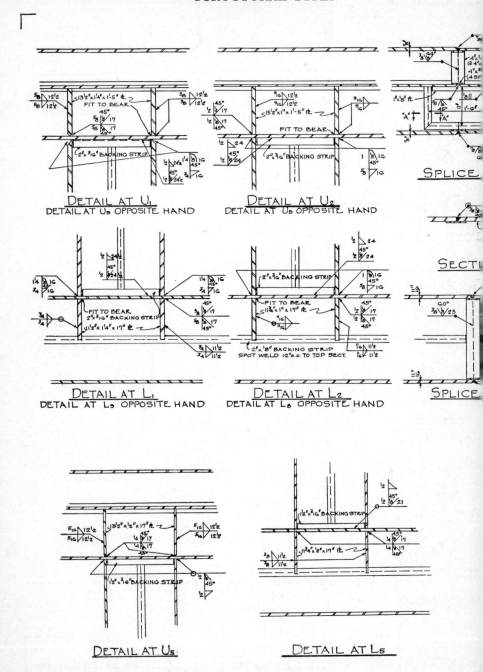

DETAIL AT U₁
DETAIL AT U₉ OPPOSITE HAND

DETAIL AT U₂
DETAIL AT U₈ OPPOSITE HAND

SPLICE

DETAIL AT L₁
DETAIL AT L₉ OPPOSITE HAND

DETAIL AT L₂
DETAIL AT L₈ OPPOSITE HAND

SPLICE

DETAIL AT U₅

DETAIL AT L₅

Figure 44

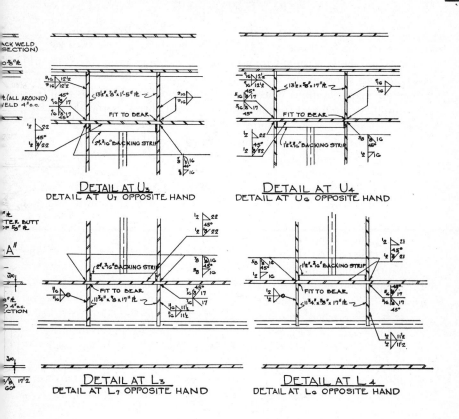

DETAIL AT U₃
DETAIL AT U₇ OPPOSITE HAND

DETAIL AT U₄
DETAIL AT U₆ OPPOSITE HAND

DETAIL AT L₃
DETAIL AT L₇ OPPOSITE HAND

DETAIL AT L₄
DETAIL AT L₆ OPPOSITE HAND

GENERAL NOTES:
RADIUS OF CHANNEL INTERIOR FILLETS = FLANGE THICKNESS
" " " EXTERIOR CORNERS = WEB "
CHORD CHANNEL FLANGES ⅜"
VERTICAL " " ½"
BOTTOM CHORD TIE " ⁵⁄₁₆"

JOINT DETAILS
OPEN WEB TRUSS DECK BRIDGE

Figure 44 (Concluded)   133

H. H. Gilbert, San Carlos, California, chose a tied arch and gave the following reasons for doing so, "The tied arch type of bridge was selected because it is especially suited to welding on account of the fact that the predominating stress in the arch rib is compression. The tied arch is also suitable for many locations where a true arch could not be used, as a true arch must have solid rock to take the horizontal thrust at the skewbacks, while a tied arch does not require a rock foundation."

The arch ribs are 30 in. in diameter and ½ in. thick. The rise at the centerline is 15 ft.-4 in. Each tie is composed of two bars, 2 in. x 6 in. All verticals are 8 in. standard pipe and are spaced every 15 ft. A hanger rod, 1½ in. in diameter, supports the tie bars at the centerline. The hollow sections of the bridge structure are to be tested under air pressure of 200 lb. per sq. in. for 24 hours and then hermetically sealed.

The plan and elevation of this tied arch bridge are shown in Figure 45, also the details of both shoes are given. Figure 46 shows two half-sections of the bridge, including the details of the floor system, and the detail of the field splice of the arch rib at the centerline. This unusual floor system consists of a reinforced concrete floor which is supported by floorbeams every 15 ft. The arched deck plate serves both as a form and as part of the steel reinforcement for the concrete slab. For additional reinforcement, ½ in. rods are placed in the concrete floor above the top of the deck plate and run in both directions with the spacing for transverse bars being 8 in. and for longitudinal bars being 10 in. The floorbeams are fabricated sections composed of ¾ in. x 10 in. flange plates and 26 in. x ½ in. web plates (24 in. x ½ in. for the end floorbeam). The cross frame members are 6 in. standard pipe sections.

J. R. Daymond and M. S. Zakrzewski, both of Durban, South Africa, used five unusual frames in the design of their bridge which they described in these words:

"The bridge consists of five longitudinal frames, each frame consisting of a beam simply supported at its ends on roller bearings and for extra support and rigidity, the beam is rigidly connected at two points in the span to inclined props, these props in turn being pin jointed at their ends to abutments. The structure may thus be regarded as a two pinned portal with inclined legs and with horizontal projecting propped cantilevers forming open spandrels. These cantilevers being an effective means of 'prestressing' the beam under load.

"The frames are rigidly connected together laterally by strong diaphragms and stiffeners enabling all five frames to form one composite section. The roadway consists of concrete placed as filling directly on the flanges of the frames with a two inch wearing surface of asphalt on the concrete with a waterproofing compound placed between the concrete and the asphalt. The deck fulfills a double role; curved plates, ⅜ in. thick, in the flanges of the frames and stiffened by the concrete fill, transfer the wheel loads to the frames and at the same time a portion of these curved plate flanges near the frame web act as the top flange of the solid web frames. The hand-railing of the bridge consists of steel verticals, and horizontals supporting light meshed steel wire panels. Drainage of the road surface is from the span centre towards the abutments."

An elevation, a plan, and a cross section of this bridge is shown in Figure 47. Details of the longitudinal frames, the diaphragms, and the bearings are given in Figure 48. Two special sections were proposed in the design and their dimensions are also given in this latter figure.

According to Messrs. Daymond and Zakrzewski, the following considerations influenced the form of the bridge as finally designed and were the factors governing their choice of structure:

1. The loads are brought directly to the abutments without using transverse or longitudinal secondary load carrying members.

2. The introduction of the inclined props to reduce the 'simply supported beam' bending moment at the centre of the span. For most and certainly for the worst conditions of loading the end beam reactions are downward, the props together with anchorage thus acting virtually as 'prestressing' agents greatly reducing stresses at the centre of the beam.

3. For reasons given in (2) the weight of the structure is reduced in the middle of the span, and concentrated more at supports, so further reducing the dead load bending moment.

4. By utilizing the curved steel flanges of the main beam to act as part of the decking, and as shuttering for the concrete, the deck structure becomes very economical.

5. The design enables the fabrication of large elements in the shop, reducing field and in situ welding to a minimum. On the site three structural elements only require in situ welding.

6. The bridge may be readily erected without the aid of auxiliary, temporary supporting structures.

7. The structure presents relatively small surface areas to transverse or wind forces. The decking provides a permanent waterproof roof to the bridge. All parts are readily accessible for painting or can be rendered waterproof and immune from corrosion. The bridge as a whole may be easily and economically maintained in a good state of preservation.

8. As finally evolved the bridge portrays simplicity, dignity and economy which should be characteristic of a welded steel structure.

P. J. Tupker, Groningen, Holland, submitted the design of a very unusual structure which he stated is, "a solid curved closed box, carrying the roadway on the top, therefore: 'Closed-Box Section' Design." This rectangular box is 26 ft. wide and varies in depth, having an end depth of 2 ft.-7½ in. and a center depth of 5 ft. (see Figure 49). Each of the four sides of this large and extremely wide box beam consists of a series of adjacent cells 4 in. wide and 4 in. high (see Figure 50). The top flange, therefore, has 79 cells and a

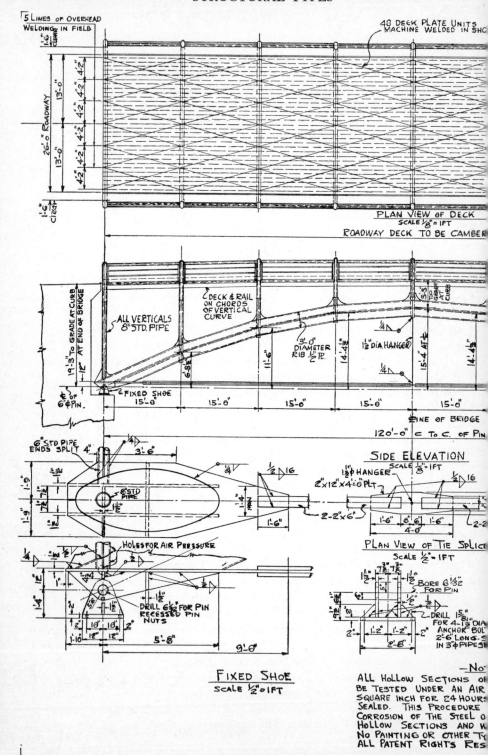

PLAN VIEW OF DECK
SCALE 1/8" = 1 FT

ROADWAY DECK TO BE CAMBER

SIDE ELEVATION
SCALE 1/8" = 1 FT

PLAN VIEW OF TIE SPLICE
SCALE 1/2" = 1 FT

FIXED SHOE
SCALE 1/2" = 1 FT

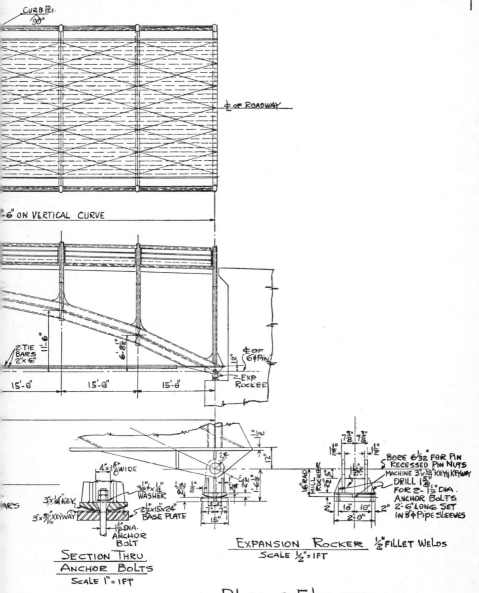

SECTION THRU
ANCHOR BOLTS
SCALE 1"=1FT

EXPANSION ROCKER ½"FILLET WELDS
SCALE ½"=1FT

PLAN AND ELEVATION –

A WELDED BRIDGE OF THE
FUTURE
FOR THE 1949 AWARD PROGRAM.
SPONSORED BY THE
JAMES F. LINCOLN
ARC WELDING FOUNDATION.

Figure 45 (Concluded)   137

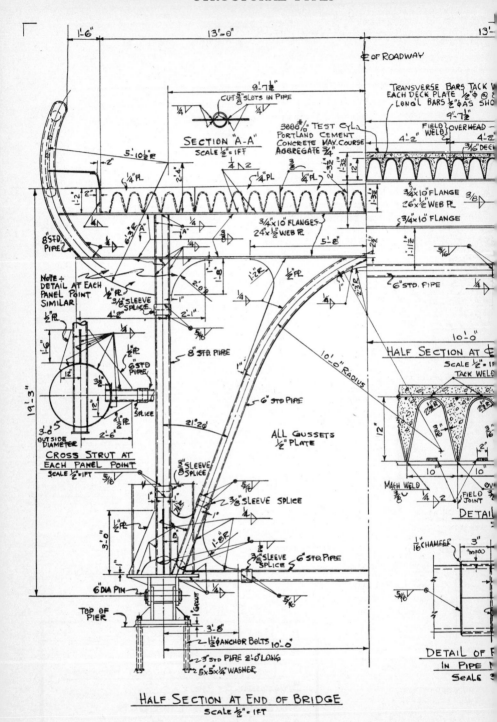

HALF SECTION AT END OF BRIDGE
SCALE ½" = 1 FT

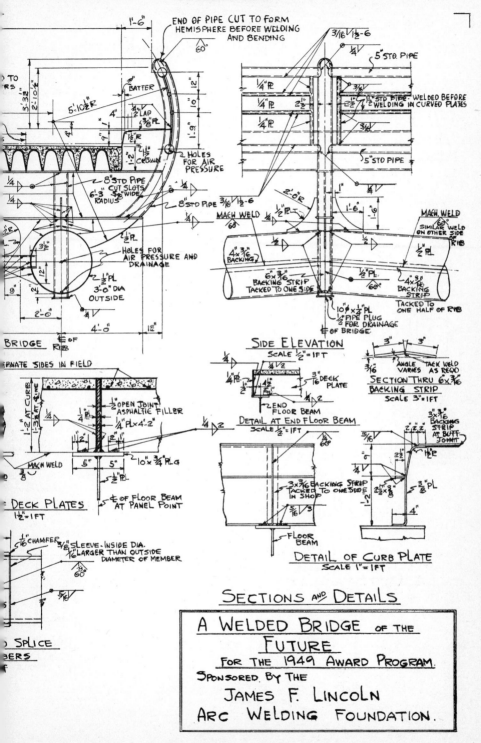

SECTIONS AND DETAILS

A WELDED BRIDGE OF THE FUTURE
FOR THE 1949 AWARD PROGRAM.
SPONSORED BY THE
JAMES F. LINCOLN
ARC WELDING FOUNDATION.

Figure 46 (Concluded)

139

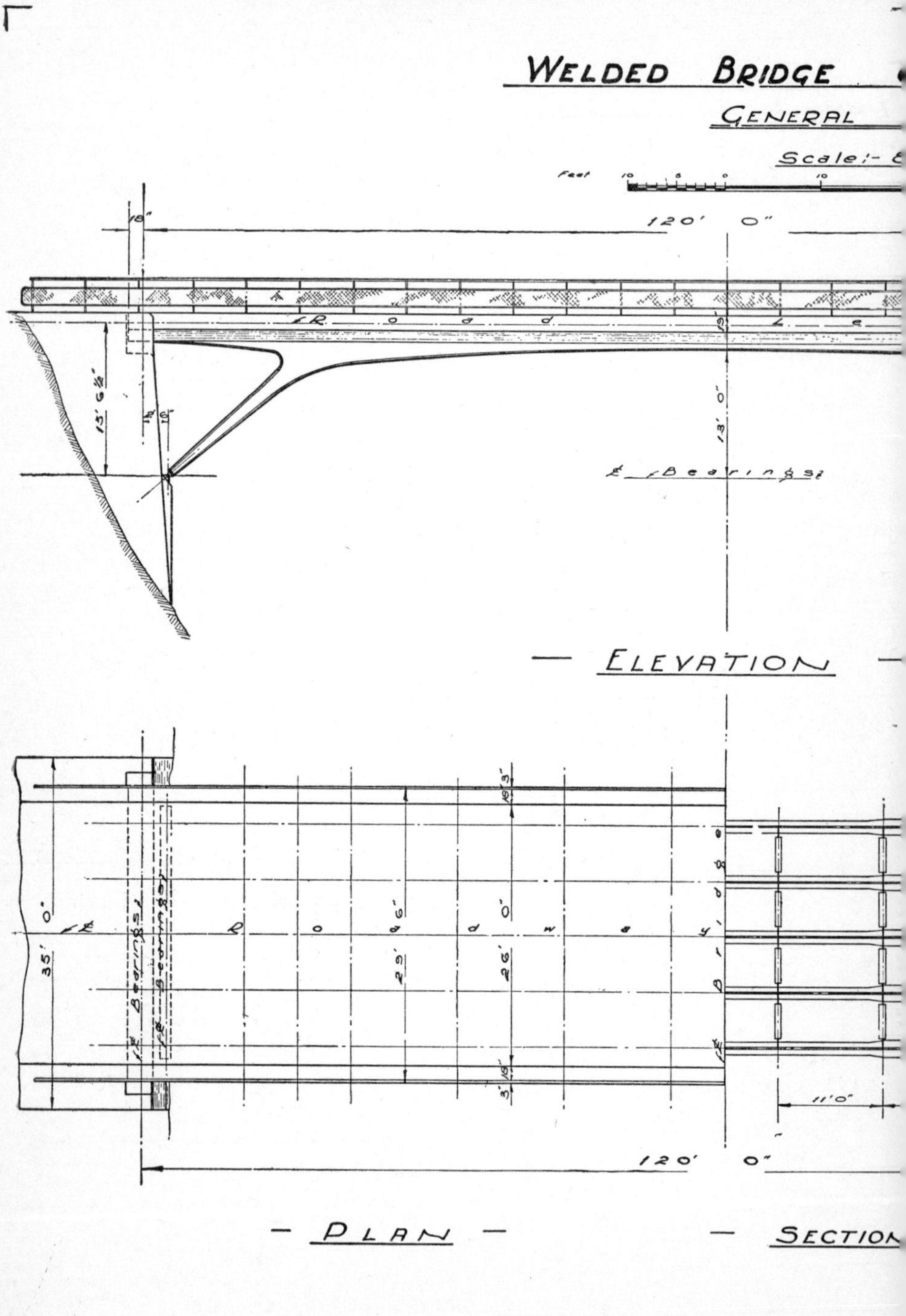

WELDED BRIDGE

GENERAL

Scale:- 8

Feet

120' 0"

Road

13' 6½"

13' 0"

℄ Bearings:

— ELEVATION —

— PLAN —

— SECTION

120' 0"

Figure 47

F THE FUTURE

LAYOUT

0" to 1."

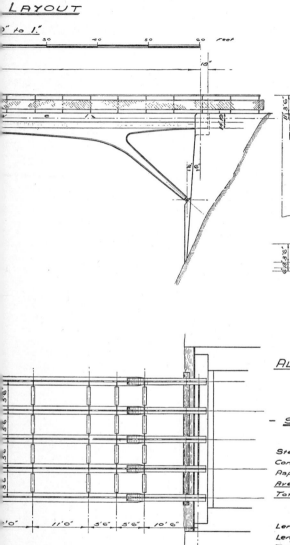

CROSS SECTION

29' 6"

2 6' 0"
Kerb and Cable Box
2" Asphalt Covering
Lightweight Filling
1" Fall

3'6" 5'6" 5'6" 5'6" 5'6" 3'9"

ALTERNATE CROSS SECTION

2" Asphalt Covering

4'3" 6'6" 8'0" 6'6" 4'3"
29' 6"

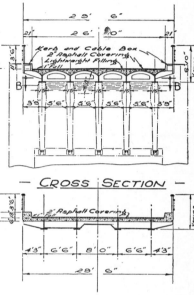

— SUMMARY OF QUANTITIES —

	Weight in lbs. per lin. foot	Total
Steel	1670	203450
Concrete 1636 c.f. at 140 lb/c.f.	1880	228800
Asphalt 3155 sq.ft.at 18 lb/sq.ft.	470	56750
Average weight per lin. ft — 4020 lbs.		
Total weight of Bridge—489000 lbs.		

	BUTT $\frac{1}{4}$	FILLET $\frac{3}{8}$ $\frac{5}{16}$
Length of Shop Welds	1898	7182 1107
Length of Field Welds	702	1026 851
Total length of Welding	2600	8208 1958

PLAN B-B —

Figure 47 (Concluded)   141

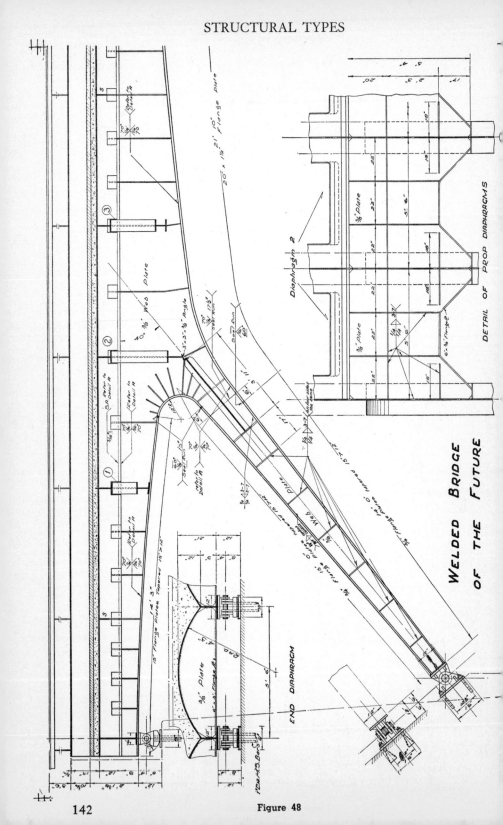

WELDED BRIDGE OF THE FUTURE

DETAIL OF PROP DIAPHRAGMS

END DIAPHRAGM

Figure 48

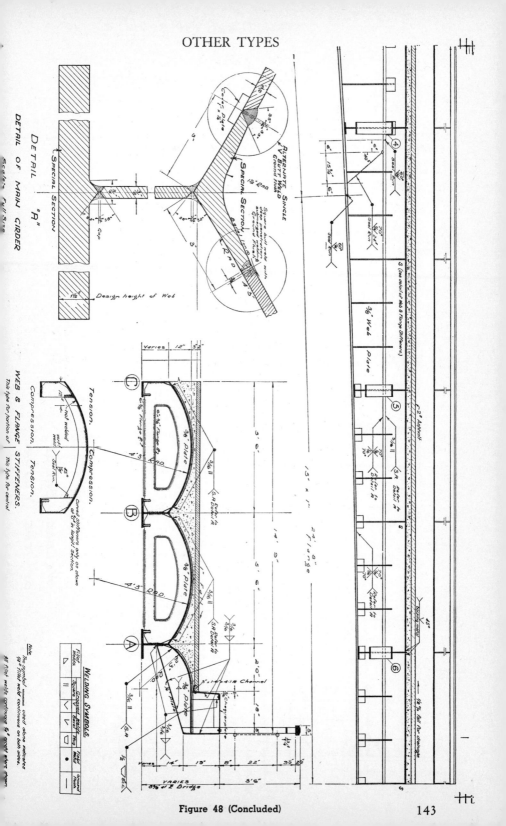

Figure 48 (Concluded)

WELDED BRIDGE OF THE FUTURE

PROPOSED TWO-LANE DECK HIGHWAY BRIDGE

SUPPORTED ON TWO END PIERS 120 FEET APART,

CENTERLINE TO CENTERLINE OF BEARINGS.

A SOLID CURVED CLOSED BOX, CARRYING THE ROADWAY ON THE TOP

THEREFORE: "CLOSED-BOX SECTION" DESIGN

SUITABLE FOR ALL LENGTHS OF SPAN — FRAMELESS CONSTRUCTION

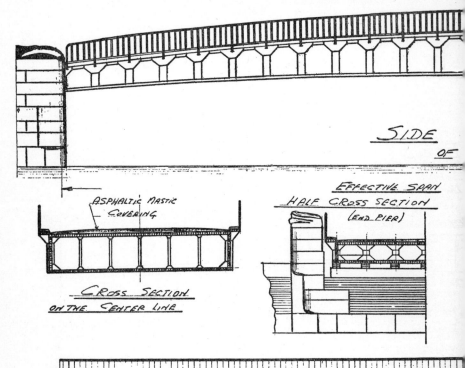

SIDE

OF

EFFECTIVE SPAN

HALF CROSS SECTION
(END PIER)

ASPHALTIC MASTIC
COVERING

CROSS SECTION
ON THE CENTER LINE

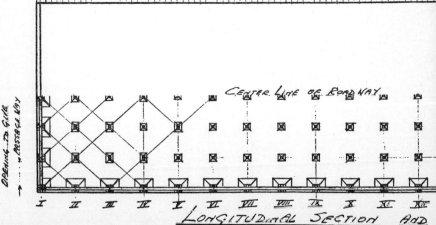

OPENING TO GIVE PASSAGE WAY

CENTER LINE OF ROADWAY

I II III IV V VI VII VIII IX X XI XII

LONGITUDINAL SECTION AND

Figure 49

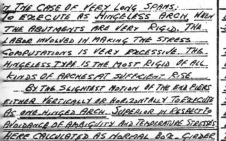

IN THE CASE OF VERY LONG SPANS: TO EXECUTE AS HINGELESS ARCH, WHEN THE ABUTMENTS ARE VERY RIGID. THA LABOR INVOLVED IN MAKING THE STRESS COMPUTATIONS IS VERY EXCESSIVE. THE HINGELESS TYPE IS THE MOST RIGID OF ALL KINDS OF ARCHES AT SUFFICIENT RISE.

BY THE SLIGHTEST MOTION OF THE END PIERS EITHER VERTICALLY OR HORIZONTALLY TO EXECUTE AS ONE HINGED ARCH. SUPERIOR IN RESPECT TO AVOIDANCE OF AMBIGUITY AND TEMPERATURE STRESSES HERE CALCULATED AS NORMAL BOX-GIRDER

ADVANTAGES

FIRST.	COMPACTNESS
SECOND.	BETTER RESISTANCE AGAINST. SHOCK AND CHECK VIBRATION.
THIRD.	LITTLE COST OF MANUFACTURE.
FOURTH.	SIMPLICITY OF THE SECTIONS
FIFTH.	LITTLE COST FOR ERECTION
SIXTH.	CAN BE HIGH OVERSTRESSED WITHOUT DANGER
SEVENTH.	LESS LIABLE TO INJURY BY ACCIDENT
EIGHTH.	MORE EASILY TO PAINT
NINTH.	MORE ACCESSIBLE TO EXAMINATION
TENTH.	LITTLE COST OF MAINTENANCE

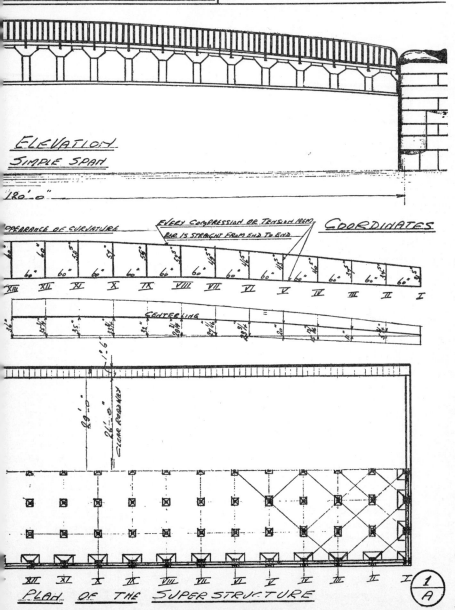

ELEVATION
SIMPLE SPAN

180'-0"

APPEARANCE OF CURVATURE

EVERY COMPRESSION OR TENSION MEM BER IS STRAIGHT FROM END TO END

COORDINATES

CENTERLINE

CLEAR ROADWAY

PLAN OF THE SUPERSTRUCTURE

Figure 49 (Concluded)

145

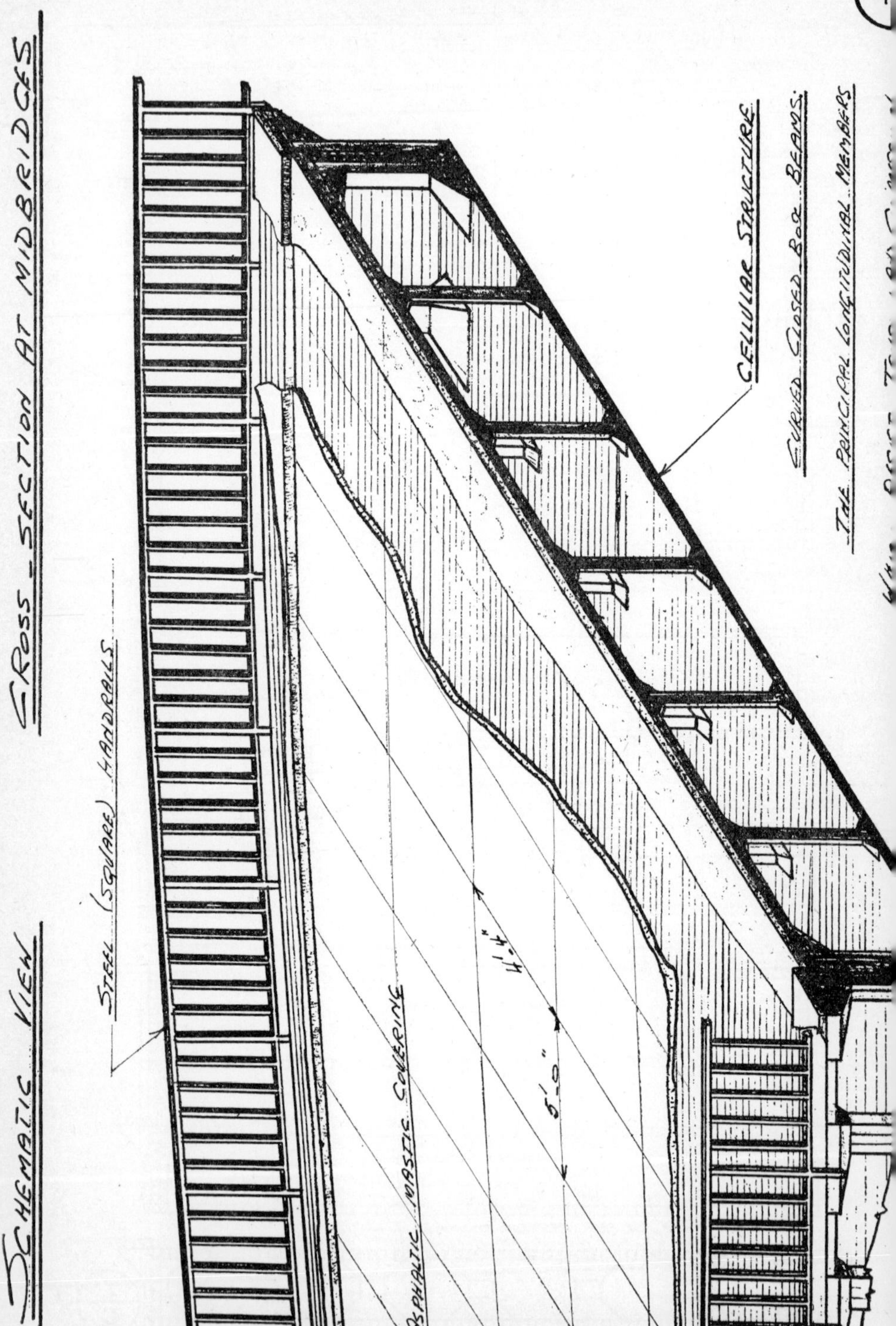

CROSS - SECTION AT MIDBRIDGES

CELLULAR STRUCTURE

CURVED CLOSED BOX BEAMS:
THE PRINCIPAL LONGITUDINAL MEMBERS

SCHEMATIC VIEW

STEEL (SQUARE) HANDRAILS

ASPHALTIC MASTIC COVERING

4'-4"

5'-0"

146

Figure 50

FOR FABRICATION BY WELDING:
ONLY CLOSED-BOX SECTIONS!
THE WHOLE CURVED-SOLID CLOSED-BOX IS A BEAM COMPOSED OF THIN
SPECIAL SHAPED PLATES WITH MANY STIFFENERS.
SCALE 1" = 4'-2"
6 x 4'-4" = 26'-0"

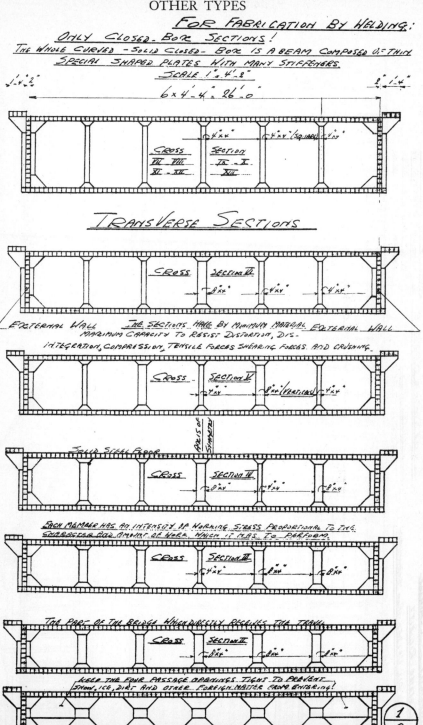

TRANSVERSE SECTIONS

EXTERNAL WALL   THE SECTIONS HAVE BY MINIMUM MATERIAL   EXTERNAL WALL
MAXIMUM CAPACITY TO RESIST DISTORTION, DIS-
INTEGRATION, COMPRESSION, TENSILE FORCES, SHEARING FORCES, AND CRUSHING.

EACH MEMBER HAS AN INTENSITY OF WORKING STRESS PROPORTIONAL TO THE
CHARACTER AND AMOUNT OF WORK WHICH IT HAS TO PERFORM.

THE PART OF THE BRIDGE WHICH DIRECTLY RECEIVES THE TRAVEL

KEEP THE FOUR PASSAGE OPENINGS TIGHT TO PREVENT
SNOW, ICE, DIRT AND OTHER FOREIGN MATTER FROM ENTERING!

FIXED SHOES ON ONE END PIER
EXPANSION SHOES ON THE OTHER

CROSS SECTION I (TAIL HALL)

$\frac{1}{C}$

Figure 51   147

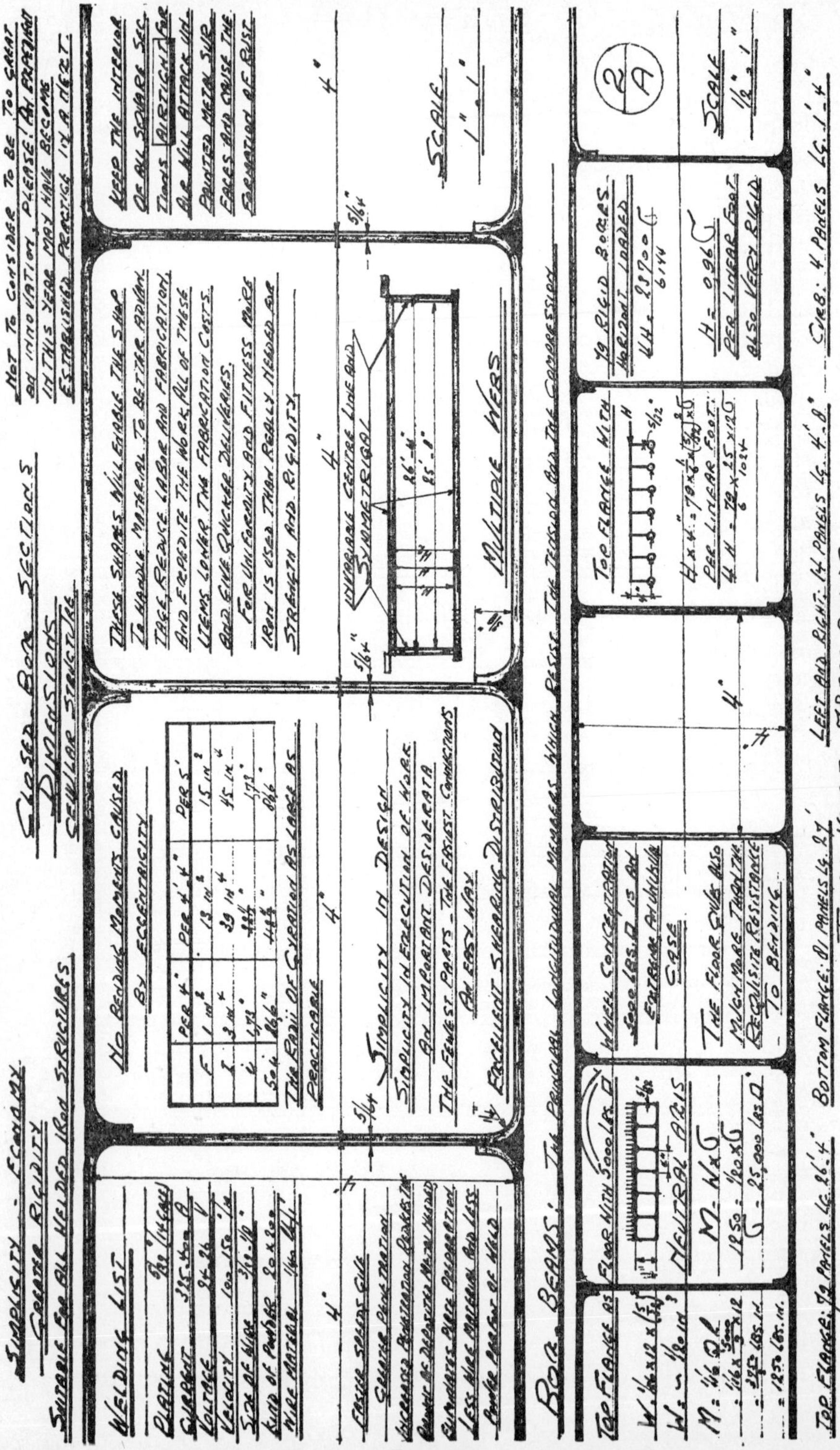

SIMPLICITY - ECONOMY
GREATER RIGIDITY
SUITABLE FOR ALL WELDED IRON STRUCTURES

CLOSED BOX SECTIONS
DIFFERS SLIGHTLY
SIMILAR STRUCTURES

KEEP THE INTERIOR OF ALL SQUARE SECTIONS PROTECTED AS THIS YEAR MAY HAVE BECOME ESTABLISHED PRACTICE IN A FLEET

NOT TO CONSIDER TO BE TOO GREAT AN INNOVATION, PLEASE AS PERHAPS OR NAIL ATTACK THE PITTED METAL SLIP EDGES AND CAUSE THE FORMATION OF RUST

THESE SHAPES WILL ENABLE THE SHOP TO HANDLE MATERIAL TO BETTER ADVANTAGE, REDUCE LABOR AND FABRICATION AND EXPEDITE THE WORK, ALL OF THESE ITEMS LOWER THE FABRICATION COSTS AND GIVE QUICKER DELIVERIES
FOR UNIFORMITY AND FITNESS THIS (RATIO) IS USED THAN REALLY NEEDED FOR STRENGTH AND RIGIDITY

SCALE
1" = 1'

MULTIPLE WEBS

WELDING LIST
CURRENT
VOLTAGE
VELOCITY
SIZE OF WIRE
KIND OF POWER
WIRE MATERIAL

Figure 52

148

width of 26 ft.-4 in. overall, exclusive of curbs. The bottom flange has a total of 81 cells and a width of 27 ft., allowing for a 4 in. overhang on each side for outside stiffeners. The webs at the center of the bridge, where the distance between flange centroids is 5 ft., have 14 cells each and a depth of 4 ft.-8 in., permitting them to be placed between the flanges (see Figure 51). Each of the 4 in. x 4 in. cells is fabricated from thin bent plate as shown in Figure 52.

The top flange, 4 in. in thickness and serving as the floor slab, is connected to the bottom flange by means of vertical columns. These columns are spaced at 5 ft. centers longitudinally and 4 ft.-4 in. centers transversely. All columns have truncated sections at both the top and bottom that serve the purpose of load distributors, and all columns are fabricated from thin bent plate. Most columns have a cross section of either one 4 in. x 4 in. cell or two 4 in. x 4 in. cells.

One stipulation which Mr. Tupker gave was that all cells were to be kept air-tight. He brought out many points in his discussion, some of which follow:

"All connections are 'balanced'—that is to say, any connection welded to plating has a welded connection to balance it on the opposite side.

"This plating without stiffeners may easily prove to be the most satisfactory welded type when regard is given to all the factors of efficiency, such as weight, durability and economy of construction.

It is comparatively easy to roll the plates to the correct curvature.
The desired standard of accuracy can be obtained without difficulty.
Only one run in each weld gives proper penetration.
The quality of that run is easy to inspect.
Reduced welding costs: result from faster travel speed.
Smaller amounts of weld metal required.
Use of electrodes with higher currents.
Only in some cases back-chipping.
No plate preparation.

"Weld strength is largely a matter of design, it is the responsibility of the welding engineer to see that the most economical procedure is chosen."

Mr. Tupker listed these ten items as advantages that his design had: (1) Compactness, structural dead weight eliminated, (2) Better resistance against shock and check vibration, (3) Low cost of manufacture, (4) Simplicity of the sections, (5) Low cost of erection, (6) Can be greatly overstressed without danger, (7) Less liable to injury by accident, (8) Ease of painting, (9) More accessible for examination, (10) Low cost of maintenance. The total weight of steel was given as 89,100 pounds. This weight will be itemized in Chapter VI where many data on cost will also be given.

T. G. Morrison, Chicago, Illinois, selected a structure that he termed a

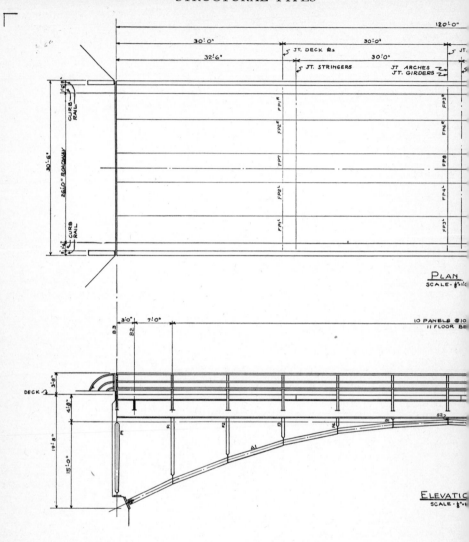

PLAN
SCALE-

ELEVATION
SCALE-

STATISTICS	
TOTAL WT. STEEL	192,400#
TOTAL WT. BITUMINOUS SURFACE	15,600#
TOTAL VOL. CURB CONCRETE	8.9 Yds.³
TOTAL WT. PER FT. OF ROADWAY	2025#/ft
DECK WT. PER FT. INCLUDING CONC. & BIT.	1398#/ft
DECK WT. PER FT. - ℞s & STRINGERS	968#/ft
SUPPORTING STRUCTURE WT. PER FT.	627#/ft
ESTIMATED COST	$16,507
EST. COST PER. SQ.FT. ROADWAY.	$5.30
ROLLED STEEL DECK ℞ ASSM. WT./FT.²	36.2#/ft

GENERAL NOTES
GENERAL SPECIFICATIONS — A.A.S.H.O.
WELDING SPECIFICATIONS — A.W.S.
LOADING H20
STRESSES - SEE DESIGN DATA

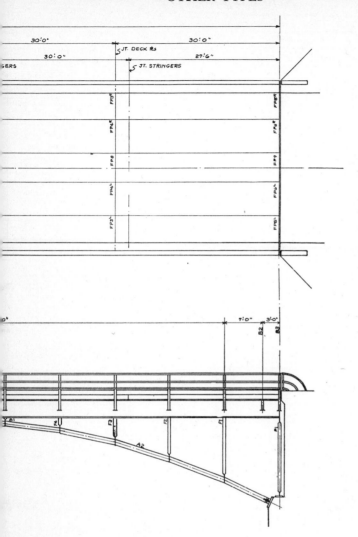

LIST OF DRAWINGS	
NO	**TITLE**
O	COVER SHEET
1	PLAN AND ELEVATION
2	CROSS SECTION AND DETAILS OF DECK PLATE
3	FLOOR BEAMS, STRUT, CURB, AND ARCH DETAILS TYPICAL BUTT WELDS
4	END GIRDER, END FRAME, AND CENTER ANCHOR
5	DESIGN DATA
6	BILL OF MATERIAL, WELD LISTS, AND ESTIMATE OF COST
7	ERECTION PROCEDURE

WELDED STEEL BRIDGE
120'-0" SPAN

PLAN AND ELEVATION

SHEET 1 OF 7

Figure 53 (Concluded)

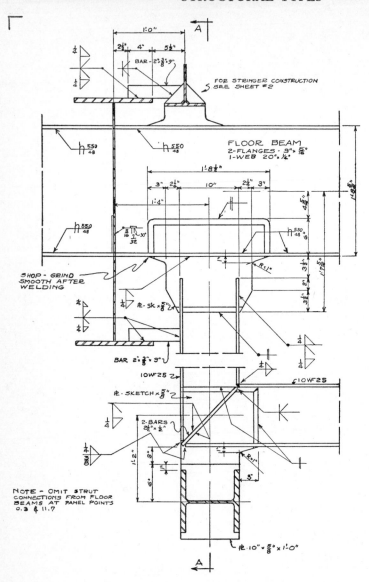

FLOOR BEAM & STRUT DETAILS

SCALE – $1\frac{1}{2}$"=1'-0"

TYPICAL BUTT WELD DETAILS & JOINT PREPARATION

Figure 54

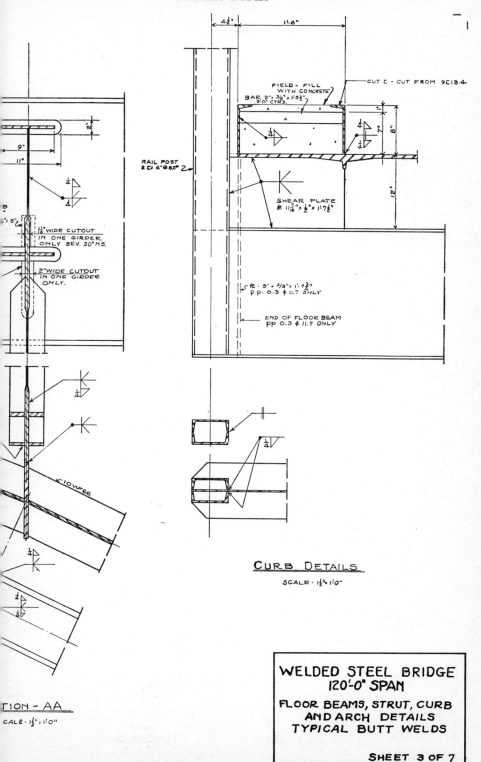

CURB DETAILS

SCALE - 1½" 1'0"

WELDED STEEL BRIDGE
120'-0" SPAN

FLOOR BEAMS, STRUT, CURB
AND ARCH DETAILS
TYPICAL BUTT WELDS

SHEET 3 OF 7

Figure 54 (Concluded)

153

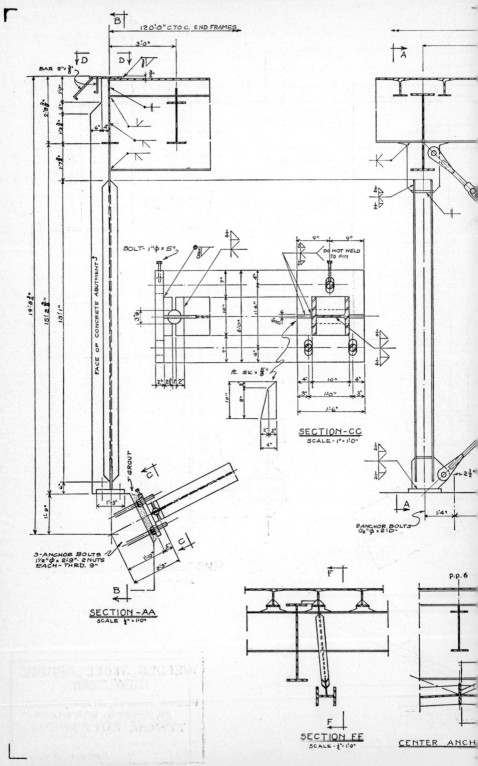

Figure 55

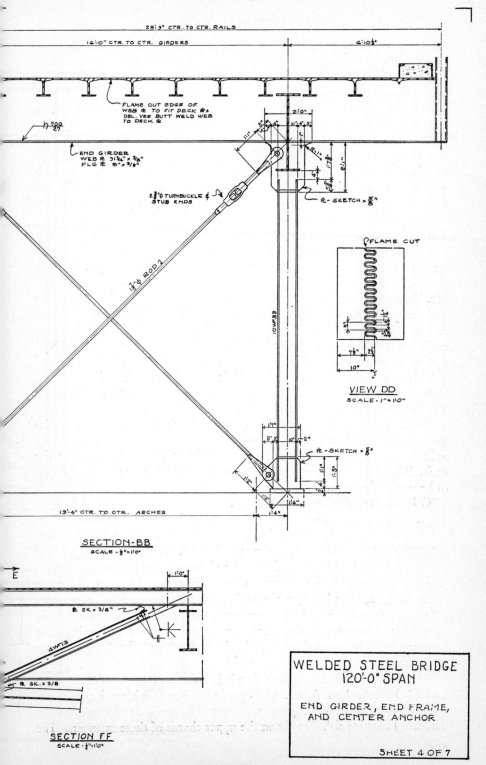

Figure 55 (Concluded)

stiffened flexible arch. His selection was due to the advantages of a stiffened flexible arch which he gave as: "(1) It is one of the naturally most beautiful bridge types. (2) Economically, it compares very favorably with plate girder construction—even for the 120 ft. span, notwithstanding the established tradition that arches are not economical for spans of less than 200 ft. (3) The flexible arch is easy to fabricate and erect."

The arches, made of 10 WF 66, are segmental with a rise of 15 ft. and spaced 13 ft. - 4 in. apart. The stiffening girders are 16 ft. apart and consist of flange plates (13 in. wide) welded to webs (38 in. x $\frac{5}{16}$ in.). The horizontal struts between the arches and the verticals at each panel point are 10 WF 25, except at the ends and at the three center panel points where verticals and struts are unnecessary.

Figure 53 shows a plan and an elevation of the bridge and Figure 70 (in Chapter III Page 199) shows a cross section, including the details of the floor system. This floor system will be elaborated upon in Chapter III. The details at a typical panel point are shown in Figure 54. About some of these, Mr. Morrison said: "At the connections of the vertical struts to the arches and floorbeams there will necessarily be a certain definite amount of hinge action. This also has been provided for by employing flexible plates. Some engineers might consider this detail in particular to be too radical and prefer, instead, a detail similar to that used at the spring lines of the arches." (Much more of his discussion of details is given in Chapter V.)

An end girder, end frame, and the center anchor are shown in Figure 55. The purpose of the center anchor was stated as follows:

"The bridge is kept centered by anchoring the deck to the arches at midspan. Slight displacements due to temperature changes or other causes induce unbalanced forces in the arches sufficiently large to re-center the deck. The deflection due to acceleration forces was investigated and found to be negligibly small.

"Other deck anchors considered were:

1. Ties made of timber or other material having a coefficient of expansion about one half that of steel, these ties to be attached to the abutments and to the girders near the opposite end. This anchor was rejected because it required the use of timber and because the ties would be loosened or damaged if the abutments tilted slightly.

2. Large springs between the ends of the girders and the abutments. Springs of a size sufficient to transmit the necessary force are readily available. However, if the frequency of oscillation of the spring-mass system is to be maintained sufficiently high, the spring force becomes excessive.

"The system adopted is unusual but it is believed quite practical."

L. C. Maugh, Ann Arbor, Michigan, used six, two-hinged continuous welded frames as the longitudinal members of his bridge and supported the reinforced concrete slab directly on the upper chords of these members. The requirements he gave for welded bridges in general, and the manner in which his design satisfied these, are as follows:

"To make welded steel highway and railroad bridges more dependable and economical in operation when subjected to heavy truck or train traffic it will be necessary to make the following changes in the present conventional welded bridges:

1. Eliminate the danger of fatigue failures by reducing the amount of fillet welds in main structural members and connections.

2. Reduce stress concentration by eliminating heavy gusset connections, floor beam and stringer connections, and by the use of the minimum number of main structural members.

3. Reduce the danger of cracking of welds and also large internal stresses in the base metal by using rolled structural shapes that spread the flange area rather than concentrating it in thick flange elements.

4. Use a sub-assembly method of erection so as to reduce the number of field connections and the amount of field welding.

"The 120 ft. span two-hinged continuous welded frame bridge shown in the accompanying drawings [Figures 56 and 57] satisfy the above requirements for a dependable and economical structure because:

1. The new type of rolled sections S1 and S2 (shown in Figure 57) not only spreads the flange material but enables connections to be made by butt welds instead of fillet welds. All corner plates are butt welded in the shop to the flanges of the new sections.

2. By placing the roadway slab directly on the upper chords of the frames all floor beams and stringer connections are eliminated, thereby reducing the amount of field welding and the danger of weld failures.

3. By using the sub-assembly arrangement shown in the erection diagram in Figure 57, the amount of field welding is not only greatly reduced but the splices can be placed where the bending moments are relatively small and the direct stress is compression. It should be noted that the parts M1, M2 and M3 can be brought together and held in position before the welding is done. All field welding can be easily performed.

4. Although the total amount of steel in the bridge can be reduced by the use of more sizes of sections it is desirable to provide duplication of details by using few sections. Therefore only two different sections have been used for all main frame members. These sections have been designed according to the stated specifications.

5. The saving in cost due to the simplification of the fabrication and erection procedures and the duplication of parts will more than offset any increase in the quantity of steel as compared to present conventional trusses.

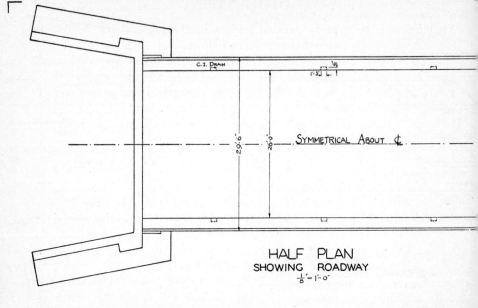

HALF PLAN
SHOWING ROADWAY
$\frac{1}{8}" = 1'-0"$

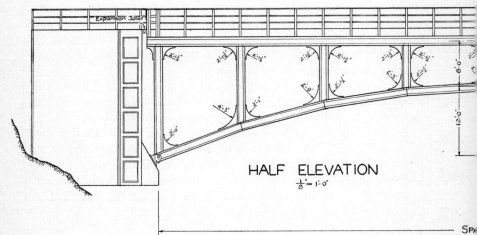

HALF ELEVATION
$\frac{1}{8}" = 1'-0"$

GENERAL NOTES

Loads and unit stresses according to AASHO specifications (1949) and standard specifications for welded highway and railway bridges (1947 American Welding Society)

Wt. of roadway per lin. ft of span	3400 lbs/lin. ft
Wt. of steel structure per lin. ft of span	1,417 "
Quantity of concrete in roadway	103 cu. yd.
Quantity of reinforcement steel in roadway	21,200 lbs.
Quantity of structural steel in bridge (including handrails)	184,000 "

Figure 56

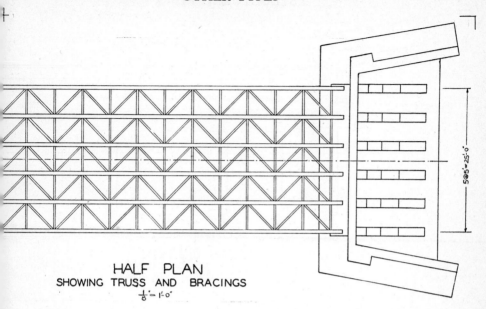

HALF PLAN
SHOWING TRUSS AND BRACINGS
$\frac{1}{8}" = 1'-0"$

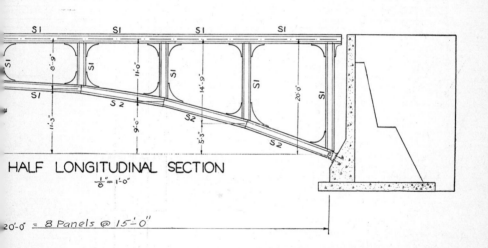

HALF LONGITUDINAL SECTION
$\frac{1}{8}" = 1'-0"$

20'-0" = 8 Panels @ 15'-0"

---

120 FT
WELDED STEEL FRAME BRIDGE
OF THE FUTURE

Sh. 1 of 2

Figure 56 (Concluded)

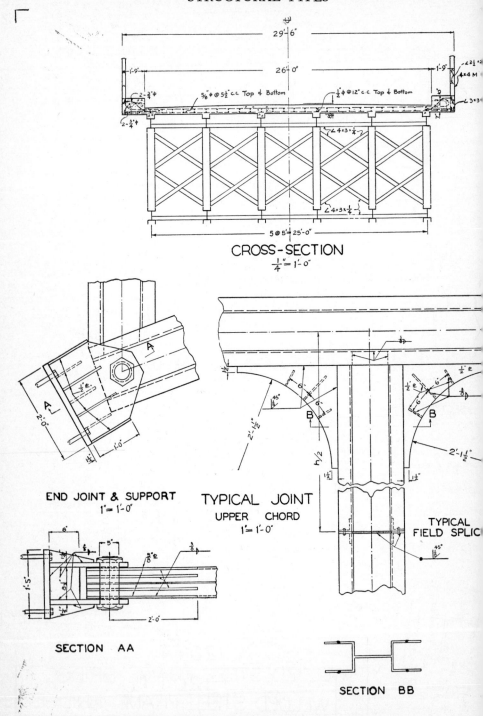

CROSS-SECTION
$\frac{1}{4}" = 1'-0"$

END JOINT & SUPPORT
$1" = 1'-0"$

TYPICAL JOINT
UPPER CHORD
$1' = 1'-0"$

TYPICAL FIELD SPLICE

SECTION AA

SECTION BB

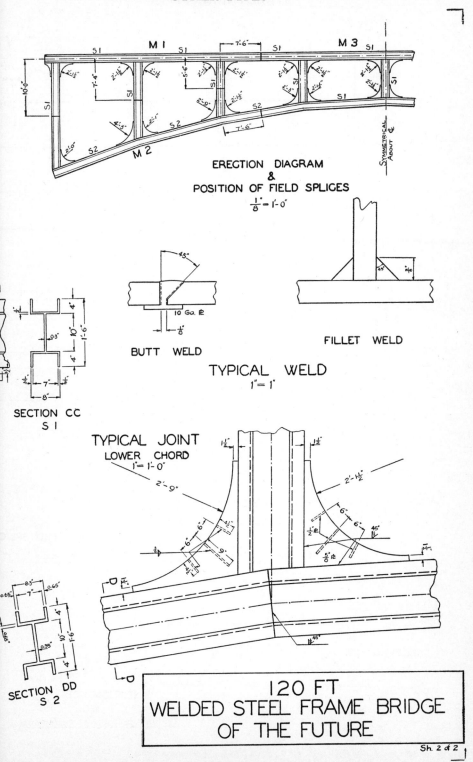

ERECTION DIAGRAM
&
POSITION OF FIELD SPLICES
$\frac{1}{8}" = 1'-0"$

BUTT WELD

FILLET WELD

TYPICAL WELD
$1" = 1"$

SECTION CC
S 1

TYPICAL JOINT
LOWER CHORD
$1" = 1'-0"$

SECTION DD
S 2

120 FT
WELDED STEEL FRAME BRIDGE
OF THE FUTURE

Sh. 2 of 2

Figure 57 (Concluded)   161

STRUCTURAL TYPES

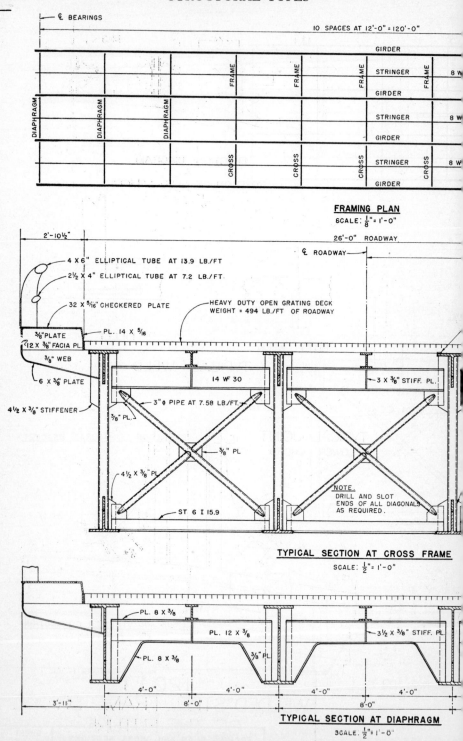

℄ BEARINGS

10 SPACES AT 12'-0" = 120'-0"

GIRDER

FRAME · FRAME · FRAME · STRINGER · FRAME · 8 W

GIRDER

DIAPHRAGM · DIAPHRAGM · DIAPHRAGM · STRINGER · 8 W

GIRDER

CROSS · CROSS · CROSS · STRINGER · CROSS · 8 W

GIRDER

FRAMING PLAN
SCALE: $\frac{1}{8}$" = 1'-0"

2'-10½"   26'-0" ROADWAY
                                    ℄ ROADWAY

4 X 6" ELLIPTICAL TUBE AT 13.9 LB./FT

2½ X 4" ELLIPTICAL TUBE AT 7.2 LB./FT.

32 X 5⁄16" CHECKERED PLATE

HEAVY DUTY OPEN GRATING DECK
WEIGHT = 494 LB./FT OF ROADWAY

⅜"PLATE   PL. 14 X 5⁄16
12 X ⅜" FACIA PL

⅜" WEB

6 X ⅜" PLATE   14 WF 30   3 X ⅜" STIFF. PL.

4½ X ⅜" STIFFENER   3"⌀ PIPE AT 7.58 LB./FT.
⅜" PL.

⅜" PL

4½ X ⅜" PL

ST 6 I 15.9

NOTE.
DRILL AND SLOT
ENDS OF ALL DIAGONALS
AS REQUIRED.

TYPICAL SECTION AT CROSS FRAME
SCALE: $\frac{1}{2}$" = 1'-0"

PL. 8 X ⅜

PL. 12 X ⅜   3½ X ⅜" STIFF. PL.

PL. 8 X ⅜   ⅜" PL

4'-0"   4'-0"   4'-0"   4'-0"

3'-11"   8'-0"   8'-0"

TYPICAL SECTION AT DIAPHRAGM
SCALE. $\frac{1}{2}$" = 1'-0"

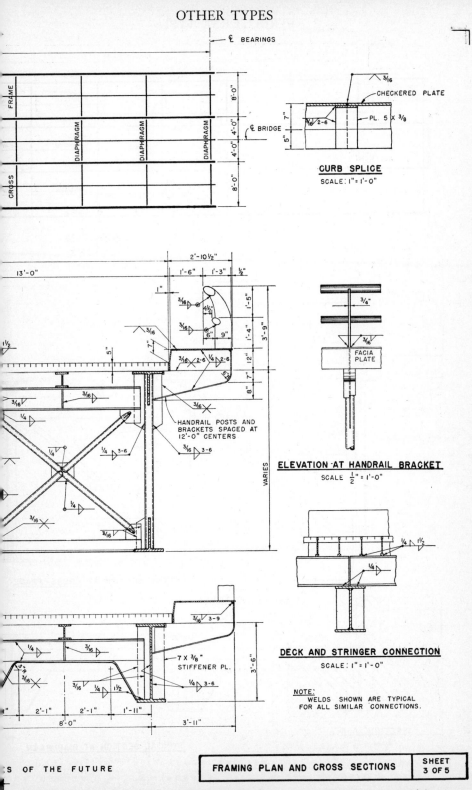

CURB SPLICE
SCALE: 1" = 1'-0"

ELEVATION AT HANDRAIL BRACKET
SCALE: ½" = 1'-0"

HANDRAIL POSTS AND
BRACKETS SPACED AT
12'-0" CENTERS

DECK AND STRINGER CONNECTION
SCALE: 1" = 1'-0"

NOTE:
WELDS SHOWN ARE TYPICAL
FOR ALL SIMILAR CONNECTIONS.

S OF THE FUTURE

FRAMING PLAN AND CROSS SECTIONS	SHEET 3 OF 5

Figure 58 (Concluded)   163

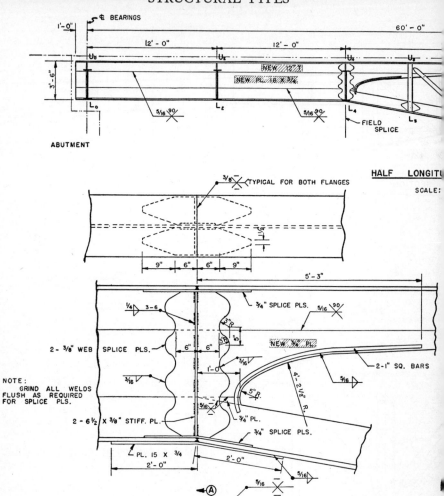

ABUTMENT

3/8 ✕ TYPICAL FOR BOTH FLANGES

NOTE:
GRIND ALL WELDS
FLUSH AS REQUIRED
FOR SPLICE PLS.

2 - 3/8" WEB SPLICE PLS.

3/4" SPLICE PLS.

5/16 90

2 - 1" SQ. BARS

4 - 2 1/2" R.

5/16

5" R.

3/4" PL.

3/4" SPLICE PLS.

2 - 6 1/2 x 3/8" STIFF. PL.

PL. 15 x 3/4

2'- 0"

2'- 0"

1/4 3 - 6

3/16

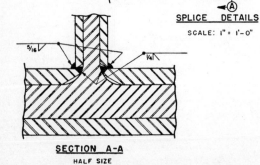

SPLICE DETAILS

SCALE: 1" = 1'- 0"

5/16 ✕

5/16 ◁ TYPICAL

1/4 1 1/2

SECTION A-A

HALF SIZE

Figure 59

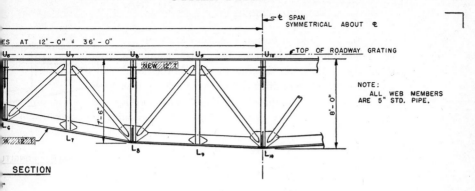

SECTION

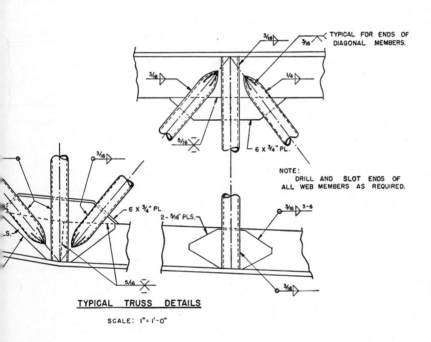

NOTE:
ALL WEB MEMBERS ARE 5" STD. PIPE.

TYPICAL FOR ENDS OF DIAGONAL MEMBERS.

6 X ¾" PL.

NOTE:
DRILL AND SLOT ENDS OF ALL WEB MEMBERS AS REQUIRED.

6 X ¾" PL

2 - ⁵⁄₁₆" PLS.

TYPICAL TRUSS DETAILS

SCALE: 1"= 1'-0"

6. If it is not desirable to design the abutments for thrust the structure can be given similar proportions by cantilevering the frame over the supports. The cantilever arrangements should be used if multiple spans supported on piers are necessary.

7. The type of bridge shown is also desirable with respect to appearance and maintenance. It does not have the confused appearance of the ordinary truss as the function of every member is apparent to any individual. All parts are easily accessible for painting.

S. K. Willis, Independence, Missouri, and C. R. Hawker and D. L. Stevens, of Kansas City, Missouri, combined the girder and truss types into a single structural unit. By spacing four of these at 8 ft. centers and placing stringers (8 WF 35) between them, the open grating deck is supported every 4 ft. Transverse members, diaphragms or cross frames, are spaced at 12 ft. centers and provide the supports for the stringers. The reasons for their choice of this type and additional description of the structure are given below:

"Since the four principal load carrying members of the bridge are a combination of girder and truss, this design incorporates the advantages of both the truss and the girder. At the ends of the bridge, where shear is a primary factor, a girder section provides the necessary area without excessive depth of structure. Throughout the remainder of the bridge, moment governs the design and a truss provides the necessary material more economically than the girder. By reverting to a truss, the depth can be increased without an increase in material, thus decreasing the stresses due to moment. This also eliminates all unnecessary web material where shear stresses are low.

"The flanges of the girder extend into the truss to form the top and bottom chords of the truss. Present rolled sections do not provide satisfactory dimensions for these members and a new Tee section was developed. The new Tee section has several advantages over present rolled sections when used as a flange for a welded girder or a chord for a welded truss. The principal difference between this new Tee and those rolled at present is that the area has been reduced in the web and is concentrated in the flange where a maximum moment of inertia can be obtained from it. The depth of the web is two-thirds the depth of present structural Tees of comparable area and weight. The web thickness was not decreased appreciably. Therefore, when used as a girder flange, the intensity of web compression at bearing points is not excessive. The new Tee resembles a built-up plate-girder flange where the center of gravity lies as close as possible to the extreme fiber. This gives an average fiber stress in the flange, which is nearly equal to the maximum fiber stress.

"Tee sections for welded structures could very easily be rolled with a double bevel on the end of the stem. This would facilitate butt welding to plates or other shapes. The double bevel was used for the Tee section developed with this design. Plates of various widths could also be rolled with this double bevel on one or both edges. This type of plate has been called for in some of the details.

"All web members are detailed as round pipe sections in the main girder-truss and in the diaphragms. This unique feature provides a minimum area with a maximum radius of gyration, which is symmetrical about any axis bending. This detail is adaptable to welding only and is far superior to the uneconomical angle sections commonly used as web members in riveted structures."

A framing plan and the details of a typical cross frame and a typical diaphragm are given in Figure 58. A half longitudinal section and the details of the girder-truss are shown in Figure 59.

CHAPTER III

FLOOR SYSTEMS

Whereas the preceding chapter dealt primarily with the main longitudinal members and their parts and secondarily with bracing, floor systems, and details, this chapter is devoted principally to floor systems, but other parts of the bridge will be discussed if they influenced the design or function of the members of the floor systems. According to the Rules and Conditions of this program, participants were required to design a floor only so far as was necessary to indicate the dimensions from which the gross weight was determined unless the floor was to contribute to the strength of the supporting structure. However, a great deal of valuable information on floor design was presented and some of it has been included in this chapter.

Among the designs of this program, the variation in the floor systems was almost as great as the variation in bridge types. As treated here, floor systems include the floorbeams and all members supported by the floor-beams. Some designs did not have floorbeams and others (having more than two principal longitudinal members) did not have stringers either. For such structures as the latter, a reinforced concrete slab or a stiffened steel plate would constitute the entire floor system.

This chapter is divided into three sections, reinforced concrete, steel grids and steel plates. Although the structures of some of the roadway surfaces do not strictly belong in any of the three sections, it is felt that each floor system can be sufficiently classified in one of the three.

Reinforced Concrete

Many designers preferred reinforced concrete slabs. The reasons given for this preference differed in number and in content, but the most common one was that concrete slabs provide a better roadway surface.

In many cases, the reinforced concrete slabs here have been reinforced in the conventional manner by common steel reinforcing bars, but some designers have used steel structural shapes exclusively, or in addition to the usual round bars. Also included in this section are slabs constructed by placing concrete on corrugated sheets, ribbed plates, or similar steel sections, and for which the steel members served both as forms and as the reinforcing material; however, regular steel grid floors filled with concrete, such as I-Beam-Lok Armored Floor Slab, are discussed in the next section under the type, Steel Grid. If concrete was added to the top of a steel floor for the purpose of providing a wearing surface and the concrete was not considered as structural material, the floor system has not been classified in this section.

The means of support varied. The usual procedure of supporting slabs on stringers that framed into floorbeams was utilized by a considerable number of the designers; however, many supported the slabs directly on floorbeams (there being no stringers), or directly on the top of the principal longitudinal members (the bridge having neither stringers nor floorbeams). A few designs had two-way slabs that were supported by the longitudinal members as well as the floorbeams.

It was not uncommon for the designers to attach the reinforced concrete slabs to the top flanges, or top chords, of the longitudinal members by means of some type of shear connectors in order to use a portion of the slab as effective flange (chord) material. This kind of composite action existed also, in a few instances, for floorbeams and stringers.

An example of the conventional floor system that consists of a reinforced concrete slab, stringers, and floorbeams is the one used by Mr. Pimenoff and described in Chapter II. As mentioned there, he adopted a concrete slab for the deck of his bridge (see Figure 24, Page 81) because of its considerably lower cost than a steel deck or grid type floor, but he said that a more expensive but lighter floor would be economical in a long span bridge.

R. A. Dunstan, V. Karmalsky, and S. C. Robertson, all of Sydney, Australia, selected a reinforced concrete slab, 5¾ in. in thickness including ¼ in. for wearing surface, supported by stringers (18 I 54.7) 4 ft. - 7 in. apart. The stringers are set ¼ in. into the slab to obtain full lateral support for the compression flange. Floorbeams every 20 ft. are fabricated by welding 11 in. x 1 in. flange plates to a 30 in. x 5⁄16 in. web. To avoid fixed end conditions in stringers and floorbeams, their end connections are made through end plates that allow a certain amount of end rotation. The curbs are reinforced to take bending stresses since the truss top chords are designed for direct compression only. These details are shown in Figure 60 which is a sectional view of the bridge.

In Chapter II, Mr. Jennison's design was discussed and three of his drawings were shown as Figures 21, 22, and 23 (Pages 75, 77 and 79). His reinforced concrete slab functions not only as a deck but also as the main compression members for the top chords of the trusses and as the upper parts of the reinforced concrete floorbeams. The discussion of this multiple purpose slab given in the previous chapter will not be repeated here, but the reinforcement and details of the slab are shown in Figure 61. The eight ⅝ in. round deformed reinforcing bar hooks and the forty 2½ in. x 2 in. x ¼ in. angle shear lugs that are welded to the steel T-sections of every floorbeam are not shown in this figure.

Another design that utilized a reinforced concrete slab as effective structural material for the floorbeams as well as the longitudinal members was the one presented by Messrs. Bleich and Schwarting (see Figure 4 Page 19), The design embodies a two-way slab with a 20 ft. span between floorbeams and a 22 ft. - 6 in. span between girders. The shear connectors are spirals with a 6 in. mean diameter. The bars are ¾ in. rounds in the end panels

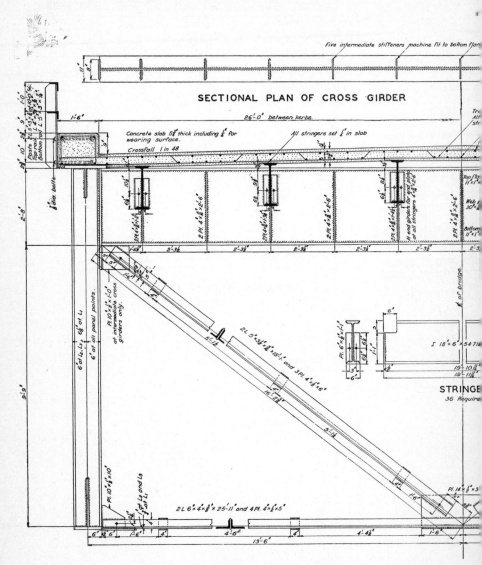

SECTIONAL PLAN OF CROSS GIRDER

DECK SLAB STRINGERS, CROSS GIRDERS, SWAY BRACING

Scale : 1 in. = 1 ft.

Notes:
¼" shop fillet weld
⅜" field fillet weld
¾" dia. erection bolts

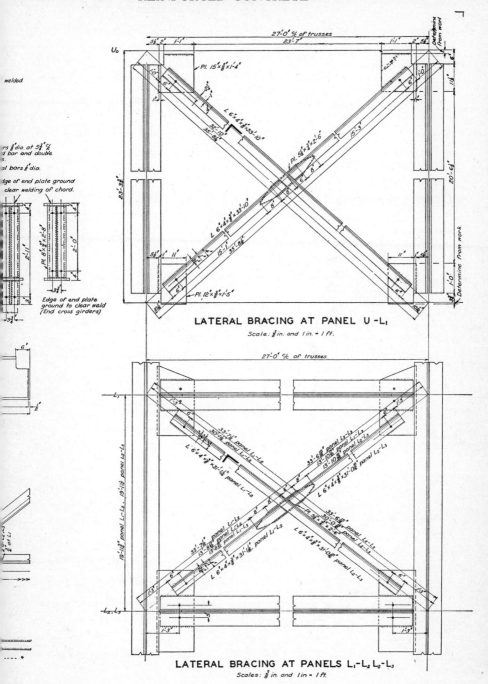

LATERAL BRACING AT PANEL U-L₁

Scale: ⅜ in. and 1 in. = 1 ft.

LATERAL BRACING AT PANELS L₁-L₂ L₂-L₃

Scales: ⅜ in. and 1 in. = 1 ft.

Figure 60 (Concluded)   171

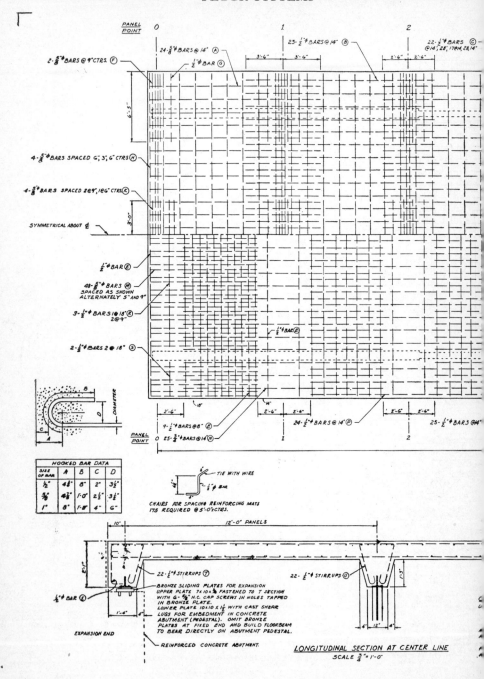

Figure 61

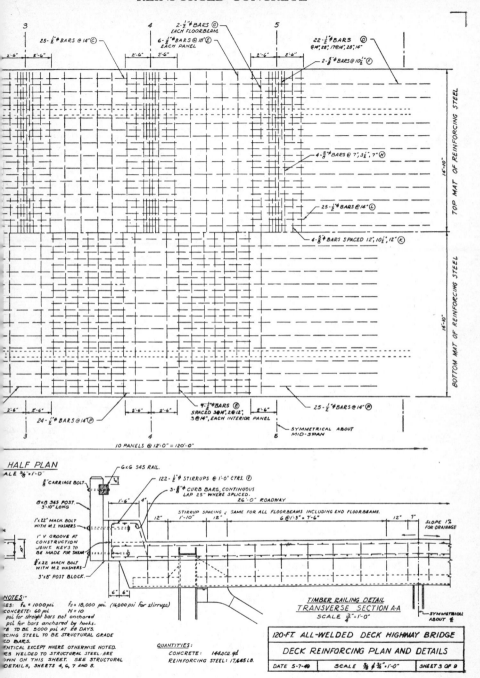

HALF PLAN
SCALE 3/8" = 1'-0"

TIMBER RAILING DETAIL
TRANSVERSE SECTION A-A
SCALE 3/4" = 1'-0"

120-FT ALL-WELDED DECK HIGHWAY BRIDGE		
DECK REINFORCING PLAN AND DETAILS		
DATE 5-7-40	SCALE 3/8 & 3/4" = 1'-0"	SHEET 3 OF 9

Figure 61 (Concluded)

173

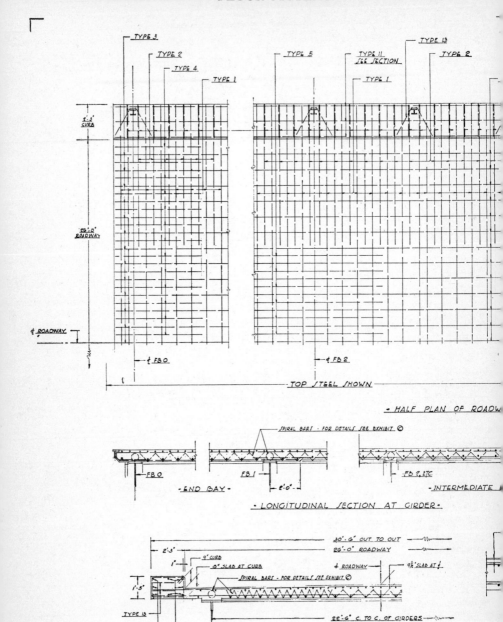

- HALF PLAN OF ROADWAY

- LONGITUDINAL SECTION AT GIRDER -

- TRANSVERSE SECTION -
- INTERMEDIATE BAY -

Figure 62

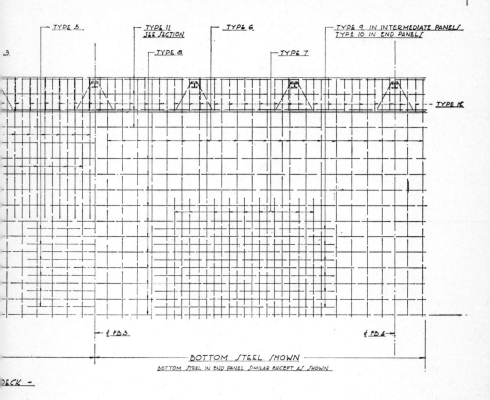

TYPE 5.   TYPE 11 SEE SECTION   TYPE 6   TYPE 9 IN INTERMEDIATE PANELS
TYPE 10 IN END PANELS

TYPE 8   TYPE 7

TYPE 12

£ FB3   £ FB4

BOTTOM STEEL SHOWN

BOTTOM STEEL IN END PANEL SIMILAR EXCEPT AS SHOWN

DECK -

VER

¼" WEARING SURFACE

VARIES

COVER

TAIL ∘

•BAR LIST•

TYPE NO.	SIZE	LENGTH
1	5/8" ⌀	30'- 3"
2	DO.	9'- 0"
3	DO.	131'- 0" *
4	DO.	8'- 0"
5	3/4" ⌀	9'- 0"
6	1/2" ⌀	30'- 3"
7	DO.	15'- 0"
8	3/4" ⌀	131'- 0" *
9	5/8" ⌀	15'- 0"
10	3/4" ⌀	15'- 0"
11	1/2" ⌀	130'- 0" *
12	3/8" ⌀	6'- 9"
13	1/2" ⌀	4'- 6"

* INCLUDES 2 LAP JOINTS

- NOTES -

1. THE FORMWORK FOR THAT PORTION OF THE SLAB BETWEEN THE MAIN GIRDERS SHALL BE SUSPENDED FROM THE FLOORBEAMS IN SUCH MANNER THAT THE FLOORBEAMS CARRY THE ENTIRE WEIGHT OF THIS PART OF THE SLAB DURING POURING.

2. ULTIMATE COMPRESSIVE STRENGTH OF CONCRETE AFTER 28 DAYS, $f_c' = 3000$ LBS/SQ.IN.

- DESIGN OF ALL-WELDED HIGHWAY BRIDGE -

• ROADWAY SLAB DETAILS•

- SCALE: ¼"=1'-0" AND AS NOTED -   - EXHIBIT Ⓔ -

Figure 62 (Concluded)

and ⅝ in. rounds elsewhere. They are welded to the top flanges of the girders or floorbeams. The spacing of the lower bars of the slab reinforcement is arranged to agree with the pitch of the spirals. The valleys of the spirals locate the positions of the reinforcing bars and it is unnecessary to thread bars through the loops of the spirals.

In discussing their two-way slab, Messrs. Bleich and Schwarting stated:

"Two-way concrete slabs of the large spans employed in the design permit a considerable reduction in the number of floor members resulting in a substantial saving of structural steel.

"Such slabs will be necessarily heavier than the usual one-way concrete slab. But by suitable selection of the panel side ratio, and by utilizing the crown of the roadway to vary the slab thickness from 9½ in. at the crown to 8 in. at the gutter, the increased weight of the deck does not upset the economy for a bridge of this span.

"The use of the two-way slab reduces the number of beams to be assembled and welded to a minimum, reducing the amount of welding and the cost of erection.

"Large span two-way slabs are particularly well suited for application in this welded bridge, where their use, together with composite floorbeams and girders, results in an extremely simple, straightforward and economical design."

A cost comparison was made to compare this design with an alternative design consisting of a one-way slab and stringers. Having a 6¾ in. slab, this alternative design required less concrete and reinforcing steel, and it saved some in the plate girders due to a decrease in total dead load. But the three stringers (18 WF 50) which were added made the total cost higher even though there was composite action between the slab and the stringers, floorbeams, and girders. The results showed the total weight of the deck in lbs. per ft. of length was 4000 lbs. to 3300 lbs. but the total cost of the deck in dollars per ft. of length was $83.95 to $102.50. Therefore, the two-way slab was heavier but cheaper.

Attention was called to the fact that the deflection of supporting beams might increase moments in two-way slabs considerably. The effect was investigated and they said: "It was found that the increases would be very large for plain rolled floorbeams, and that even for the composite sections used in this design noticeable increases of moments occur.

"The proposed design avoids any such increase of moments by suspending the formwork for the slab from the floorbeams in such manner that these beams carry, during pouring of the concrete, all the weight of the slab situated between the main girders."

The slab details are shown in Figure 62.

The floor system for Mr. Ullman's design is a reinforced concrete slab 8½ in. deep (see Figure 63). It is supported by and anchored to the four top chords of the three space trusses. The slab has three continuous spans

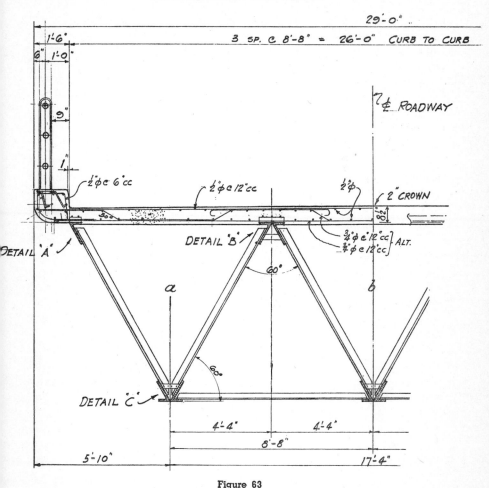

Figure 63

of 8 ft. - 8 in. each. The shear lugs, $2\frac{1}{2}$ in. x $\frac{1}{2}$ in. bars, are welded to the top chords and are spaced at 12 in. centers. Welded to the top of these shear lugs and connecting them together are $\frac{5}{8}$ in. round deformed bars that provide anchorage for the slab. This anchorage plus the shear connections assure slab participation in resisting the live load stresses in the top chords. The details of this design are given in Figures 32 and 33 (Pages 105 and 107) and a discussion of the space trusses is included in Chapter II.

Mr. Ullman said: "A reinforced concrete deck slab was selected because requirements of modern vehicular traffic demand a uniform, hard continuous surface and a slab of adequate weight and depth. A deck consisting of 'T' or 'J' beam Lok construction would have required approximately four times as much steel as the reinforcing steel required for the concrete deck. Because of a lighter weight, some saving would have resulted in the weight of the supporting structure. However, it was felt that a greater dead weight of the bridge is more desirable than a lighter weight structure. Furthermore, a shallower deck on beams cannot be considered to participate in the composite action of the bridge as the submitted concrete slab does."

The design of Messrs. Fietz and Walt is described in Chapter II. The bridge consists of three longitudinal girders, four transverse stiffening gird- ers, and a reinforced concrete floor slab. Not only does the 10 in. slab serve as the entire floor system, but also it is used structurally as top flange material for the three girders with each flange having the same effective slab width. The shear connectors, 63 per girder, are tees welded to the top flanges with the 6 in. webs pointed toward the ends. They project 4 in. into the slab. A transverse section of this floor including the reinforcement details is shown in Figure 64.

A slab very similar to the one above is the slab designed by Messrs. Brigham and Steiner and shown in Figure 41 (Page 125). Here again, there are no stringers or floorbeams, and a 10 in. slab is the complete deck as well as effective top chord material. This slab, however, has a transverse span of 11 ft. and the shear anchorage, as shown in Figure 39 (Page 121), is entirely different. Pertinent to these points of composite action and shear connections of slab and chords, Messrs. Brigham and Steiner made these statements:

"As reinforced concrete and welded steel are the most suitable building materials for monolythical structures, composite beam action should be made use of wherever possible. Structures built accordingly have greater rigidity, a greater factor of safety, and require less steel. Besides, steel surfaces enveloped in concrete need no maintenance.

"Composite beam action can be fully utilized only when the weight of the concrete floor, usually about ⅔ of the total D.L., is carried by the action of the composed steel and concrete members. For such a case falsework is indispensable. The presented design would have been even more economical if composite beam action had been fully utilized. The latter calls for well designed, adequate shear anchors. The shear anchors shown have been successfully tested previously in similar structures. Having a relatively great contact surface with the concrete over a wide floor area, this shear anchor assures a fairly well distributed transmission of stresses, thus avoid- ing critical stress concentrations. Here, as well as in welded connections, the stress paths cannot be neglected."

Messers. Bresler and Lin used sheet steel in their bridge. Their design is discussed in Chapter II and some details are shown in Figure 5 (Page 23), including those of the corrugated deck floor and floorbeams. As mentioned there, this floor system acts as a form for the concrete, as the roadway, as the stringers, as the compression flanges of the main girders, and as the top lateral bracing. The floor deck is supported by floorbeams at 6 ft. centers and is continuous over the supports. It consists of a series of adjacent 6 in. hats. Each 30 in. width contains 5 hats, 6 in. in height and 6 in. in width. The top of each hat is 2½ in. wide. They are made from No. 12 gage sheet steel. Using these corrugations as forms, lightweight concrete is poured until the top of the hats are covered by 1½ in. of concrete. Stresses were computed on the basis that the corrugation only was effective and also on the basis that the corrugation and concrete (reinforced) acted together. The stresses were not high either way. Concerning stresses in the floor deck, the authors said:

"The floor deck elements, forming the compression flange of the girder, receive or give up their normal stresses due to bending by means of shear stresses in the flat sheet of the deck system and in the vertical webs. The conventional flexure theory neglects the effect of shear deformation on the normal stress distribution. This effect may become important in structures made of light gage steel where the flange elements are distributed over a large width, and particularly if the shear rigidity of the flange elements is relatively small. The effect of shear deformations is to increase the normal bending stresses near the connection of the flange to the vertical webs, and to decrease the normal stresses in the region away from the webs. This change in the stress due to shear deformations is essentially local, and is most severe at the point of application of the concentrated loads or at the points of change in the cross-section. The problem of this local stress concentration, known as 'shear lag', has been thoroughly investigated in connection with the design of aircraft structures. The effect of shear deformations on the normal stress distribution was considered in this design. An approximate solution of this problem indicates an increase in the compression stress at the top corners of the girder cross section of 2300 psi. This increase occurs in the flange area immediately adjacent to the vertical web. Its effect is not critical since the stress in this area is due to girder action only and is computed to be 8900 psi. Thus, the maximum stress at the corner, including the effect of shear deformation, is not critical."

Figure 10a (Page 39) shows a section of the bridge Messrs. Borton and Borton designed. The floor system is composed of special channels, filled and covered with concrete, supported on floorbeams at 10 ft. centers. Their reasons for choosing a concrete surface were:

"The concrete was adopted because—

1. It contributes rigidity and mass to the structure making it more resistant to lateral forces and reducing the vibration due to heavy, rapid moving traffic loads.

2. It can be easily molded or crowned to facilitate surface drainage, without complicating the supporting structure.

3. It provides a finished surface proven satisfactory for traffic. The use of air entraining cement in proportioning the concrete gives satisfactory durability and permanence. The surface is skid resistant and can be finished to match the approach roadway, thereby removing the hazard

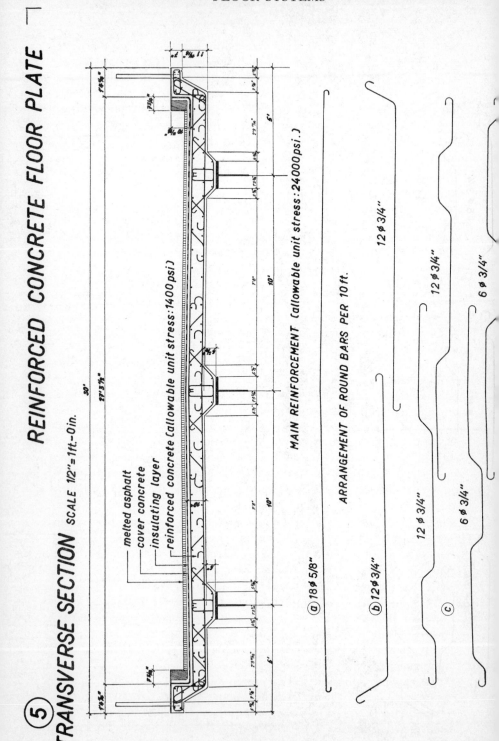

REINFORCED CONCRETE FLOOR PLATE

⑤ TRANSVERSE SECTION SCALE 1/2"=1ft.-0in.

melted asphalt
cover concrete
insulating layer
reinforced concrete (allowable unit stress:1400 psi)

MAIN REINFORCEMENT (allowable unit stress: 24000 psi.)

ARRANGEMENT OF ROUND BARS PER 10 ft.

ⓐ 18 φ 5/8"

ⓑ 12 φ 3/4"   12 φ 3/4"   12 φ 3/4"   12 φ 3/4"

ⓒ   6 φ 3/4"   6 φ 3/4"

Figure 64

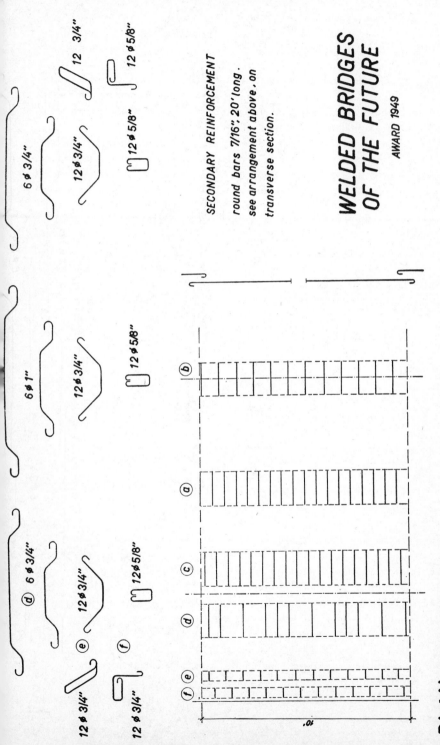

6 ∅ 3/4"

12 ∅ 3/4"

12 ∅ 5/8"

6 ∅ 1"

12 ∅ 3/4"

12 ∅ 5/8"

12   3/4"

12 ∅ 5/8"

ⓓ 6 ∅ 3/4"

ⓔ 12 ∅ 3/4"

ⓕ 12 ∅ 5/8"

12 ∅ 3/4"

12 ∅ 3/4"

SECONDARY REINFORCEMENT

round bars 7/16", 20' long.
see arrangement above, on
transverse section.

WELDED BRIDGES
OF THE FUTURE

AWARD 1949

PLAN SCALE 1/2"=1ft.-0in.

10'

ⓑ ⓐ ⓒ ⓓ ⓔ ⓕ

Figure 64 (Concluded)

191

from a change in either the appearance or texture of the pavement. It is possible that a light weight concrete could be used to advantage although this weight differential has not been utilized in the design. Future surfacing imposing an unanticipated weight is always a possibility. It is therefore desirable that a reasonable factor of safety be built into the deck system. If asphalt surface is used on the approaches the bridge deck should be filled with concrete to the top of the floor plate ribs and the asphalt topping applied above.

The dimensions of the deck channel are given in Figure 10a and the designers described its advantages as follows: "The floor shapes are designed to support the floor fill and the concentrated wheel loads including impact. While various weights could be devised to suit different loads and spans, we have selected a 24 in., 70.3 lb. section for this design supporting an H-20 truck loading on a 10 ft. span. The shape selected corresponds approximately to a channel with two intermediate ribs. One flange is rolled one half inch narrower than the other, one inch narrower than the intermediate ribs to allow for joining the sections by welding. The advantages of this ribbed floor channel are:

1. Good bond with the roadway fill so that floor channel and concrete fill act as a reinforced unit.

2. Relatively smooth under deck surface, reducing corrosion area, and simplifying maintenance.

3. A section modulus which permits the member to span from floor beam to floor beam eliminating stringers.

4. A web sufficiently thick and well reinforced to serve as the top flange of the bridge girder, as well as the floor support. Due to the fact that it is generally advisable to limit the use of the floor system as a structural part of the girder, we have reduced the area of flange considered effective in resisting girder stresses to a strip about 40 inches wide directly over the girder where bending stresses in the floor are a minimum.

5. The sections can be easily welded along the flanges to form an integral floor unit.

"Standard rolled wide flange sections are proposed for floor beams. These are readily available and a depth of section has been selected which is somewhat in excess of design requirements, to provide additional stiffness and frame resistance to unsymmetrically applied loads."

Mr. Spaulding incorporated some unusual features in his floor system. The stringer system he chose is termed the Restrained Cantilever Beam System. In this floor, the end spans (16 ft.-8 in.) are shorter than the intermediate spans (21 ft.-8 in.) so that all maximum positive bending moments will be substantially equal and all maximum negative bending moments will be substantially equal throughout the length of the bridge. Composite action between the floor slab and the stringers is effected where the top flange is in compression. To obtain better efficiency in composite beam action, Mr. Spaulding suggested a new I beam that had considerably more metal in the bottom flange than in the top. The spacing of the stringers across the roadway is not uniform, the edge bays of the floor slab having shorter spans. He said: "This is not only more efficient as to the floor slab itself but effects a better transverse distribution to the several stringers of critical point load reactions in mid-span. A transverse equalizer beam (or diaphragm) is placed at the point of normal maximum positive bending moment. This, together with the unbalancing of the stringer spacing, is most effective in the distribution to the stringers of critical point loadings."

The trusses of this design are discussed in Chapter II and shown in Figures 25 and 26 (Page 87). A partial framing plan of the floor is given here as Figure 65 and a transverse truss and floor cross section are shown in Figure 66. The reinforced concrete slab is 6⅜ in. thick. The proposed stringers weigh 30 lbs. per lin. ft., are 12 in. deep, and have flanges 4 in. wide but of unequal thickness. The transverse equalizing beams are 12 WF 27.

Mr. Spaulding called attention to the following point: "In the design submitted it is to be noted that the floor system may expand and contract from the center of the bridge in both directions independent of the carrying trusses. The vertical supports to the floor system have sufficient 'spring' so that no overstressing is developed."

Mr. Faltus used for his design a floor system composed of strips of precast reinforced concrete, 2 ft. wide, laid across the top flanges of his four main girders. After putting the girder flanges in tension by erection supports at the third points, the shear connectors embedded in the slab strips are welded to the top flanges. These details are discussed more fully in Chapter II and a longitudinal section is shown in Figure 7 (Page 29).

Steel Grid

Of the designs using this kind of flooring, about half had concrete filled grid floors, the others had open decking. Generally, lightweight concrete was the filler material. The two reasons most commonly given for having filled decking were to provide a better roadway surface and to protect the structure beneath. Those who preferred the open decking did so to have less weight and no drainage or snow removal problems.

The conventional supporting structures for steel decking, comprising either sills, stringers, and floorbeams, or stringers and floorbeams, in accordance with the kind of decking, were only slightly more common than floor systems having fewer members. Some designers having as many as four top chords placed the decking directly on the chords and omitted the stringers and floorbeams.

A transverse section of Mr. Kavanagh's bridge in Figure 29 (Page 97) shows the floor system composed of decking, sills, stringers, and floorbeams.

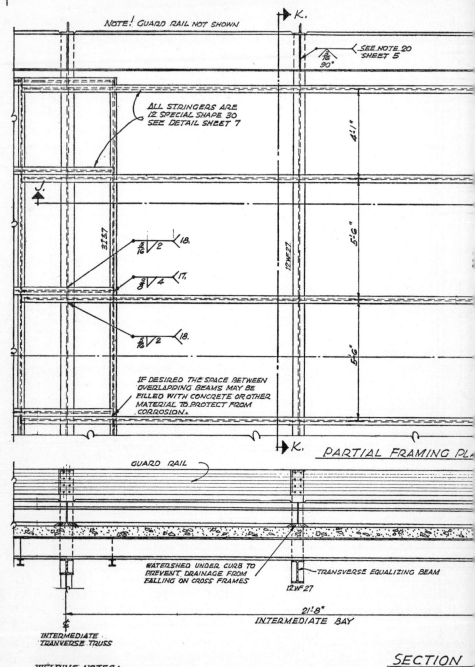

NOTE! GUARD RAIL NOT SHOWN

⊢ K.

SEE NOTE 20
SHEET 5

ALL STRINGERS ARE
12 SPECIAL SHAPE 30
SEE DETAIL SHEET 7

4'-1"

5'-6"

5'-6"

31 ST 7

12 WF 27

18.

17.

18.

IF DESIRED THE SPACE BETWEEN
OVERLAPPING BEAMS MAY BE
FILLED WITH CONCRETE OR OTHER
MATERIAL TO PROTECT FROM
CORROSION.

K. PARTIAL FRAMING PL

GUARD RAIL

WATERSHED UNDER CURB TO
PREVENT DRAINAGE FROM
FALLING ON CROSS FRAMES

12 WF 27

TRANSVERSE EQUALIZING BEAM

21'-8"
INTERMEDIATE BAY

INTERMEDIATE
TRANVERSE TRUSS

SECTION

WELDING NOTES:

17. TYPICAL WELD AT ENDS OF ALL CANTILEVER TIPS.

18. TYPICAL WELD WHERE STRINGERS CROSS TRANVERSE TRUSSES.

19. CURB PLATE BEING CONTINUOUS OVER END TRANVERSE TRUSSES,
IT IS NECESSARY TO WELD UNDERNEATH.

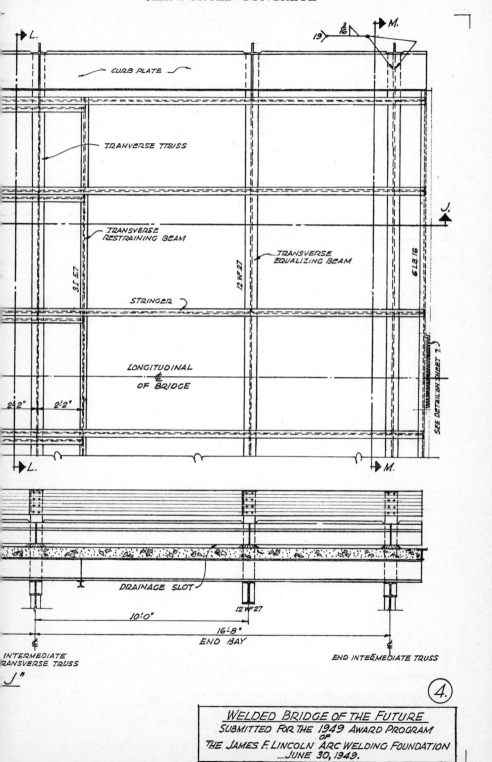

CURB PLATE

TRANVERSE TRUSS

TRANSVERSE
RESTRAINING BEAM

TRANSVERSE
EQUALIZING BEAM

STRINGER

LONGITUDINAL
℄
OF BRIDGE

2'2"   2'2"

3'-1.57

12 W 27

6'-1.816

SEE DETAILS ON SHEET 7.

DRAINAGE SLOT

12 W 27

10'-0"

16'-8"
END BAY

INTERMEDIATE
TRANSVERSE TRUSS

END INTERMEDIATE TRUSS

WELDED BRIDGE OF THE FUTURE
SUBMITTED FOR THE 1949 AWARD PROGRAM
OF
THE JAMES F. LINCOLN ARC WELDING FOUNDATION
JUNE 30, 1949.

Figure 65 (Concluded)   185

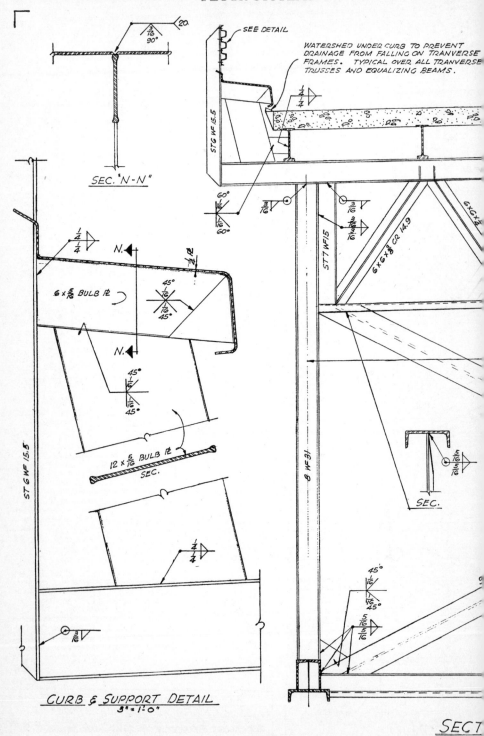

SEC. "N-N"

SEE DETAIL

WATERSHED UNDER CURB TO PREVENT DRAINAGE FROM FALLING ON TRANVERSE FRAMES. TYPICAL OVER ALL TRANVERSE TRUSSES AND EQUALIZING BEAMS.

6 x ⁵⁄₁₆ BULB ℞

12 x ⁵⁄₁₆ BULB ℞
SEC.

SEC.

CURB & SUPPORT DETAIL
3" = 1'-0"

SECT

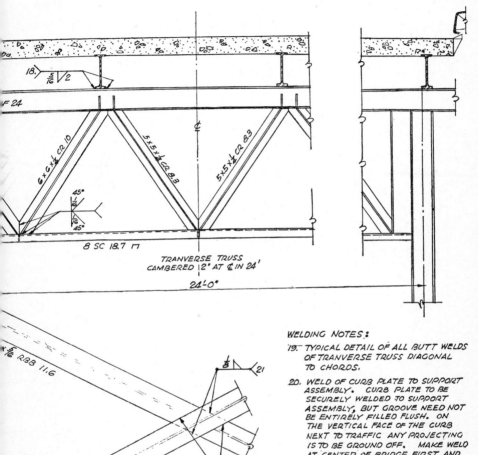

TRANVERSE TRUSS
CAMBERED 2" AT ℄ IN 24'

24'-0"

WELDING NOTES:

19. TYPICAL DETAIL OF ALL BUTT WELDS OF TRANVERSE TRUSS DIAGONAL TO CHORDS.

20. WELD OF CURB PLATE TO SUPPORT ASSEMBLY. CURB PLATE TO BE SECURELY WELDED TO SUPPORT ASSEMBLY, BUT GROOVE NEED NOT BE ENTIRELY FILLED FLUSH. ON THE VERTICAL FACE OF THE CURB NEXT TO TRAFFIC ANY PROJECTING IS TO BE GROUND OFF. MAKE WELD AT CENTER OF BRIDGE FIRST AND THEN WORK PROGRESSIVELY FROM CENTER TO ENDS TO AVOID ACCUMULATING "DRAW" OF WELDS UPON COOLING.

21 SEAL WELD. CARE IS TO BE TAKEN THAT NO NOTCH EFFECT IS INTRODUCED WHERE WELD BEAD PASSES OVER THE INTERSECTION FROM NEAR SIDE TO FAR SIDE. THIS DETAIL APPLIES TO ALL JOINTS WHERE TENSION MEMBERS CROSS, AS AT TRUSS DIAGONALS AND LOWER CHORD LATERAL DIAGONALS.

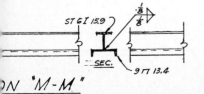

⑤.

WELDED BRIDGE OF THE FUTURE
SUBMITTED FOR THE 1949 AWARD PROGRAM
OF
THE JAMES F. LINCOLN ARC WELDING FOUNDATION
JUNE 30, 1949

ON "M-M"

Figure 66 (Concluded)   187

The decking is Irving bridge decking weighing 15¼ lbs. per sq. ft. It is tack welded to the sills with ¼ in. x 3 in. fillet welds about every 10¼ in. The sills are 7 in. channels (9.8 lbs. per ft.) spaced at 18 in. centers. The five interior stringers are 16 WF 40 and have spacing of 4 ft.-4 in. The exterior stringers are 8 WF 35. The sills rest on the stringers, but the stringers frame into the floorbeams. The floorbeams, 15 ft. apart, are constant in depth for the middle 17 ft.-4 in., but taper at the outer ends. There, middle parts are 18 WF 50 and the outer ends (cantilevers) are cut from 18 WF 50. Mr. Kavanagh said, "The use of grating flooring, while not an essential feature of this design, permits considerable savings in maintenance, particularly during bad weather conditions, such as with snow removal." He also mentioned the advantage of weight saving.

Mr. Dumbauld made designs for four types of floor slab and their supporting floorbeams and stringers. He said, "Their weight and costs were compared, using unit prices that were the Engineering News-Record national average for the same material in 1948 where available, and average bid price in this state [Ohio] for fall of 1948 for remaining items.

"The types designed were:—

    a. 5″ I-Beam-Lok Open Grid Floor

    b. 4¼″ I-Beam-Lok Armored Floor Slab

    c. Reinforced Concrete Slab

    d. Battle Deck Floor

"There was very little difference in the cost of the first three types, but the 5″ I-Beam-Lok Open Grid Floor was selected as the first cost did not seem excessive, and its light weight and other advantages made it first choice for more general use than the other three."

The size and spacing of the floorbeams and stringers are shown in Figure 2 (Page 13) and the manner in which the girders support the stringers directly at the outer edges of the roadway is shown in Figure 3. Some reduction of the possible moment in the floorbeam is accomplished by spacing stringers so that no concentrated load is carried at the center of its span.

In discussing the advantages of his open decking, Mr. Dumbauld stated: "The advantages gained in the design of this welded bridge with an open grid floor are many and should be given serious consideration when comparing with other types. The writer thinks this type of floor slab will permit the most economical design of structural steel floor system and girders for first cost and maintenance, because:—

    1. *Light Weight*. The light weight reduces the amount of dead load. This reduces the required size of stringers, floorbeams and girders and results in a savings of structural steel and cost of the structure.

    2. *No Crown Required*. The elimination of the crown, required for drainage on solid floors, cuts bridge construction costs by simplifying drafting. It eliminates crowning of end finish and the filler plates welded

to tops of floorbeams under stringers to form the crown. This advantage is greater when structures are constructed on skews and grades.

3. *Speed and Ease of Placing.* The deck requires only 20 pieces 6'-0" x 25'-9" weighing about 2900 lbs. each. This should all be placed at one time before welding. It requires 65 lbs. of ¼ in. x ½ in. fillets to weld to stringers; and 35 lbs. of ¼ in. x 4½ in. fillets to splice the units together. Welding time required to melt (100 lbs. weld metal) 500 ft of ¼" intermittent fillets at 50 ft. per hour is 10 hours at 100% operating factor. One welder and two helpers should weld this floor in place in three days. Speed is important at this stage of erection, as it is the end of the superstructure construction, and the contractor can submit his work for approval and payment and move to next job in a minimum amount of time.

4. *Safety and Accident Maintenance.* The rolled serrations on the top of the 'I' beams and the grid-like surface of the open slab form a wearing surface having greater skid resistance than either wet or dry concrete surface. This tends to reduce accidents to traffic and damage to curbs and railings. This reduces maintenance cost.

5. *Traffic Maintenance Reduced.* Traffic maintenance on structure in icy weather is reduced as the ice and snow are crushed and fall through the open grids. A ventilated floor dries faster than a solid wearing surface.

6. *Scuppers and drains not required.* The vented floor allows use of a vented curb. Scuppers and drainage systems are not required as no large concentrated streams of water are collected. This saves structural steel and drafting.

7. *Better and Easier Inspection.* Better and easier inspection of deck members is possible with an open grid floor.

8. *Wind Pressure Reduced.* Vented floor and curb reduces wind pressure on the structure. This reduces wind stresses in bridge members.

9. *Seasonal Construction Less Important.* Structural steel can be installed in all seasons with less protection from the elements.

10. *Fewer Classes of Skilled Workers.* Structural steel workers, crane operators, welders and common laborers are the only craftsmen to remain on the job for superstructure work. The carpenters, reinforcing steel placers, concrete finishers, concrete mixers and truckers are ready to move to another job when the substructure is completed. The concrete backwall above the bridge seat and the approach slab are considered as part of the approach pavement construction.

He also mentioned that, "The open grid floor permits rain and some sunshine to fall on the berms and slopes underneath the bridge. This makes it possible to raise a better type of vegetation on the berms and slopes and make them more in harmony with their surroundings."

The maximum tensile and compressive stresses were computed for the decking, stringers, floorbeams, and girders. It was found that for the decking, these were quite low, and for the stringers, floorbeams, and girders, while not excessive, they were higher. His statement relative to these findings was, "The light weight of the open grid floor reduces the size of stringers, floorbeams, and plate girders required for the total moment so much that there is a greater variation in stresses with live load and impact than in a structure with a greater dead load. This increases the importance of a study of the distribution and frequency of heavy freight vehicles and the ultimate development of the highway for future traffic, as related to fatigue failure of members and their connections."

Figure 14 (Page 51) contains a transverse section of the bridge designed by Messrs. Cassidy and Otto. The floor system shown there has a 3 in. U.S.S. Armored I-Beam-Lok floor filled with concrete to provide a 1 in. wearing surface. This floor is supported in the center by the box girder and on each side by two stringers (12 WF 40). These stringers are continuous across the cantilever floorbeams and are butt welded at the splices. The spacing of the floorbeams is 17 ft. As shown in Figure 14, the floorbeams are tapered by fabricating them from 24 WF 84 sections so as to have a depth of 3 ft.-5 in. at the box girder and about a 6 in. depth at the outer end.

About this grid floor, the designers said, "For the floor system, a proprietary steel grid flooring presented two definite advantages. It was the lightest type of floor that could handle the design loads. And it was of simple construction and could be easily assembled and welded into the bridge at the site. This decrease in dead load because of the light weight was of considerable consequence. A steel floor including wearing surface and weighing 60 lbs. per sq. ft. carried the load that would normally require a concrete floor weighing approximately 125 lbs. per sq. ft. Over the total floor area of about 3100 sq. ft. this was a weight saving of 201,500 lbs. This can be compared with the overall bridge weight as designed of 307,-500 lbs. Any saving in the use of the cheaper concrete floor would have quickly been lost in the added weights of all the steel supporting structure."

Some of the details of the design submitted by Messrs. F. W. and L. W. Cox are given in Figure 6 (Page 26). The cross section shows that the 4 in. concrete filled, steel grid floor is supported by the floorbeams whose spacing of 5 ft.-5 7/16 in. make stringers unnecessary.

To bring out the principal features of the floor system, the authors made the following remarks: "The concrete filled, steel grid floor is light in weight as compared to an all concrete floor. By designing it heavy enough to span directly between floor beams, the cumbersome method of placing beams on top of each other or any other complicated framing method is avoided, valuable vertical overall height is saved, and a better stability and better firmness under traffic is attained.

"The floor is adaptable to the use of traffic markers and in this design we suggest one row of grid cells adjacent to each curb and two rows of cells along the center line of roadway, to be finished with 'Ribbed White Concrete Markers'. We understood that these markers are not patented.

"The light weight of this floor reduces the weight of steel required for the main structure as compared to an all concrete design. For a general case, it is preferred to an open deck type as having a more general application to the various conditions and locations throughout the country. For instance, where there is likelihood of women pedestrians crossing the bridge, the heels of their shoes will be caught in and damaged in an open deck type. The herds of sheep, thousands of which in one herd are still driven over some of our western roads, could not cross over an open deck type. An overhead crossing over a street with pedestrian traffic would have its disagreeable aspects. Where an open type of grid floor is suitable, modifications in this bridge type can readily be made such as to accommodate it.

"The ¾ in. width main grid floor bars are to be deformed where in contact with concrete so that, like regular reinforcing bars, they will have a better bond with the concrete. The exposed surfaces are not to be deformed nor is it necessary for the web to be deformed. A thin web is used between the top and bottom bar flanges, not primarily for strength, as the concrete can carry the shear, but to insure a uniform depth of floor and a true alignment of the top surface. Using 4000 lbs. per sq. in. concrete at 28 days and the specification steel at 18000 lbs. per sq. in., and neglecting the 22 gage bottom pan, the transformed section develops 65,500 in. lbs. Working stress in the concrete is below the A.A.S.H.O. specification value of 1333 lbs per sq. in. The 22 gage bottom pan is used as a form so as to speed up erection work and lower the costs. It is to be bent down at beams so that the concrete will bond to the top flanges, all as indicated on the drawings. It is not required that the pans be detailed with accuracy as to top flange fits, since at these points, they can easily be supplemented with other forms.

"It is intended that the steel grid floor be shop fabricated in such sized sections as to be mutually agreeable to the shop and to the contractor, except that they must be in sufficiently small sections to conform reasonably close to the contours of the specified roadway surface. Lugs are welded to the shop sections along the lines of floor beam locations and tapped for tap bolts. They are to be used to bring the grid floor to proper height and line before welding the field sections together and to hold the sections in position until the concrete is poured."

Details of the grid floor are shown in Figure 67.

Two transverse sections of the bridge designed by Messrs. Willis, Hawker, and Stevens are shown in Figure 58 (Page 163). The 5 in. heavy duty, open grating deck has 6 spans of 4 ft. each, being supported alternately by girder-truss flanges and stringers. The stringers are 8 WF 35, placed midway between girder-trusses. They rest on transverse members that occur every 12 ft. These transverse members are diaphragms near the ends where the

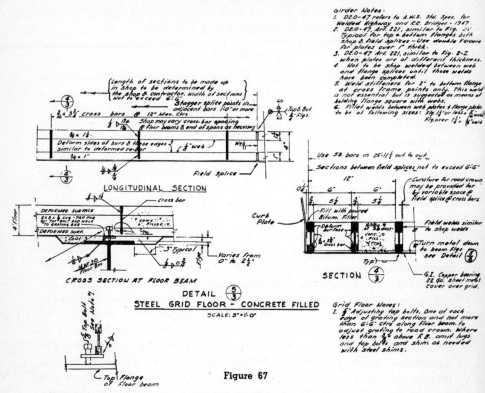

Figure 67

girder section exists and cross frames in the middle where the longitudinal members are trusses.

H. A. Balke, Cincinnati, Ohio, selected a 4¼ in. steel grid floor. He supports the decking directly on the top chords of his four trusses, having neither stringers nor floorbeams. He said: "The use of a steel grid floor spanning the 7 ft.-3 in. spacing between the trusses was a natural choice to obtain the results required. To reduce the total weight, a light weight concrete fill is specified, and to waterproof the surface for added protection of the entire structure, an asphaltic wearing surface has been provided."

A cross section of this bridge is shown in Figure 88 (Page 231) of Chapter V where the connections of Mr. Balke's pin connected trusses are discussed.

The floor system shown in Figure 37 (Page 113) is part of the design of Messrs. Armitstead, Brown, Henegan, Minnich, and Wheeler. These men use 4¼ in. I-Beam-Lok Armored floor, filled with concrete, as the decking between floorbeams, except at the truss top chords where bulb angles replace the steel grid. The eight bulb angles at each top chord serve as truss chord area in addition to being part of the deck. These bulb angles are also filled with concrete and then the entire surface of the slab is topped with a one inch thick layer of asphalt to provide a wear course. The floor is

192

supported by floorbeams 6 ft.-8 in. on centers. The intermediate floorbeams are 18 WF 55, and the end floorbeams are 24 WF 160.

Steel Plates

A considerable number of designers chose steel plates as the structural slabs for their floor systems. The plates were used in a variety of ways and many were attached to the longitudinal members in a manner such that they could be utilized as effective flange or chord material. Some were covered with a wearing surface, but others were traffic plates and served as such.

The unusual floor system that Mr. Lazaro used in his design is shown in Figure 1 (Page 11). The ⅝ in. floor plate is welded to Y-sections to form a continuous structural unit (similar to slab and stringers) that is supported by floorbeams every 20 ft. An 88½ in. width of this combination is considered as effective top flange material for each girder. Of the 88½ in., 33½ in. of plate with one Y-section are on the cantilever side of the girder web, and 55 in. of plate with two Y-sections are on the inside of the girder web (see Figure 68). A 30 in. width of this same floor plate is assumed to be the top flange for each floorbeam.

The distance between the tops of the inclined legs of the Y-section is 11 in. and the distance center to center of Y-sections is 22 in.; thus, the floor plate has longitudinal supports every 11 in. The steel plate is to be covered by two layers of asphaltic concrete, each being 1¼ in. thick. The dimensions of the Y-section, or Y-beam, are given in Figure 68. These stringer members are assumed fully continuous since they are inserted through the webs of the floorbeams by punching or cutting out by torch Y-shaped slots through the floorbeam webs as shown in Figure 69. These 17 in. x ½ in. floorbeam web plates are welded at the top to the floor plate or to the Y-beams and at the bottom to temporary floorbeams. The temporary floorbeams are 12 in. WF tees at 42 lbs. with 4 in x ½ in. plates welded to the tops of the webs of the tees. They serve as floorbeams during erection and become the lower parts of the final floorbeams as soon as the 17 in. x ½ in. plates are attached.

Figure 69 shows the floor system assemblies that are placed as units on the temporary floorbeams.

Mr. Lazaro explained the shop assembly of floor systems as follows:

1. Floor plates consist of three pieces each 121 ft. long and 7 ft., 6 ft., and 7 ft. wide each. The Y-beam stringers shall be cut in lengths of 121 ft. also.

2. Weld triangular fillers in web of the Y-stringers where they coincide with the webs of the floorbeams.

3. Automatic weld the Y-stringers to each plate, 4 to the 7 ft. plates and 3 to the 6 ft. plate, thus forming three rigid pieces each 121 ft. long.

4. Then cut each piece into 40 ft., 40 ft., and 41 ft. lengths. Automatic

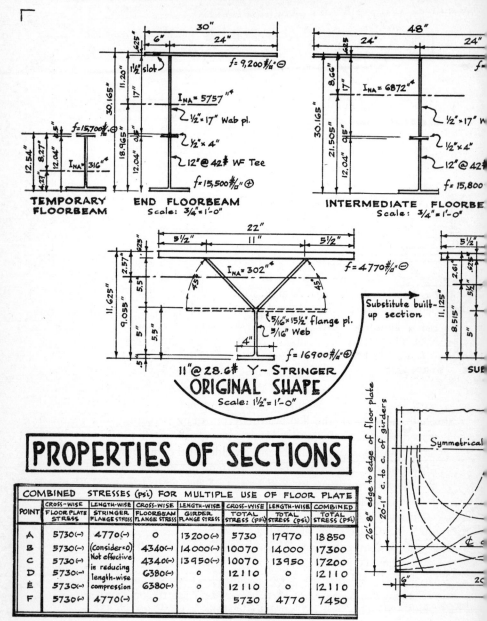

Figure 68

weld three corresponding 40 ft. lengths with the 6 ft. plate in the middle, thus forming a piece 40 ft. long and 20 ft. wide. This is either Floor System XI or XII.

Do likewise with the three 41 ft. lengths to form Floor System X which is 41 ft. long and 20 ft. wide.

5. Cut or stamp out the pattern for floorbeam web plates and slide them into place along the Y-stringers. Then weld the webs into place.

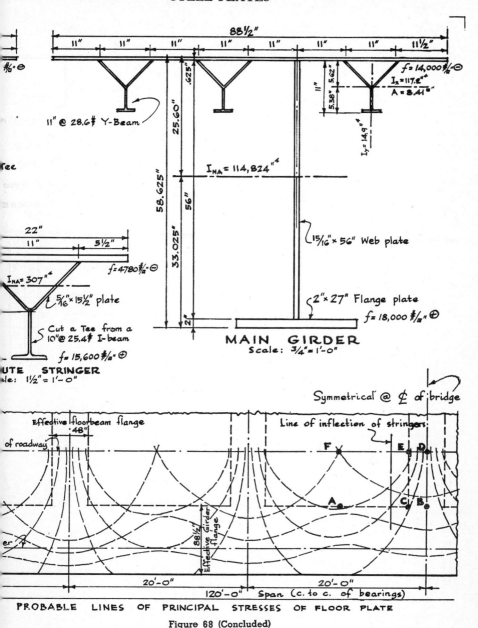

PROBABLE LINES OF PRINCIPAL STRESSES OF FLOOR PLATE

Figure 68 (Concluded)

Stitch welds (to satisfy specification requirements) can be reached at either ends of the 40 ft. lengths since they are only 6 in. within the Y's of the stringers.

For the other three intermediate floorbeams, cut 5 in. x 8 in. holes alternately on each side of the web of the Y's and stitch weld to floor plate. Then reweld the holes.

6. Mark each corresponding section of the floor system (as cut in step

195

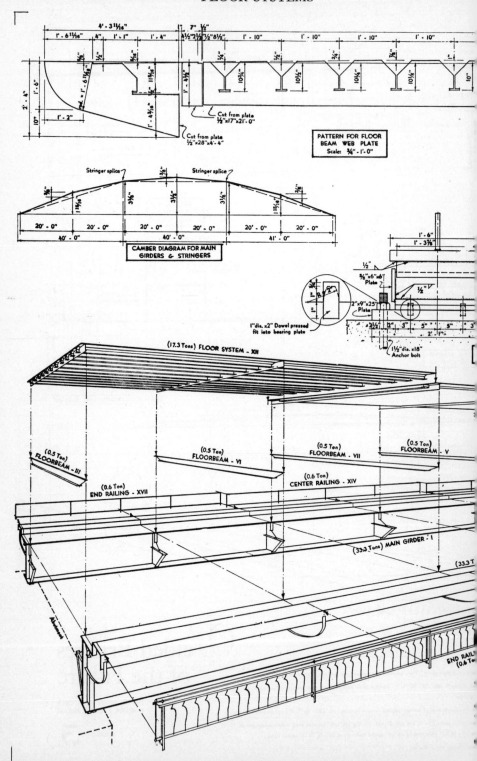

PATTERN FOR FLOOR
BEAM WEB PLATE
Scale: ¾" - 1'-0"

CAMBER DIAGRAM FOR MAIN
GIRDERS & STRINGERS

(17.3 Tons) FLOOR SYSTEM - XII

(0.5 Ton)
FLOORBEAM - III

(0.5 Ton)
FLOORBEAM - VI

(0.5 Ton)
FLOORBEAM - VII

(0.5 Ton)
FLOORBEAM - V

(0.6 Ton)
END RAILING - XVII

(0.6 Ton)
CENTER RAILING - XIV

(33.3 Tons) MAIN GIRDER - I

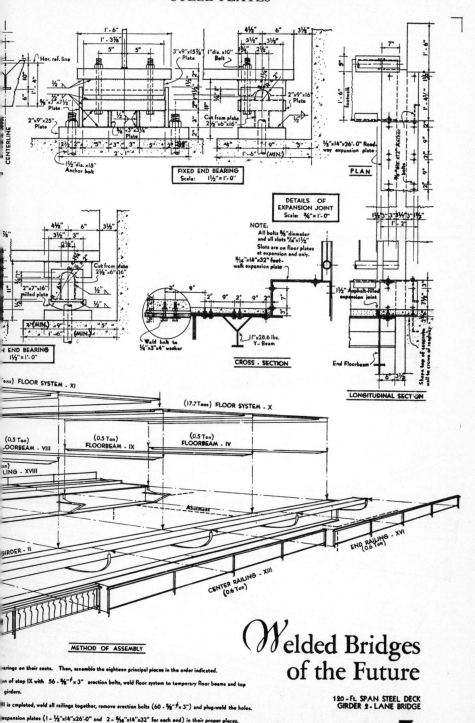

FIXED END BEARING
Scale: 1½"=1'-0"

PLAN

DETAILS OF EXPANSION JOINT
Scale: ¾"=1'-0"

NOTE:
All bolts ⅝"diameter and all slots ¾₆"x1½".
Slots are on floor plates at expansion end only.
⁵⁄₁₆"x14"x32" footwalk expansion plate

CROSS - SECTION

END BEARING
1½"=1'-0"

LONGITUDINAL SECTION

(... ons) FLOOR SYSTEM - XI

(17.7 Tons) FLOOR SYSTEM - X

(0.5 Ton) FLOORBEAM - VIII

(0.5 Ton) FLOORBEAM - IX

(0.5 Ton) FLOORBEAM - IV

... LING - XVIII

Abutment

... GIRDER - II

END RAILING - XVI
(0.6 Ton)

CENTER RAILING - XIII
(0.6 Ton)

METHOD OF ASSEMBLY

... arings on their seats. Then, assemble the eighteen principal pieces in the order indicated.

... n of step IX with 56 - ⅝"ᶠx 3" erection bolts, weld floor system to temporary floor beams and top girders.

... Il is completed, weld all railings together, remove erection bolts (60 - ⅝"ᶠx 3") and plug-weld the holes.

... expansion plates (1 - ½"x14"x26'-0" and 2 - ⁵⁄₁₆"x14"x32" for each end) in their proper places.

... re 70 - ⅝"ᶠx3" bolts with ½"x4"x4" welded washers and 70 - ¾"ᶠx 12" anchor bolts.)

... asphalt concrete surfacing.

*W*elded Bridges of the Future

120-Ft SPAN STEEL DECK GIRDER 2-LANE BRIDGE

PLATE **3**

Figure 69 (Concluded)

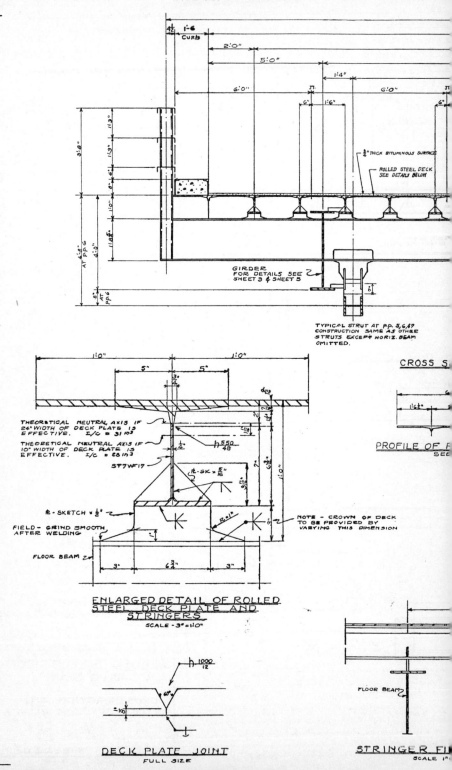

CROSS S

PROFILE OF F
SEE

ENLARGED DETAIL OF ROLLED STEEL DECK PLATE AND STRINGERS
SCALE - 3" = 1'-0"

DECK PLATE JOINT
FULL SIZE

STRINGER FI
SCALE 1"

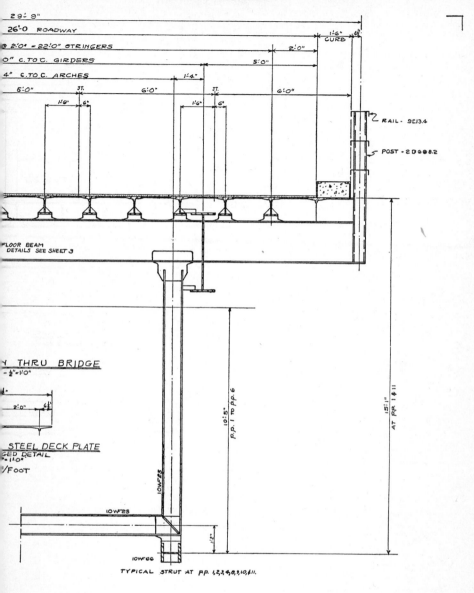

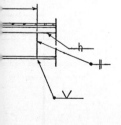

WELDED STEEL BRIDGE
120'-0" SPAN

CROSS SECTION AND
DETAILS OF DECK PLATE

SHEET 2 OF 7

Figure 70 (Concluded)

IV) in order to get a close fit when assembling them on site.

7. Weld the backing and stiffening strips in place.

8. Floor Systems are completely assembled, welded, lifted, and transported in the same position throughout (upside down) and only turned over when all ready to be laid in place at site.

The floor system of Mr. Miller's design is shown in the cross section of Figure 18 (Page 67) and in longitudinal section of Figure 20 (Page 71). The $\frac{7}{16}$ in. floor plate has a $2\frac{1}{2}$ in. wearing course of bituminous concrete and is stiffened underneath by the 4 in. x 3 in. x $\frac{5}{16}$ in. angles at 15 in. centers. These angles are each 1 ft.-8 in. long and do not attach to the stringers which are 2 ft.-7 in. apart. They are placed with the 4 in. legs vertical and the 3 in. legs horizontal, the tops of the 4 in. legs being welded to the underneath side of the floor plate by $\frac{3}{16}$ in. intermittent fillet welds on both sides, 4 in. lengths at 8 in. centers. The 14 WF 34 stringers frame into floorbeams. The floorbeams are 18 WF 70 sections, spaced 20 ft. center to center. The floorbeams rest on the top chords of the trusses and cantilever 6 ft.-3 in. beyond. The cantilever portions are tapered.

Mr. Morrison used a rolled steel deck plate covered with $\frac{3}{4}$ in. of bituminous concrete as a roadway slab. The covering serves only as a wearing surface. The steel plate is a special rolled section, essentially a $\frac{9}{16}$ in. plate with ribs every 2 ft. Actually, the plate is tapered for 5 in. on both sides of each rib from $\frac{9}{16}$ in. of thickness to 1 in. of thickness as shown in Figure 70. Each rib is welded to a ST 7 WF 17 tee section to form a stringer; thus, the deck plate is supported at 2 ft. centers and is not only a floor plate but also the top flanges for the stringers.

About the deck plate, Mr. Morrison said: "Conventional battledeck construction suffers from the serious disadvantage that fillet welds must be used at the toes of the stiffening beams, points subjected to high bi-axial stresses of opposite sign. The rolled deck plate assembly submitted avoids this shortcoming and effects a substantial saving of material as well. The deck assembly is designed to place the weld at or near the neutral axis. Since there is some doubt as to the exact amount of plate functioning as top flange for the stringer, the shape was designed so that the weld would be near the neutral axis and the value I/c nearly constant for both extreme conditions. According to Timoshenko (Strength of Materials, Vol. II, page 55, paragraph 9) the full deck plate will be effective. Full width has been used in design.

"Present day research strongly indicates that the failure of ductile materials subjected to multi-axial stress is related closely to the resultant octahedral shear. The deck plate has been designed so that the maximum octahedral shear developed is less than 45% of the octahedral shear at yielding in an ordinary tension test

"The deck plate design submitted is actually only a first approximation. Considerable study would be necessary before selecting a final design.

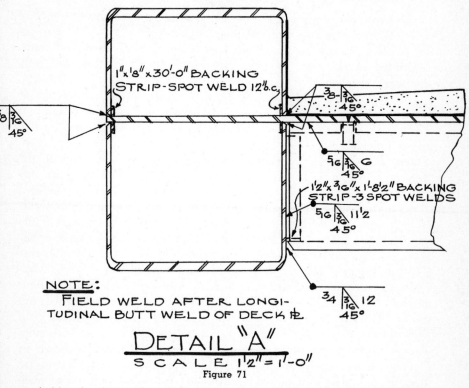

$\frac{3}{8} \frac{3}{16}$ 45°

1"×!8"×30'-0" BACKING STRIP-SPOT WELD 12"o.c.

$\frac{3}{8} \frac{3}{16}$ 45°

$\frac{5}{16} \frac{3}{16}$ 6 45°

1'2"×$\frac{3}{16}$"×1-8!2" BACKING STRIP-3 SPOT WELDS

$\frac{5}{16} \frac{3}{16}$ 11'2 45°

$\frac{3}{4} \frac{3}{16}$ 12 45°

NOTE:
FIELD WELD AFTER LONGI-
TUDINAL BUTT WELD OF DECK ℄.

DETAIL "A"
SCALE 1'2" = 1'-0"
Figure 71

Probably the bottom surface between the thickened edges should be curved making the plate thick at the center and thin at the quarter points. Such a plate would be lighter and the stress distribution considerably more favorable."

The stringers are supported at the floorbeams by connection plates designed for a certain definite, predictable flexibility. Many of the designer's comments about flexible connections are given in Chapter V. Details of the floorbeams are shown in Figure 54 (Page 153). The floorbeams are 10 ft. apart and are composed of flange plates, 9 in. x $\frac{5}{16}$ in., welded to 20 in. x $\frac{1}{4}$ in. webs. The floorbeams also have flexible plates connecting them to the verticals.

The members of Mr. Asrow's Vierendeel truss are rectangular in shape, the rectangles being formed by welding together two channels. These channels are special sections having wide flanges and thick webs. This same type of channel is used for the floorbeams. They are welded to the $\frac{5}{8}$ in. deck plate, as shown in Figures 42 and 43 (Page 131), in a manner that makes the deck plate function as the top flanges. These floorbeam channels are approximately 12 in. wide and 12 in. deep, spaced 3 ft. apart. Figure 71 shows the attachment of a typical floorbeam to the top chord of the truss. The floor channel is welded to the lower top chord channel, but

201

the floor plate is welded to another ⅝ in. plate that extends between the two top chord channels. This latter plate is part of the area of the top chord.

Mr. Asrow made the following comments concerning his floor system:

"Wide steel plates support a flexible bituminous pavement integrally tied to the surface to prevent creep and separation. The steel plates which form a continuous beam are utilized as the top flange of the floor beam. The plates are designed in accordance with present specifications but in light of recent battle deck floor investigations, the design is rather conservative. Research investigation should indicate the use of much higher permissible stresses. This deck also serves as the stiffened web of a deep rigid horizontal plate girder; the top chord serving as the flanges. Bolting the plate directly to the abutment eliminates the necessity for transferring the horizontal loads to the abutment through the use of a rigid end portal.

"Due to the torsional stiffness of the chords and rigid lateral frame formed by the deck, verticals and the bottom chord ties, the floor beams are partially fixed-ended. These beams can be shallow since deflection is decidedly reduced by partial fixity as are the design moments. An easily rolled thick web channel forms the web and bottom flange of a torsion resistant tee-beam having a sealed closed shape. This torsional resistance will tend to reduce deflections of the floor plate due to concentrated loads. Full wheel loads are used in the design of the floor beams without reduction for support contributed by adjacent floor beams. Experimental investigation should reveal a permissible distribution factor. Attaching three of the thick web channels to a single large plate by long continuous machine-made shop welds reduces the number of pieces to be handled and erected."

The method by which Mr. McBroom utilized his ⅝ in. traffic plate as effective top chord material for the four trusses is shown in Figure 27 (Page 89), and discussed in Chapter II. Between trusses, the plate is supported by 8 I 18.4 stringers, but at each truss, two channels (8 in. channels weighing 13.75 lb. per ft.) replace a stringer, and in combination with the traffic plate, constitute the top chord. The stringers span the 10 ft. between the floorbeams. Floorbeams are 10 I 40 sections that frame between the trusses. A wearing surface of ¼ in. of asphalt latex is applied to the traffic plate.

Mr. McBroom suggested the following points as some advantages of a steel floor plate:

"For a 120 ft. span and a 26 ft. roadway the conventional present day design would probably consist of two steel girders with a concrete deck and curbs and possibly a steel handrailing.

"It is the designer's belief a concrete deck is not the most economical type of bridge floor even though the cost of the slab itself appears to be less than for other types of flooring. The excessive weight requires larger and heavier supporting members and foundations which nullifies any saving made in the bridge floor itself.

"The weight, although more than if open grid flooring had been used, is much less than the concrete slab steel girder combination previously mentioned. The new design weighs 2200 pounds per lineal foot of bridge whereas the slab combination weighs approximately 5500 pounds per lineal foot.

"Battle deck flooring when used in an overcrossing structure spanning a street or parkway has the advantage over open grid flooring of being a solid membrane which would prevent falling objects from becoming a hazard to the traffic below. In the case of burning gasoline resulting from a traffic accident this would be particularly advantageous."

The details of Mr. Wake's floor system are shown in Figure 12 (Page 47). The top flange of each of the two box girders is an $^{11}/_{16}$ in. plate which serves as an 8 ft. width of roadway. The center 8 ft. of roadway is termed a "sandwich" deck section. It consists of a top plate $\frac{1}{2}$ in. in thickness, a bottom plate $\frac{1}{4}$ in. thick, longitudinal tees, and transverse tees. These tees are special sections with a 14 in. depth and a 2 in. flange width. The webs of the longitudinal tees are welded to the bottom plate in the shop with tees spaced 1 ft.-4 in. apart. This center deck section is fabricated in the shop in 12 ft. lengths, except for the top plate which is attached to the flanges of the tees by field welds. Each 12 ft. length has a transverse tee shop welded to the ends of the webs of the 5 longitudinal tees and also to the bottom plate. The additional foot of roadway on each side is added in the field along with the curb plate and cantilever brackets. This roadway plate is $\frac{1}{2}$ in. thick.

Mr. Wake said, "The battle deck floor which contributes to the strength of the supporting structure would eliminate costly forming and pouring of a concrete slab. A two or three inch bituminous coat would be applied as a wearing surface."

A schematic view of Mr. Tupker's bridge is shown in Figure 50 (Page 146), and a cross section of it is shown in Figure 72. This unusual structure is described in Chapter II, and is considered again here because the top of the principal structure is itself the roadway for the bridge; that is, the top row of cells is the top side of a box structure and also the roadway structure. Mr. Tupker stated that these 4 in. x 4 in. cells of the roadway should be provided with a wearing surface in the following manner: "On the clean and dry surface of the metal, a waterproof anti-rust coating is first to be applied. On this, refined asphalt is laid, melted at a temperature of between 300 degrees and 400 degrees F., and while the material is still hot, there shall be placed on it one layer of asphalt felt. Finally the asphaltic mastic blocks in melted asphalt are placed in position."

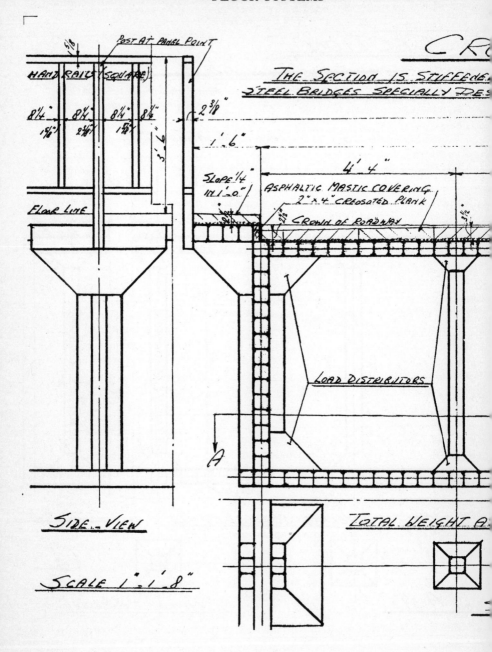

CR...

THE SECTION IS STIFFENE...
STEEL BRIDGES SPECIALLY DES...

POST AT PANEL POINT

HAND RAILS (SQUARE)

8¼" 8¼" 8¼" 8¼"
1⅝" 2⅜" 1⅝"

2⅜"

3'-6"

1'-6"

4'-4"

SLOPE ¼"
IN 1'-0"

ASPHALTIC MASTIC COVERING
2"×4" CREOSOTED PLANK
CROWN OF ROADWAY

3½"

FLOOR LINE

LOAD DISTRIBUTORS

A

SIDE - VIEW

TOTAL WEIGHT A...

SCALE 1" = 1'-8"

Figure 72

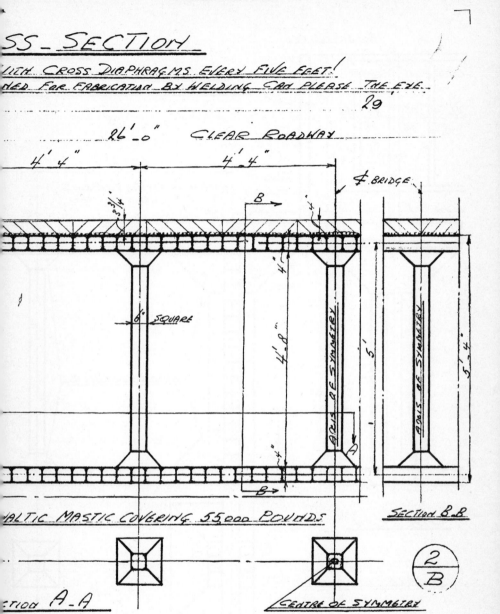

SS - SECTION

WITH CROSS DIAPHRAGMS EVERY FIVE FEET!
DED FOR FABRICATION BY WELDING CAN PLEASE THE EYE

29

26'-0" CLEAR ROADWAY

4'4"   4'.4"

⏚ BRIDGE

B →

6" SQUARE

4'-8"

AXIS OF SYMMETRY

5'

AXIS OF SYMMETRY

5'-4"

Section B.B

ALTIC MASTIC COVERING 55,000 POUNDS

CTION A-A

CENTRE OF SYMMETRY

2/B

Figure 72 (Concluded)   205

CHAPTER IV
NEW SECTIONS

The designs entered in the program were not limited to the use of present structural steel shapes. In fact, the participants were encouraged to incorporate sections in their designs that were not then available provided the design could be improved thereby. The only limitation in this regard was that the new sections specified must be of such shape that they could be readily produced if a sufficient demand developed.

Although in Chapter II new sections are mentioned in discussing the designs that used them, they are of primary interest in this chapter and will be described in detail here. Also, being grouped with similar sections, it will be possible to more easily compare the advantages of each new section proposed. Not all of the new shapes suggested in the program are included in this chapter, but the intention has been to describe one or more of each basic type.

Plates

The sections of this group are modified rolled plates in that they are not truly rectangular in shape. They have ribs, special edges, bulb ends, or a combination of these.

Mr. Dumbleton used three new sections which essentially were plates. The webs of his girders are very thin ribbed plates 120 in. wide. The web itself is ⅛ in. thick and the ribs on each side are ⅛ in. thick. These ribs are 10 in. apart.

Another new section is for the bottom flange of the girder. He named it a "Bobbin Plate". It is 24 in. wide, and 2 in. thick at the edges; however, the thickness decreases from each edge toward the center, with the middle 6 in. having a constant thickness of ¼ in. He wanted the variable thickness to allow a gradual change over from the thin web plate in order to give a smooth stress flow and eliminate the common difficulty of welding thin plates to thick plates due to unequal heat capacity.

The third new section is a ribbed plate in the floor. It is ⅛ in. thick with ribs 2 in. high on only the upper side. The spacing between ribs is 4 in. This plate is both the form and the steel reinforcement for the reinforced concrete slab as well as effective top flange material for the girder.

Messrs. F. W. Cox and L. W. Cox in the design of their girders had both edges of all flange plates and one edge of all stiffener plates rounded. They claimed three advantages for plates with rounded corners: (1) rounded corners are more effective in transmitting stresses; (2) they hold paint more efficiently and therefore lessen the cost of maintenance; and (3) rounded corners add to the esthetic appearance of the structure. The authors said that they knew of no mills rolling plates of the sizes they used with one or both edges rounded, although some types of plates with rounded

New Slab Form Section

The following is the new slab form section proposed to carry deck dead load and eliminate forming.

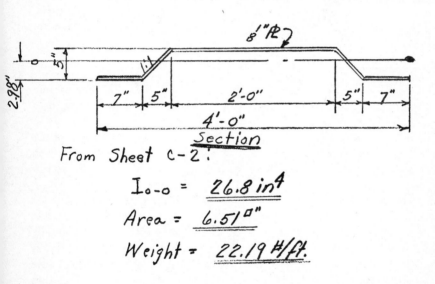

Section

From Sheet C-2:

$$I_{o-o} = \underline{26.8 \ in^4}$$

$$Area = \underline{6.51 \ \square''}$$

$$Weight = \underline{22.19 \ \#/ft.}$$

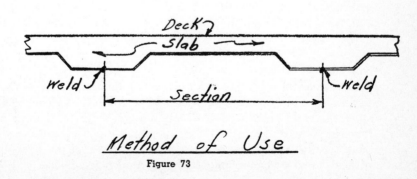

Method of Use

Figure 73

edges are in common use. Also, that a good demand should develop for the suggested rolled plates because of the advantages they have over square cornered plates in welding, even though in riveted work they are not well adapted due to the edge distances required and the common practice of detailing one plate on top of another.

The reinforced concrete slab in Mr. Hants' design is poured on a slab form section. This new shape is shown in Figure 73. It is an ⅛ in. plate rolled so as to form a trough that can be used as a concrete form having

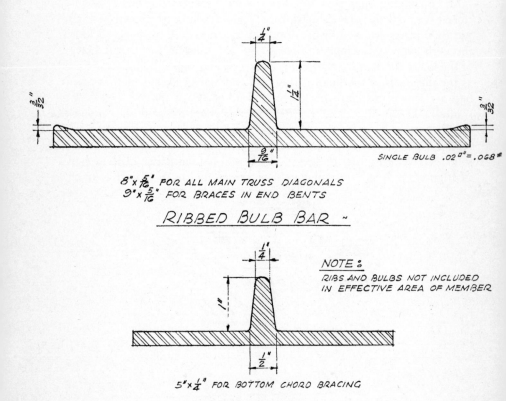

SINGLE BULB .02 ᵈ" = .068 #

8" x 5/16" FOR ALL MAIN TRUSS DIAGONALS
9" x 5/16" FOR BRACES IN END BENTS

RIBBED BULB BAR ~

NOTE:
RIBS AND BULBS NOT INCLUDED
IN EFFECTIVE AREA OF MEMBER

5" x 1/4" FOR BOTTOM CHORD BRACING

RIBBED BAR

DOUBLE BULB .04 ᵈ" = .136 #

BULB PLATE ~

Figure 74

the required strength to resist dead loads. Mr. Hants said: "The proposed new steel deck form can be put on the girder and welded automatically. Attention is directed to the fact that the structure is entirely self-supporting for dead load. This fact eliminates the necessity for costly forming for the concrete deck, as well as falsework for the main girder. Thus, the concrete deck should be poured at minimum expense." Figure 16 (Page 57) shows the girder mentioned, as well as the reinforcing bars which are welded to the steel deck form in order to provide composite action between the concrete and the plate for dead load plus live load and impact.

Mr. Spaulding suggested three new rolled shapes: the bulb plate, the ribbed bar, and the ribbed bulb plate. These sections are shown in Figure 74. Bulb plates are used in the details of the transverse members including the curb support assemblies; ribbed bars are used as the lateral bracing of the lower chord and guard rail post braces; and ribbed bulb bars are used as the diagonals of the main trusses and end bents. Details of these members are shown in Figures 26 (Page 87) and 65 (Page 185).

Messrs. Daymond and Zakrzewski said this about the plate they proposed for the bottom flange of their five longitudinal frames: "This section is already in use in Germany and was extensively used there prior to 1939 in solid web welded girder bridges." The special bottom flange plate is shown in Figure 75. It is a rectangular plate except for the V-shaped bead that

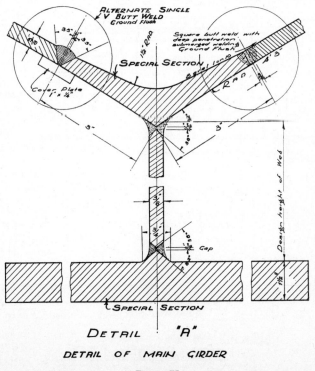

DETAIL "A"

DETAIL OF MAIN GIRDER

Figure 75

would be rolled onto the top face. This plate would be ready for butt welding without requiring any shop preparation.

Angles

The special angles presented in the designs and proposed for new rolled shapes differed from those currently available in one of the following ways: the length of legs were longer; the angle between legs was greater or less than 90 degrees; or the ends of legs were beveled or provided with lips. Included in this group are the suggested curved plates that would be used in lieu of angles. For welded box sections, it is not necessary to have sharp corners; in fact, the rounded corners made possible by special curved plates would be better structurally.

Figure 76 shows a modified angle which was discussed to some extent in Chapter II. Mr. Kavanagh acknowledged the superiority of tubular or box cross sections in making more efficient use of materials, but pointed out the difficulty of butt welding such shapes since specifications prohibit one-sided butt welds. Therefore, he designed the new angle and new tee as chord members for his space truss. These shapes provide simple butt welding of the 10″ WF sections of his web system and result in details that

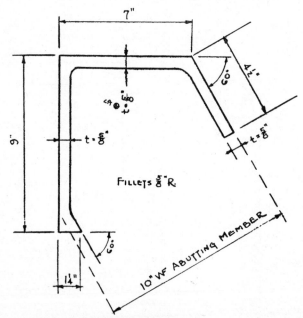

SECTION "W" (AS SHOWN) FOR $U_6 U_2$.
SECTION "X" FOR $U_2 U_4$: SPREAD
ALL ROLLS SO t = $\frac{15}{16}$".

Figure 76

are improved over the comparable section composed of shapes and angles. The angle has legs of 9 in. and 7 in. The 9 in. leg is thickened at the edge. The 7 in. leg has a lip added which is 4½ in. long and inclined at an angle of 60 degrees.

The special 60 degree, 12 in. x 6 in. angles that Mr. Ullman used as the top and bottom chords of his inclined trusses are shown in Figure 32 (Page 105). The 60 degree angle between the legs agree with the inclination of the web systems of his trusses. The 12 in. leg permits him to weld the web members directly to the chord angles eliminating the need of gusset plates. Mr. Ullman said that if fillet welding to the angle faces were considered unfavorable, it would be possible to butt weld the flanges of the tees of the web members to the outer edges of the top and bottom chord angles, and then fillet weld the webs of the tees to the angle faces.

Mr. Grinter stated that the fabrication of structures with inclined webs such as his Vee-girder would be simplified by the availability of angles rolled at some standard slope (such as 60 degrees) between the legs. This would eliminate the expense of rerolling a standard angle to close it to the desired shape. He proposed the angle shown in Figure 8 (Page 33).

Messrs. Cassidy and Otto proposed that new angles, as shown in Figure 77, be rolled. The section is essentially a plate curved 90 degrees rather

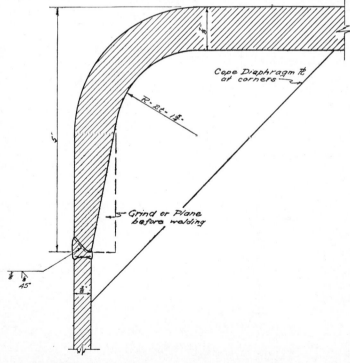

DETAIL B

Figure 77

than an angle; however, it would serve the purpose of an angle and also eliminate the sharp corner that is undesirable in a structure subjected to torsion. The inside radius is twice the plate thickness. For welded box girders, they prefer a single plate with both ends curved. Such a rolled shape would save the welding of a flange plate between two curved angles. The angles for their design are 5 in. x 5 in. x ⅞ in.

The open angle shown in the upper part of Figure 75 is a portion of the flange of a frame. The pointed corner at the intersection of the legs makes the section ready for butt welding without any shop work.

Mr. Faltus combined an angle and a plate for each bottom flange of his four girders by rotating the angle so that the girder web was butt welded to the backside of the intersection of the legs and the flange plate was welded to the edge of both legs. This type of flange is shown in the transverse section of Figure 7 (Page 29). Also illustrated in the horizontal section of this figure is the manner in which he rotated the stiffener angles in order to weld both legs to the web of the girder to form a tubular section. Mr. Faltus said that angles now fabricated could be used here both as the flange angles and as the stiffener angles, but that they were not very suitable. Therefore, he proposed an improved new shape as shown in Figure 78 which he termed the "New Angle".

Mr. Faltus stated: "This shape would be very advantageous for welded constructions and it would substantially enlarge the number of forms which are obtainable by welding.

"The 'New Angle' differs from a normal angle in these points:

(1) A bevel is formed on the projecting flanges, so that is is possible to join the angle by means of ordinary fillet welds after setting it on the plate.

(2) The edge of the angle is cut off and so a level surface is formed on which plates may be joined by the means of fillet welds. In Figure 73 is shown how 'New Angles' of the same size but different thickness are rolled in a similar way as normal angles.

(3) The rounding of the edges r_1 is as small as possible. The top radius ($r_2 = 1.5d$ min.) is larger than on normal angles and provides a level edge large enough for the attachment of plates with fillet welds.

"The ratio of width w to height h of the 'New Angle' is 2:1 for the most used medium thickness of each size.

"Some shapes which are easily formed of the 'New Angles' are shown in Figure 78.

(1) The cruciform shape is suitable for poles, flanges of the lattice girders, etc. The advantage is the easy joining of the two angles and then the easy joining of gusset plates without necessity of chamfering. It is easy to join plates having a slope of 45° to the legs of the 'New Angles'. For medium thickness of the legs of

"New Angle"

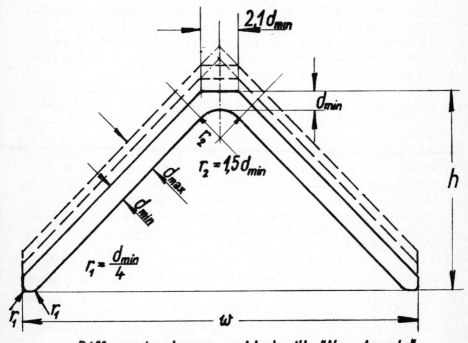

$2.1d_{min}$

d_{min}

r_2

$r_2 = 1.5d_{min}$

d_{max}

d_{min}

$r_1 = \dfrac{d_{min}}{4}$

h

r_1 r_1

w

Different shapes welded with "New Angels"

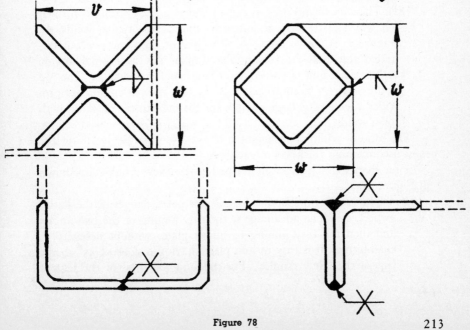

v

w

w

w

Figure 78

213

'New Angles' of each size the legs are in alinement and the out-line is a true square.

(2) This cross-section consists of two angles which are put together into a shape U. It is again favorable that welding is done without bevelling and then that the gusset plates are easily attached.

(3) A tube profile formed by two new angles is suitable for poles and as flange of latticed girders. The easiness of joining gusset plates is again very advantageous.

(4) *T—form*. The advantages are the same as of the above mentioned cross-sections.

"It is not impossible to form all the mentioned and many other profiles, which may be easily formed with the 'New Angle', with normal angles too, but every expert in welding will appreciate the outstanding advantages given by the 'New Angles'."

Tees

Many tees now available were chosen by a large percentage of the participants as the best shapes for a variety of bridge members. Also, a considerable number of the designers preferred tee sections not now rolled, and the number of new or modified tees proposed was greater than for any other single shape.

Mr. Dumbauld designed a series of 20 in. x 6 in. tees for flanges of girders. Figure 79 gives the dimensions, areas, and weights of his proposed tees. His remarks about this new section were:

"One of the most important types of bridge construction in the future will be the deck type welded plate girder bridge, built of web plates with special flange sections. These flanges will be 'T' sections, and will consist of a heavy flange with a thin stem having various patterns on the tip for fillet welding and the many different types of butt welds. For girders using a fillet weld to join the flange section and web plate the stem must be thick enough to accommodate the web plate, 2 fillet welds and clearance for fillets from edge of stem. In the girder designed in this paper the stem thickness would have to be $1\frac{1}{8}$ in. thick to accommodate two $\frac{5}{16}$ in. fillet welds and a $\frac{3}{8}$ in. web plate.

"The type chosen for the girder flange section in this paper was a 'T' section with a 20 in. wide flange, and a 6 in. stem with a $\frac{3}{8}$ in. web having a square tip suitable for making a tight square butt, automatic welded joint by shielded metallic arc operation where permitted. Where beveled or 'J' joints are required the bevels are to be cut on the web plates at the same time the web plates are cut for camber.

* * *

"The special Teed Flange sections (20 x 6 TF) required or investigated for this girder are detailed and described in Figure 79.

"The advantages of this type of section are:—

1. The welding of a thin plate to a thin plate eliminates the pre-heating required when welding a thin web plate to a thick flange plate.

2. The speed of welding is increased, and the quality of welds improved by eliminating the preheating. This reduces the cost.

3. A generous and constant stem depth (6 in.) permits use of a greater number of flange thicknesses and use of a constant depth web plate.

4. A generous stem depth allows for easier adjustment on a jig or table for automatic welding and flux material.

5. More accessible for back welding and inspection.

6. The butt welding of flange section to web can be made automatically with greater speed, using more current, voltage and submerged arc. Butt welds have much higher fatigue values than fillet welds. This permits use of higher design stresses in butt welds and longer life for the structure.

7. By keeping the top of flange level, a surface suitable for a deck resting directly on it is furnished without the addition of any other leveling plates.

Proposed New Structural Steel Shapes

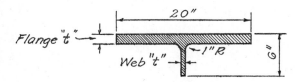

TEED-FLANGE SECTION · 20×6 TF ·

Section Number	Weight. Lbs. per ft.	Area. Sq. Inch	Depth of Tee. Inches	Flange	
				Width. Inches	Thickness. Inches
20×6 TF	59.2	17.40	6	20	$3/4$
20×6 TF	67.5	19.85	6	20	$7/8$
20×6 TF	75.9	22.35	6	20	1
20×6 TF	84.2	24.75	6	20	$1\frac{1}{8}$
20×6 TF	92.5	27.20	6	20	$1\frac{1}{4}$
20×6 TF	100.9	29.70	6	20	$1\frac{3}{8}$
20×6 TF	109.2	32.20	6	20	$1\frac{1}{2}$
20×6 TF	117.6	34.60	6	20	$1\frac{5}{8}$
20×6 TF	125.9	37.10	6	20	$1\frac{3}{4}$
20×6 TF	134.2	39.50	6	20	$1\frac{7}{8}$
20×6 TF	142.6	41.90	6	20	2
20×6 TF	150.9	44.40	6	20	$2\frac{1}{8}$

Figure 79

Messrs. Fietz and Walt used special tees for the flanges of their three girders. These tees are new rolled sections with webs 4 in. high and ⅝ in. thick. Both corners at the end of each tee web are beveled ready for the butt welding of these flange tees to the girder web plate. The flanges of the tees vary in thickness and in width, but by having flange tees rather than flange plates, it is not necessary to weld thin girder webs to thick flange plates. The girder webs and tee webs are practically equal in thickness.

Another advantage of flange tees that the authors mentioned is that the location of the weld occurs at a position of smaller stress. They were concerned about the unequal shrinkage due to different temperatures within the penetration zone which results during the welding of plates whose thicknesses differ considerably. They stated that the number of types of this rolled tee could be comparatively small since the unrestricted height of the web plate would guarantee full utilization of the shapes. The following range in dimensions were suggested: ½ in. to ¾ in. for the thickness of the tee web, 3 in. to 5 in. for web height, 1 in. to 2 in. for the radius of the fillet between the web and the flange, 1 in. to 3½ in. for the flange thickness, and 12 in. to 30 in. for the width of the flange.

The mono-truss bridge designed by Mr. Scheyer is shown in Figure 17 (Page 63) and briefly discussed in Chapter II. The new tee sections proposed by Mr. Scheyer are dimensioned on Figure 80. About these tees, he said: "The use of one heavy truss creates the necessity of heavy shapes

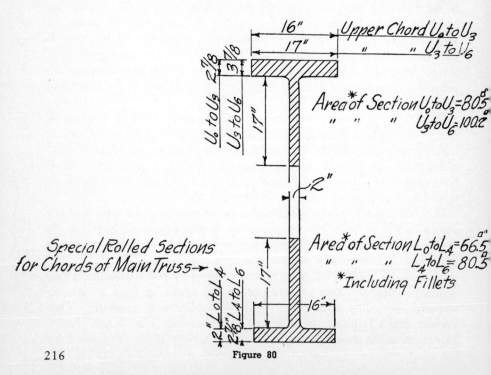

Figure 80

216

which, once the rolls are provided, would appear to be more economical than an equal weight of a number of lighter shapes. Only one cutting to length and measurement therefore at the mill is required. Less painting on of identifying marks is required.

"A lesser number of passes through the rolls to reduce the ingot to finished size and shape is required. If the 62 ft. length of the longest truss segment shown on the drawing, should prove to be too great for the rolls to produce from a practicable size ingot, such length could be reduced by breaking the truss at another location. Reference to Table 4, Sheet 3, shows that breaking the upper chord between U_3 and U_4 instead of between U_2 and U_3 would increase the weight only of the lighter portion of the chord section, shown on Sheet 1, by about 50 lbs. per lineal foot to account for the increase in stress of 202,000 lbs.

"A further advantage of the new sections, which are T-shaped, is that the stem portion can be made of sufficient depth to allow space for the welding to it of the web members of the truss. Even the connections shown on the drawings for the web members of the main truss might be simplified by using a deeper stem than shown. The ST sections now obtainable, even if the stem section is of sufficient depth to provide room for members to be welded to it, in most instances has its ratio of depth to thickness too great. The present practice for highway bridges limits this ratio to a maximum of 12 for members taking direct stress. The light T-section used for the chords of the transverse truss was primarily provided for the purpose of obtaining sufficient depth of stem for welding and at the same time to satisfy the 12 ratio. The controlling factors, therefore, in the design of the new T-sections, are the provision of a heavy section which at the same time can be given plenty of welding space, or where a light section only is needed, to provide a deep enough stem for convenient welding and at the same time conserve the 12 ratio."

Mr. Scheyer also mentioned the important consideration of keeping the center of gravity as near to flange of the tee as possible. He did this by making the flange thicker than normal. This increases the effective depth of the truss, and since the web members of a truss at a panel point should have their centers of gravity intersect at the center of gravity of the chord, it makes more welding space available.

M. J. Greaves, Pittsburgh, Pennsylvania, incorporated the two new tees shown in Figure 81 in the design of his three longitudinal members. In discussing them, he said: "Welding tees were introduced for more efficient fabrication. They may be produced by first rolling special H sections and hot slitting by blunt V shears to produce a properly prepared edge for butt welding. These tees have a thinner flange and stem edge for a given cross-sectional area, thus permitting considerable splice weld economy. Their shallow depth facilitates bending and straightening. The thinner flanges also result in less shrinkage forces."

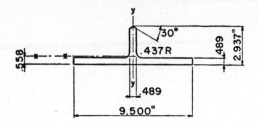

WELDING TEE
9½ x 3 WT 20

WT. PER FT. (LBS.)   20.00
AREA OF SECTION (IN²)   5.88
I_{xx} (IN⁴)   2.93
S_{xx} (IN³)   1.20
r_{xx} (IN)   .71
I_{yy} (IN⁴)   34.96
S_{yy} (IN³)   7.36
r_{yy} (IN)   2.44

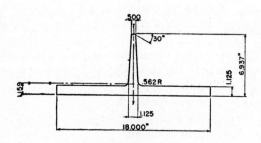

WELDING TEE
18 x 7 WT 85

WT. PER FT. (LBS.)   85.00
AREA OF SECTION (IN²)   25.00
I_{xx} (IN⁴)   52.90
S_{xx} (IN³)   9.06
r_{xx} (IN)   1.45
I_{yy} (IN⁴)   547.07
S_{yy} (IN³)   60.79
r_{yy} (IN)   4.68

Figure 81

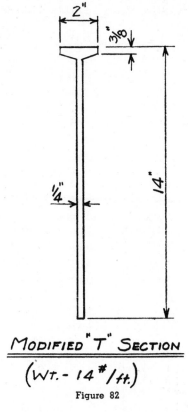

MODIFIED "T" SECTION

$$\left(WT. - 14^{\#} / ft. \right)$$

Figure 82

The tee section used by Mr. Wake in his "sandwich" deck section is shown in Figure 82. The flange is 2 in. wide and is tapered with an edge thickness of ⅜ in. The web is ¼ in. thick and 14 in. deep. These tees are the webs of the deck section. The bottom of the web is shop welded to a bottom plate, but the flange of the tee is necessary for the field plug welds to the top plate.

Beams, Channels, Miscellaneous Shapes

This group includes rolled beams of I shape with unequal flanges or special dimensions, channels of uncommon dimensions, Y sections, cruciform shapes, and other unusual shapes.

In addition to the three sections shown in Figure 74, Mr. Spaulding used the two sections shown in Figure 83. The "cross" shaped section is employed as the web members of the transverse trusses as shown in Figure 66 (Page 187). The sizes are 6 in. x 6 in. x ⅜ in., 6 in. x 6 in. x ¼ in., and 5 in. x 5 in. x ¼ in. The proposed I beam has unbalanced flanges. It is a stringer in the floor system and, being anchored to the reinforced concrete slab for composite action, the tension flange is made thicker than the compression flange in order to save steel.

As stated in Chapter II, Mr. Gottfeldt incorporated two new shapes in the design of his space truss. They are referred to as the Y-shape and the cruciform, or X-shape. The chords are Y-shapes and the members of the web system including the end posts are X-shapes. Figure 84 shows the details of the Y-shape. The X-shapes are like the "cross" shown in Figure 83; however, for each size, the leg width is 16 times the leg thickness. Therefore, an X9 has four legs, each 9 in. wide and each $\frac{9}{16}$ in. thick. Although it is called an X-shape, the angle between legs is 90 degrees.

Mr. Gottfeldt stated that welding has greatly simplified the fabrication of space structures that require connections at other than right angles, but that the advantages of welding and space trusses have not been fully realized because the available standard rolled shapes were—and still are—those developed originally for riveted structures. He said:

"It is therefore suggested to introduce a new range of shapes, the Y-shape, as illustrated in Figure 84. It is proposed to roll the edges of this new shape with a bevel of 45 degrees (or thereabouts), so as to facilitate the butt welding of other members to them." He also pointed out that much larger girder flange plates could be welded to the ends of the two flanges of the Y than could be welded to a girder web.

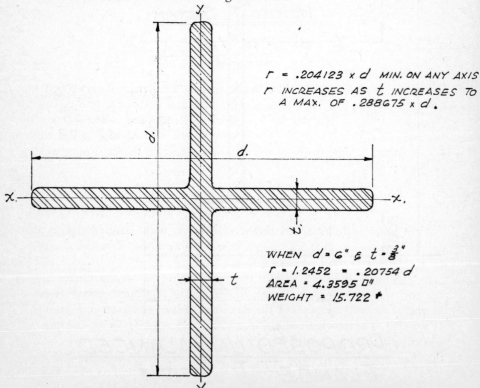

$$r = .204123 \times d \text{ MIN. ON ANY AXIS}$$

r INCREASES AS t INCREASES TO A MAX. OF $.288675 \times d$.

WHEN $d = 6"$ & $t = \frac{3}{8}"$
$r = 1.2452 = .20754\ d$
AREA = 4.3595 □"
WEIGHT = 15.722 #

Figure 83

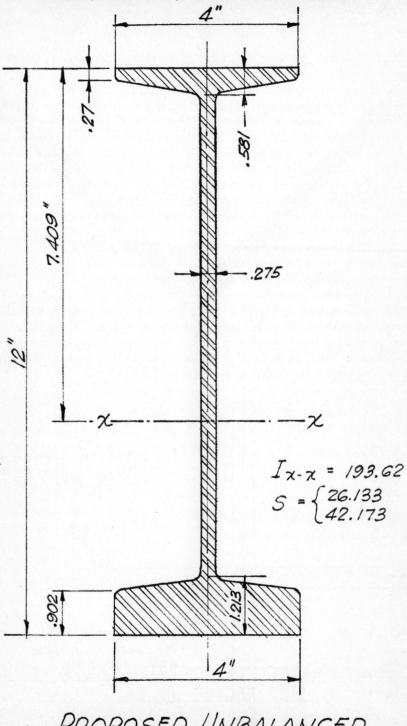

$$I_{x-x} = 193.62$$
$$S = \begin{cases} 26.133 \\ 42.173 \end{cases}$$

PROPOSED UNBALANCED
FLANGE I BEAM

Figure 83 (Concluded)

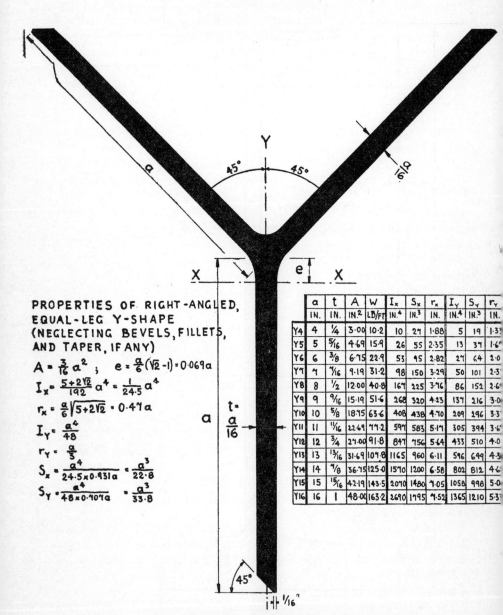

PROPERTIES OF RIGHT-ANGLED, EQUAL-LEG Y-SHAPE (NEGLECTING BEVELS, FILLETS, AND TAPER, IF ANY)

$A = \frac{3}{16}a^2$; $\quad e = \frac{a}{6}(\sqrt{2}-1) = 0.069a$

$I_x = \frac{5+2\sqrt{2}}{192}a^4 = \frac{1}{24.5}a^4$

$r_x = \frac{a}{6}\sqrt{5+2\sqrt{2}} = 0.47a$

$I_Y = \frac{a^4}{48}$

$r_Y = \frac{a}{3}$

$S_x = \frac{a^4}{24.5 \times 0.931a} = \frac{a^3}{22.8}$

$S_Y = \frac{a^4}{48 \times 0.707a} = \frac{a^3}{33.8}$

	a IN.	t IN.	A IN.²	W LB/FT	I_x IN.⁴	S_x IN.³	r_x IN.	I_Y IN.⁴	S_Y IN.³	r_Y IN.
Y4	4	1/4	3.00	10.2	10	2.7	1.88	5	1.9	1.3
Y5	5	5/16	4.69	15.9	26	5.5	2.35	13	3.7	1.6
Y6	6	3/8	6.75	22.9	53	9.5	2.82	27	6.4	2.0
Y7	7	7/16	9.19	31.2	98	15.0	3.29	50	10.1	2.3
Y8	8	1/2	12.00	40.8	167	22.5	3.76	86	15.2	2.6
Y9	9	9/16	15.19	51.6	268	32.0	4.23	137	21.6	3.0
Y10	10	5/8	18.75	63.6	408	43.8	4.70	209	29.6	3.3
Y11	11	11/16	22.69	77.2	597	58.3	5.17	305	39.4	3.6
Y12	12	3/4	27.00	91.8	847	75.6	5.64	433	51.0	4.0
Y13	13	13/16	31.69	107.8	1165	96.0	6.11	596	64.9	4.3
Y14	14	7/8	36.75	125.0	1570	120.0	6.58	802	81.2	4.6
Y15	15	15/16	42.19	143.5	2070	148.0	7.05	1058	99.8	5.0
Y16	16	1	48.00	163.2	2690	179.5	7.52	1365	121.0	5.3

Y-SHAPE. PROPERTIES, PROPOSED RANGE; ALSO FULL-SIZE SECTION OF Y6.

Figure 84

He continued: "It is well-known that butt welds are superior to fillet welds in all cases of dynamic loads, and in order to comply with this fact to the greatest possible extent it is suggested to introduce a further standard series of shapes for use with all diagonal and vertical members, namely the cruciform or X-shape. Such shapes are even now being rolled occasionally, but as far as is known none of the steel producing countries has a standard range of them.

* * *

"The cruciform section has a smaller stiffness than, for instance, a tube of comparable weight, but the connections it makes possible are better (especially when used together with the Y-shape), and in bridge work the slenderness ratio of most members is normally anyhow on the small side.

"In many cases the full cross-sectional area of the X-shape will not be required at the joints, and the outstanding legs of the main diagonal members have then been cut back accordingly [see Figure 36 Page 111]."

Mr. Lazaro's floor system is discussed in Chapter III and a cross section showing his Y-section is given in Figure 1 (Page 11). Figure 68 (Page 195) shows that the Y-section could be produced either by welding a bent plate to a tee, or better, by rolling an unbalanced I beam with a wide top flange and then rolling each side of the wide flange upward to an inclination of 45 degrees to form a Y-section.

Two of the advantages that Mr. Lazaro listed for the Y-section were: this section makes possible a smaller span for thin floor plates with increased rigidity and reduced tendency to cupping; and it has a natural 45 degree inclination at the ends of the Y flanges that is ideal for butt welding to plates.

The WF shapes proposed by Messrs. Brigham and Steiner, shown in Figure 41, (Page 125) has constant flange widths of 14 in. and constant depths of 21 in. The flange and web thicknesses are varied. They remarked that these sections were not indispensable for their Vierendeel trusses, but the sections eliminate eccentricities and protruding parts and offer greater lateral rigidity and resistance against buckling than standard sections available.

The new channels used by Mr. Asrow both in his Vierendeel trusses and in his floor system have wide flanges and thick webs. They are combined together or with plates to form torsionally rigid sections. Dimensions of the floor channel are shown in Figure 42 (Page 129) as are the widths and depths of the truss channels.

The deck channel proposed by Messrs. H. T. Borton and J. L. Borton is shown with its dimensions in Figure 85. It is utilized as effective area of their two box girders in addition to being part of the floor system. It is essentially a 24 by 4 in. channel with two intermediate ribs. The advantages offered by this ribbed floor channel are listed in Chapter III where the floor system is discussed.

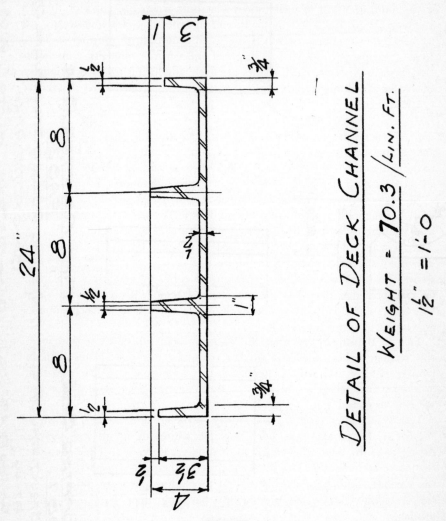

Figure 85

The "Pipe Adapter Bar" conceived by Mr. Miller is discussed in Chapter II and its use is illustrated in Figure 19 (Page 69). The dimensions of bars for 10 in. and 12 in. pipe are shown in Figure 86.

The new section Mr. Maugh used as the chords of his six, two-hinged continuous welded frames is shown in Figure 87. Size S1 is dimensioned in Section CC and size S2 in Section DD. The shape is symmetrical about both the vertical and horizontal axes and could be described as two channel shapes connected by a web. This shape spreads the flange material and enables connections to be made by butt welds.

224

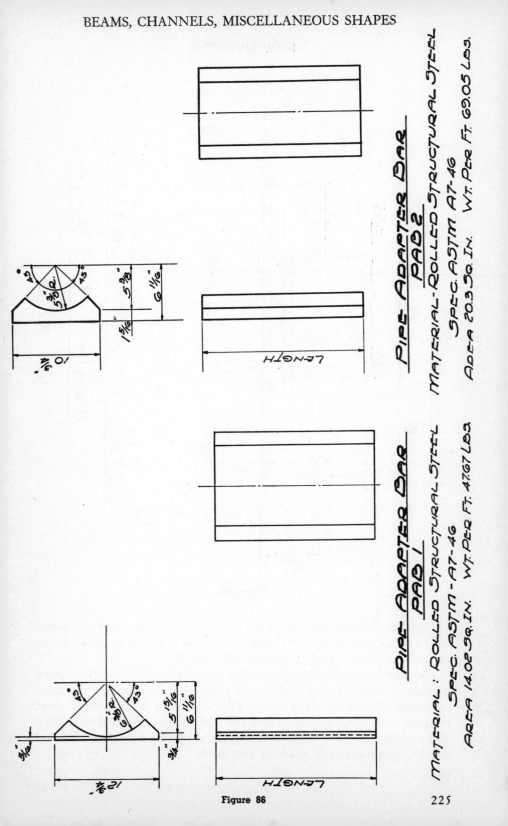

Figure 86

225

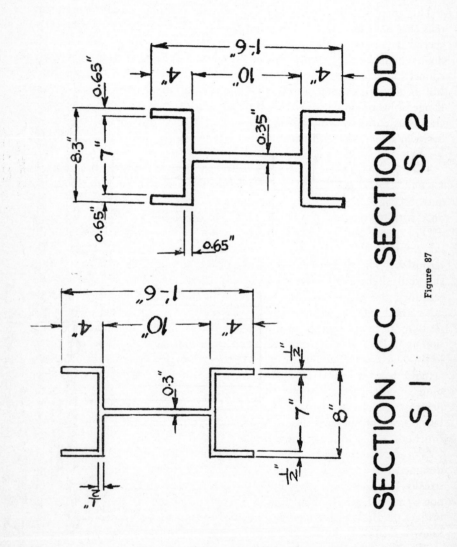

SECTION CC   SECTION DD

S 1   S 2

Figure 87

CHAPTER V

SPECIAL CONNECTIONS AND DETAILS

This chapter is devoted to the less common types of connections and details that have not already been described in the preceding chapters. Many special details were mentioned at the time the longitudinal members, the floor systems, or the new shapes were discussed. A few examples of unusual connection details previously covered are: Mr. Miller's "Pipe Adapter Bar"; Mr. Scheyer's channel braces used to provide lateral support for tension flange of his mono-truss; Mr. McBroom's single gusset plates; the use of top chords as curbs by Mr. Asrow and others; Mr. Asrow's bolted connection between floor plate and abutment; and Mr. Morrison's center anchor for his arch.

The design of Mr. Morrison's stiffened flexible arch is discussed in Chapter II and the details and connections are shown in Figures 54, 55, and 70 (Pages 153, 155, 199). The connections were made flexible in accordance with his remarks on details which were as follows:

"For years many riveted structures have been designed as statically determinate when, actually, the construction used has been highly indeterminate. The designers have tacitly placed considerable reliance on rivet slip and slight flexibilities in the connections, without ever having determined the magnitude of these relieving factors. When such practices are carried over to welded details, failures often result. The welded connections are more rigid than similar riveted details, but this rigidity is their undoing. In a welded joint subjected to fatigue loading there are no relieving factors. Therefore, it is necessary that the designer consider the actual effect on connections of forces transmitted by them. Possibly even more important, the designer should take pains to insure that, during the deformation of the structure under loads, no forces are applied to the details other than the ones they are designed to carry. 'Secondary' or 'assisting' functions, not computed, are ruinous to welded details.

"For the reasons stated above, all connection plates used in the bridge are designed for a certain definite, predictable flexibility so that participation stresses of appreciable magnitude do not develop and their transfer does not wreck the details. Had standard riveted connections been used for this bridge, the deck plates would certainly function to a considerable, but unknown, degree as top flange for the girders and floor beams.

"At the connections of the vertical struts to the arches and floor beams there will necessarily be a certain definite amount of hinge action. This also has been provided for by employing flexible plates. Some engineers might consider this detail in particular to be too radical and prefer, instead, a detail similar to that used at the spring lines of the arches.

"The problem of design of welded details resolves to a study of deformations rather than working stresses. When the edge of a plate is welded to a flexural member the stress in the fibres of the plate parallel to the member and close to it will be the same magnitude as the stress in the member. This participation stress cannot be suddenly developed at the edge of the plate. If the plate edge is perpendicular to the beam there will exist a high stress concentration at the corner. This situation has been prevented by smoothly merging the plate into the beam. The 1 inch by 3 inch triangle used is only an approximation that seems reasonable. Before finished design of a bridge was completed, tests could be conducted to determine the best size and shape for the concentration reducer. A photoelastic analysis would settle the problem.

"The rollers usually used at the ends of bridges are a frequent source of trouble. Where provision for uplift must also be made, the complications and consequent maintenance problems are greatly increased. This trouble spot can be eliminated by using welded frames and flexible connections. The cost of the additional steel will be at least partly offset by the elimination of machine work."

Mr. Spaulding extended the verticals of his trusses up through the upper chord in order to support the floor system with a member having sufficient "spring" so that the floor system could expand and contract from the center of the bridge in both directions independent of the trusses (see Figure 25, Page 85 and 66, Page 187). Figure 66 shows how the curb is supported by a plate attached to the top chord of the transverse truss. The curb is not attached to the floor slab.

For his space truss, Mr. Gottfeldt said that the forces in the two top chords were independent of the transverse position of the live load; and that this was true because these top chords formed also the flanges of a horizontal member for which the battledeck floor was the web. In order to prevent the outer stringers from acting as flanges, sliding joints as shown in Figure 35 (Page 110) were provided in the outer parts of the floor; that is, one end of each 30 ft. length of floor plate to which an outside stringer was attached was not welded to the floorbeam bracket.

Although pin connected bridges are common structures, the details Mr. Balke used in his design are quite ingenious. In discussing the pin connections, he stated:

"The use of pins for connecting the units, I believe, offers a novel method of facilitating the erection of welded highway structures. The writer's many years of observation of highway and railroad pin connected bridges has led him to the conclusion that highway bridges can be economically built as pin connected spans without incurring the wear that is evidenced in railroad structures which are subjected to much greater racking and resultant wear. To minimize the likelihood of wear however, the pin sizes have been made generous to reduce the bearing pressure of the parts on the pins.

"The eye bars have been picked from commercial sizes of forged bars still manufactured for the trade, however the writer has repaired and reinforced numerous pin connected railroad bridges requiring eye bars of sizes up to 16 in. x 2¼ in. which were made by butt welding flame cut plates to bars to produce the equivalent of forged bars. These welds were radiographed and the smaller ones were X-rayed to prove the quality of the welds. This is mentioned to bring out the fact that the bars also could be welded instead of forged.

"The details have been planned to eliminate all pockets which could collect dirt and moisture, and all parts are completely accessible for cleaning and painting. The end shoes are high to eliminate the failure of the shoes and end details due to excessive corrosion of poor details. All parts are made massive, and simple, and the sole plates of the expansion rocker are made of type 410 stainless corrosion resisting steel to further reduce the possibility of failure from corrosion.

* * *

"The various details should offer little opportunity for racking, particularly because of the complete bracing system alternating between the top and bottom panel points to serve the double function of lateral bracing and transverse distributing frames to distribute eccentric lane loading to the four trusses."

Figure 88 shows the details of the connections for Mr. Balke's design.

As shown in Figure 60, Messrs. Dunstan, Karmalsky, and Robertson weld a plate to each end of a stringer, and then the edges of this plate are welded to the web of a floorbeam. This is done to allow a certain amount of end rotation and avoid fixed end conditions. In like manner, a plate is welded to each end of a floorbeam, and the edges of the plate then welded to a vertical of the truss.

C. T. Blake, Ambridge, Pennsylvania and W. A. Brown, Sewickley, Pennsylvania designed a triangulated truss bridge. The two top chords are framed together by means of diagonal floorbeams which form the web system of a horizontal Warren truss between the two upper chords. Hence, all secondary bracing is eliminated. The connection for stringer to floorbeam and diagrammatic plan and elevation are shown in Figure 89.

With the floorbeams placed diagonally, the inclined web members of the principal trusses are so arranged that only diagonals from one truss will be framed at a panel point except at Ll and Ll prime. The entire bridge is made up of plates welded into sections with the exception of the expansion dams and stringers.

The details of end bearings, or shoes, for many designs have been shown in the preceding figures. The details of the end bearings for Mr. Lazaro's bridge are shown in Figure 69, (Page 197) and the shoes used by Mr.

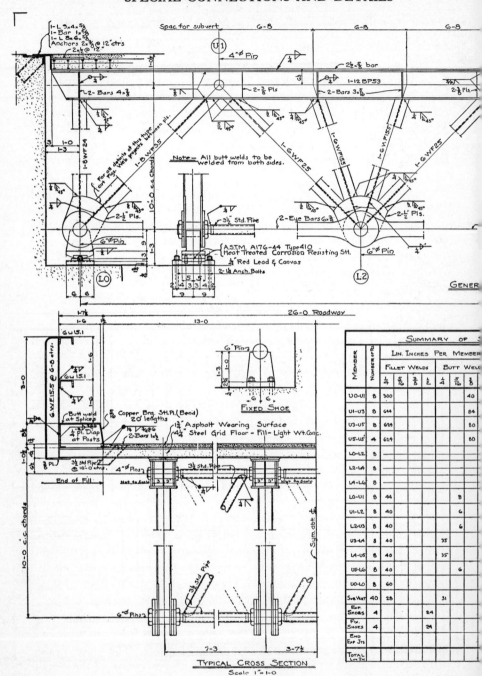

Note.— All butt welds to be welded from both sides.

TYPICAL CROSS SECTION
Scale 1"=1-0

FIXED SHOE

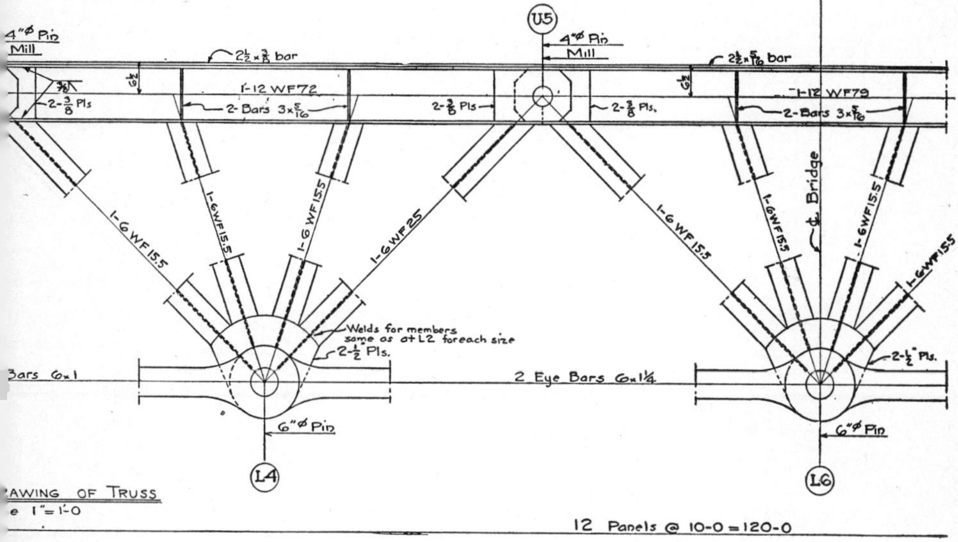
U5
4"Ø Pin
Mill
4"Ø Pin
Mill
2½ x ⅜ bar
2½ x 5/16 bar
1-12 WF72
1-12 WF79
2-⅜ Pls
2-Bars 3x5/16
2-⅜ Pls
2-⅜ Pls.
2-Bars 3x5/16
1-6 WF15.5
1-6WF15.5
1-6 WF15.5
1-6 WF25
1-6 WF15.5
1-6WF15.5
1-6WF15.5
1-6WF15.5
℄ Bridge
Welds for members same as at L2 for each size
2-½ Pls.
2-½" Pls.
Bars 6x1
2 Eye Bars 6x1¼
6"Ø Pin
6"Ø Pin
L4
L6
RAWING OF TRUSS
e 1"=1'-0
12 Panels @ 10-0=120-0

VELDS						
OTAL INCHES FOR BRIDGE						
LLET WELDS			BUTT WELDS			
5/16	3/8	1/2	1/4	5/16	3/8	1/2
					320	
					670	
					640	
					320	
				64		304
				48		232
				48		232
			280			
			280			
				48		232
						208
			1240			
		96				
		96				
		192	1800	208	1950	1208

SUMMARY OF FIELD WELDS

PART	NUMBER OF PCS	LIN. INCHES PER MEMBER								TOTAL INCHES PER BRIDGE							
		FILLET WELDS				BUTT WELDS				FILLET WELDS				BUTT WELDS			
		1/4	5/16	3/8	1/2	1/4	5/16	3/8	1/2	1/4	5/16	3/8	1/2	1/4	5/16	3/8	1/2
END EXP DAMS	2		500								1000						
CURBS	240 LIN FT	2400					480			2400					480		
RAIL P.	40	60								2400							
RAILING	4	240						35		960						140	
PIPE ST.	52	22								1140							
PIPE BR	48					30								1440			
GRID FL	3180 □'	.76		.18		.21				2400		580		670			
TOTAL LIN IN										9300	1000	580		2110	480	140	

MATERIAL CLASSIFICATION

ITEM	WT. #
12" WF	31200
8" WP	5200
6" WF	19000
6" Forged Eye Bars	24000
4" Pins & nuts	1400
6" " "	3600
Stain. Stl Type 410	200
Plates	7000
Bars	3000
9x4x5/8 Ls	1600
8x6x5/8 Ls	1700
1/4" Copper brg. pls	8800
6" Ship [illegible]	7600
Shop Weld Wire	700
Field " "	600
3½" Std Pipes	5400
Total Wt.	125,000#

STEEL ESTIMATE

TRUSSES	89000
SHOES	3000
BRACING	10000
END DAMS	3000
RAILING & CURBS	20000
TOTAL WT.	125,000#

FLOOR GRID ESTIMATE

3180 sq. ft. 4¼" GRID	47000
35 yards Light Wt. Conc.	90000
3180 sq ft of 1½" Asphalt	53000
TOTAL WT.	190000#

COST ESTIMATE

62½ Tons Struct Stl. Del @ $250	15600
" " " " " @ $96	6000
3180 □' Grid Fl in Place @ 3.60	11500
" Conc Fill " @ .35	1100
" Asphalt " @ .25	800
TOTAL EST COST	$35,000

WELDED BRIDGES OF THE FUTURE

1949 AWARD PROGRAM

THE JAMES F LINCOLN ARC WELDING FOUNDATION

CLEVELAND OHIO

Figure 88 (Concluded)

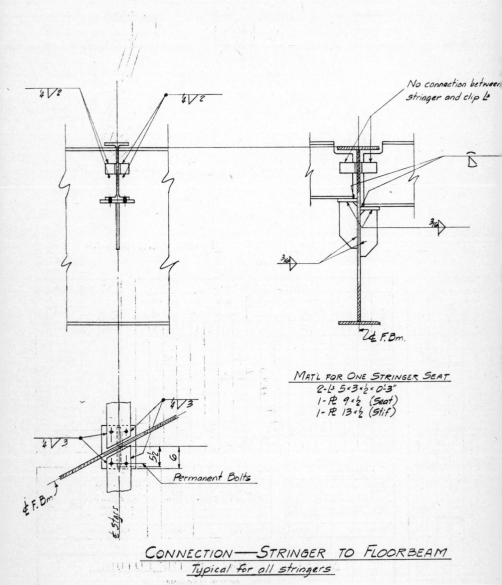

No connection between stringer and clip L

$4\bigvee 2$ $4\bigvee 2$

3/16

3/16

℄ F.Bm.

MAT'L FOR ONE STRINGER SEAT
2-L° 5×3×½×0′-3″
1- ℞ 9×½ (Seat)
1- ℞ 13×½ (Stif.)

$4\bigvee 3$

$4\bigvee 3$

5½   6

Permanent Bolts

℄ F.Bm.

℄ Stgrs.

CONNECTION—STRINGER TO FLOORBEAM
Typical for all stringers

Figure 89

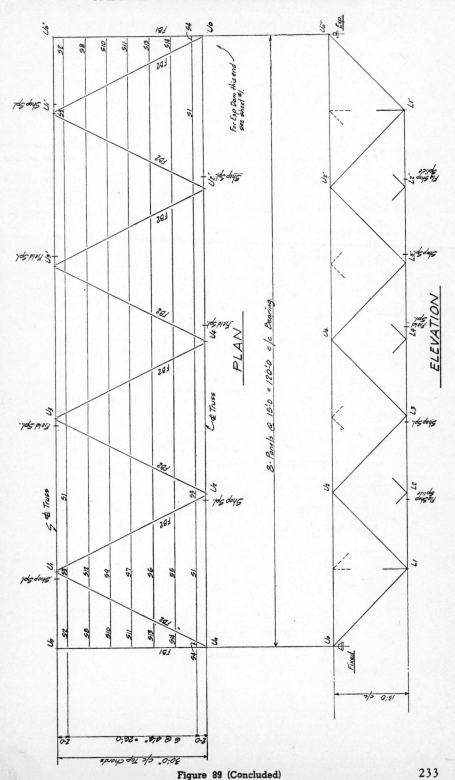

Figure 89 (Concluded)

233

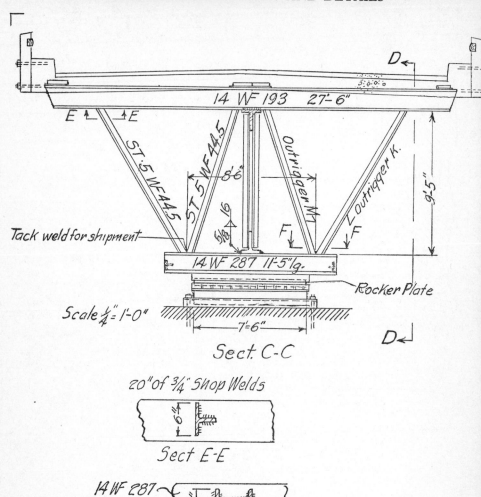

14 WF 193   27'-6"

ST 5 WF 445

ST 5 WF 445

8'-6"

Outrigger M

Outrigger K

9'-5"

Tack weld for shipment

5/8 16

F

F

14 WF 287 11'-5" lg.

Rocker Plate

Scale ¼" = 1'-0"

7'-6"

Sect. C-C

20" of ¾" Shop Welds

6"

Sect. E-E

14 WF 287

6"

40" of ¾" Field Welds

Sect. F-F

Scale ½" = 1'-0"

Figure 90

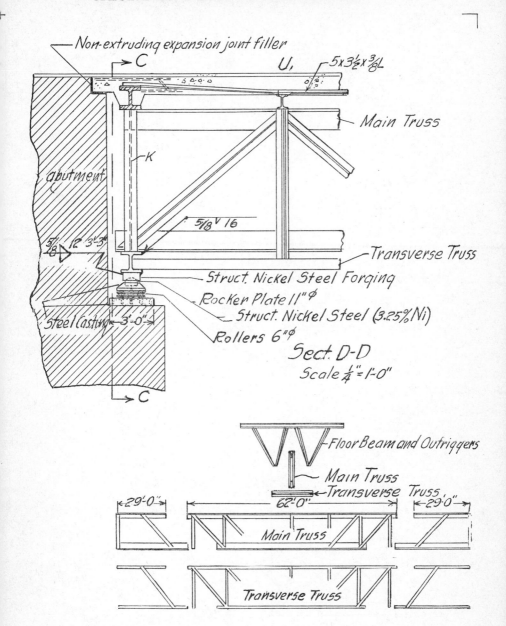

Non-extruding expansion joint filler

C

U, ——5x3½x⅜L

Main Truss

K

abutment

⅝ V 16

Transverse Truss

Struct. Nickel Steel Forging

Rocker Plate 11"ᵠ

Struct. Nickel Steel (3.25% Ni)

⅝ 12 3'-3"

Steel Casting ←3'-0"→

Rollers 6"ᵠ

Sect. D-D

Scale ¼"=1'-0"

C

Floor Beam and Outriggers

Main Truss

Transverse Truss

←29'-0"→ ←————62'-0"————→ ←29'-0"→

Main Truss

Transverse Truss

Method of Erection and Fabrication Diagram

Figure 90 (Concluded)   235

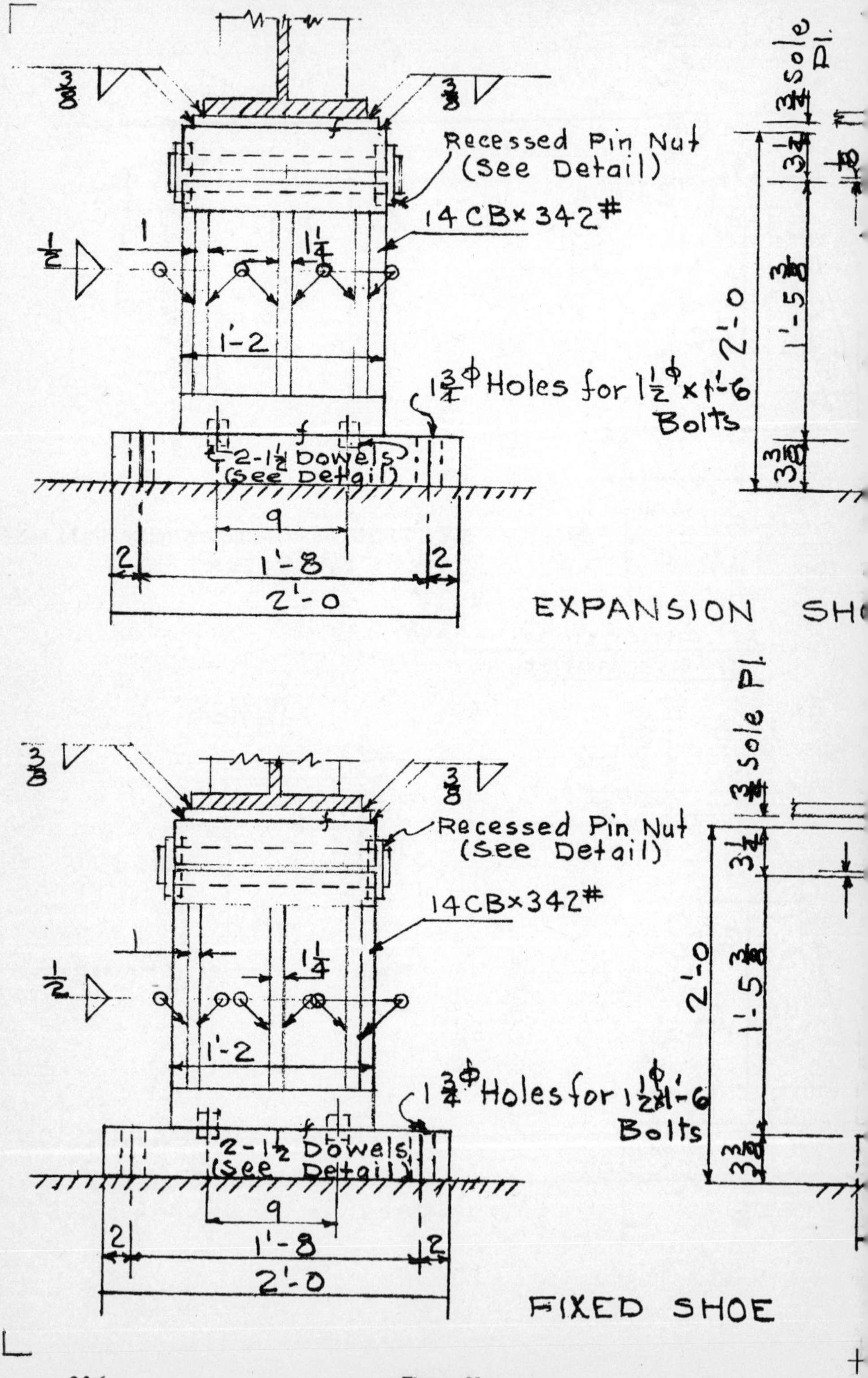

EXPANSION SHOE

FIXED SHOE

Figure 91

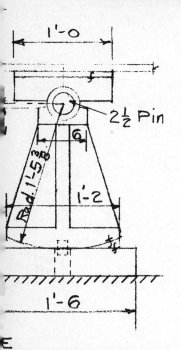

2½ Pin

Rad. 1'-5⅜"

6

1'-2

1'-6

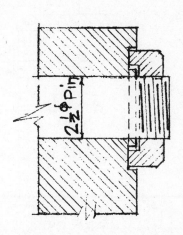

2"∅ Pin

SECTION OF RECESSED PIN NUT
SCALE 3 = 1'-0

E

<u>All dimensions inches unless noted</u>

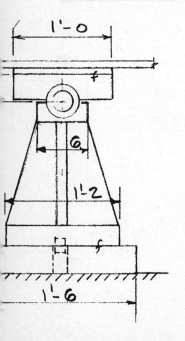

1'-0

6

1'-2

1'-6

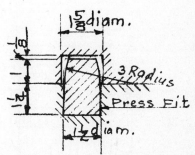

1⅝ diam.

⅛

3 Radius

Press Fit

1½ diam.

SECTION THRU DOWEL
SCALE 3 = 1'-0

DETAILS OF EXPANSION AND FIXED SHOES
SCALE 1 = 1'-0 UNLESS NOTED

Figure 91 (Concluded)   237

Balke in Figure 88, but the details of the bearings for fourteen of the other designs are all included in the figures of Chapter II.

Because Mr. Scheyer had a single vertical truss (mono-truss), the dimensions of the end bearings are unusual. In discussing the size of abutment and end bearings, he said:

"One of the advantages of the mono-truss bridge is that the part of the abutment, which takes the load, need not be anywhere near the width of the bridge as is the case with bridges having a plurality of spaced trusses or ribs. A large proportion of the cost of a bridge project is for its abutments. In good soil or rock the load carrying part of the abutment for the mono-truss bridge can readily be kept narrow. In poor soil, piles can be used. The cost of the abutment is greater where the piles must be spread apart to range over a large width rather than to concentrate them under the narrow width where the principal load is to be carried. It is for the reason of keeping the width of the abutment small, that the rocker plates have been kept down to a length of 7 ft.-6 in. and structural nickel steel, which has a high yield point, is used. However, the length of the rocker plate and the base in general depend on local conditions at the abutment foundation, and may be varied from that shown as determined by the designer. A sufficient increase in length will also bring down the pressures so that ordinary structural steel can be used for the rocker plate and nickel steel forging.

"The pressure on the nickel steel forging under the 14 WF 287 abutment beam has a triangular distribution to resist the overturning moment. Superimposed upon the maximum pressure induced by the moment, which maximum pressure is twice the average pressure or 224,000 lbs. for the end foot of the rocker plate, is the uniform pressure received from the reaction of the main truss with one lane loaded, which is 53,000 lbs. per linear foot. The maximum combined pressure of these two, which may occur at either end of the rocker plate, is 277,000 lbs. per linear foot."

To a very small scale, the fixed shoe of Mr. Scheyer's design is shown in Figure 17, (Page 63) but Figure 90 here shows the bearings at the roller end to a larger scale. The length of rollers is 7 ft.-6 in. There are three rollers, each 6 in. in diameter.

The shoes Mr. Fischer used for his Vierendeel trusses are shown in Figure 91. They are weldments. The top and bottom bearing plates have recesses machined into them to fit recessed pin nuts for pins 2½ in. in diameter.

CHAPTER VI

QUANTITIES AND COSTS

According to the Rules and Conditions of this program, each participant was required to include, as part of his exhibit, a table or tables giving the total quantity of steel required and tables giving the total quantity of welds required. The various sizes of steel shapes or plates (except sketch plates of the same thickness) were to be listed separately. The various sizes of the various types of shop welds and of field welds were to be listed separately.

These tables were provided by the designers. In some cases, the tables were a part of the drawings; and therefore, in presenting the figures of the preceding chapters, some have contained tables of quantities. The following figures have the quantities of steel and welds used in the respective designs; they are Figures 2, 11, 17, 38, 47, and 88. Figures 30 and 53 include summaries of steel weights.

A few tables not already given will be shown here as a means of illustrating, for these particular designs, the relative weights of the different parts of the structures and the relationship between amount of welding and the amount of steel.

Total costs and unit costs are appropriately considered in this chapter along with quantities and weights. Costs vary and change under economic conditions from year to year, or even from month to month. Between countries at any given time, costs will differ considerably, and to a lesser extent they vary within a single country. The costs quoted in this book were the best estimates of the authors at the time they submitted their designs.

The quantities for Mr. Kavanagh's bridge are shown in Tables 2 and 3. The costs are given in Table 4, but he emphasized that the figures were merely typical since neither job nor shop conditions had been defined.

Mr. Dumbauld made elaborate calculations for the cost of his design. He said:

"The costs for this structure were estimated, using labor and material costs edited in the March 10 and March 17, 1949 issues of the Engineering News-Record. The costs for welding, gas flame cutting and gouging were analyzed from methods described in the American Bridge Company Handbook on 'Metal Arc Welding' and 'Procedure Handbook of Arc Welding Design and Practice' of the Lincoln Electric Company, eighth edition. Office records of contract bid prices and office engineering estimates were also available.

"As the entire superstructure is structural steel the only two items to thoroughly investigate were steel and paint, with proper dividing of costs among the various items of base price, transportation, fabrication, overhead, taxes, labor and profit.

239

Table 2

Final Steel Weights

The quantity of steel in various sizes and shapes is tabulated below:

	Total Lbs.	Lbs. per ft. of bridge
Grating, Irving Bridge Decking or equal		
26′ x 121.5′ x 15¼ lbs./sq. ft.	48,200	401.7
Sills, 7 Channel 9.8		
26′ x 120 x 12/18 x 9.8 lb./ft.	20,400	170.0
Stringers: 16 WF 40 5 x 120′ x 40 lb./ft........	24,000	200.0
8 WF 35 2 x 120′ x 35 lb./ft........	8,400	70.0
Clip angles 2½ x 2½ x ⅜ x 3″		
2/x 7 x 9 x 3″ x 5.9 lb./ft.	186	1.6
Int. Fl. Bms. 18 WF 50 7 x 29.5′ x 50 lb./ft.......	10,300	
End Fl. Bms. 12 WF 40 2 x 29.5′ x 40 lb./ft......	2,360	105.5
Railings: 6 x 120′ x (5″ x ½″)	6,130	51.1
Posts: 3½″ Ex. Str. Pipe 30 @ 5′ x 12.51 lb./ft......	1,880	15.7
Straps: 30 @ 2″ x ⁵⁄₁₆ x 12″	63	0.5
Curb plates (bent) 53″ x ⁵⁄₁₆″ x 120′ x 2	13,560	113.0
Total flooring, etc..........................	135,479	1,129.1
Upper Chord "W": 12.2 sq. in. x 120′	5,000	41.6
Upper Chord "X": 18.7 sq. in. x 126′............	8,000	66.7
Lower Chord "Y": 22.5 sq. in. x 60′................	4,600	38.3
Lower Chord "Z": 30.5 sq. in. x 33′................	3,450	28.8
Diags. 10 BP 42 x 16 x 21.2′	14,200	118.3
Verts. 10 WF 33 x 14 x 15.5′	7,160	59.7
Lateral Diags. 6 ST WF 15.5 x 16 x 8.17′	2,030	16.9
Rockers (2) and attachments.....................	750	
Bolsters (2) and attachments.....................	470	12.3
4 Pins 3½″ x 11″ plus nuts	150	
Grand Totals	181,289	1,511.7

"There is a very great variation in the average bid prices for the fourth quarter of 1948 for structural steel used in highway construction in the different states. The unit price per pound of structural steel in various states listed below show the wide bid range:—

"Connecticut—$.188, George—.110, Florida—.108, Louisiana—.287, Michigan—.103, Ohio—.157, Washington—.234, Oregon—.180, with the bid average of all states being $.158 per pound for the entire year of 1948. This indicates a variation of almost 300% between the high and low state average.

"The labor rate estimated for skilled laborers in structural iron work,

Table 3

Quantity of Welds Required

A tabulation of the total quantity of welds required, by sizes and types, for the entire bridge including tack welding of the decking, is given below:

Type of weld	Size	Equivalent Wt. lbs./ft.	Length of Weld Shop	Length of Weld Field	Weight of Weld Shop	Weight of Weld Field
Fillet	1/4	.106	739 ft.	929 ft.	78.5#	98.8#
	3/8	.239	16		3.8	
	3/4	.955	15		14.3	
V Groove 60°	7/16	.518		4		2.1
	9/16	.791		11		8.7
Double V Groove 60°	7/16	.600	48	48	28.8	28.8
	5/8	.724		6		4.4
	1 1/2	3.00		1 1/2		4.5
Single Bevel 45°	1/2	.53	271	73	144.0	38.7
	9/16	.64		22		14.1
Double Bevel 45°	5/8	.54	92		49.6	
Total Weld Weight,* lbs.					319.0	200.1

Ratio of total weld weight* to total weight of steel (including decking):

$$\frac{519.1 \text{ lbs.}}{90.64 \text{ Tons}} = 5.73 \text{ lbs.* per ton.}$$

*Deposited weld metal.

crane operators, welders and flame gougers is $2.38 per hour and $1.42 per hour for common labor, with ratio of skilled labor to common labor as 1 2/3 to 1 for welding and 1 1/4 to 1 for flame cutting. The average labor rate used for painting was $2.00 per hour. The cost of welding rod is estimated at $.10 per pound, and electric power at $.03 per kilowatt. Overhead costs include maintenance, depreciation, water, heating, lighting, drafting, bookkeeping, taxes, insurance and pension payments."

The total cost for flame cutting and gouging, Mr. Dumbauld found to be $270. He obtained this value by first estimating the cost to flame cut various thicknesses of metal, in eighth inch increments from 1/4 in. to 1 in. and quarter inch increments from 1 in. to 2 in. For 1/2 in. plates, the estimated cost to flame cut was 21.9 cents per ft., 32.6 cents for 1 in., and 54.4 cents for 2 in. From very detailed computations, he obtained the cost per foot for various sizes of fillet and butt welds and used them in Table 5 which shows the weights and the total costs of his welds. Table 6 gives his estimated cost of structural steel as 12.2 cents per lb. The painting cost

Table 4

Welded Triangular Section Truss Bridge

Steel, Structural 133,089 lbs. @ 2.53¢ (mill plus 10%) . . $3,370.		
Decking 48200 lbs. at say 12.5¢ . . . . 6,020.		$ 9,390.
Freight to mill to shop		400.
Fabrication—Dwgs., genl. handling, inspection		
133,089 @ .05	670.	
Manipulation 133,089 @ .0015	260.	
Flame cutting 1000′ @ .10	100.	
Arc welding (all) 1709′ @ .20	341.	
577′ @ .40	231.	1,602.
Freight to site 181,289 @ .05		906.
Erection: Assume same as riveted truss		
Labor—flooring	1,690.	
Labor—trusses	1,240.	
Labor—painting etc.	300.	3,230.
Equipment* Crane, transp., erect.,		
welding, painting etc.		1430.
Overhead 10% x steel	819.	
35% x labor	1,170.	
5% equipment	72.	2,061.
Total		19,019.
Profit 10%		1,902.
Total Cost		$20,921.

was calculated to be 0.015 cents per lb. For 118,820 lbs. of superstructure framework, the total cost was $16,378.34. With the grid floor at $3.00 per sq. ft. plus painting amounting to slightly over $10,000, the total cost of the bridge was $26,400.

Of the 118,820 lbs., the girders accounted for 72,385 lbs., the floorbeams and stringers for 30,950 lbs., and the curb and railing for 11,545 lbs. The weight of the open grid floor was 57,500 lbs.

The summary of weights for Mr. Tupker's "cellular" bridge made of thin sheet metal were as follows:

Box and curb girders	71,500 lb.
Structural handrails	3,400
Columns and column ends	3,000
Side stiffeners	9,030
Summary	86,930 lb.
Variations in rolling thicknesses and paint 2½%	2,170
Weight of welded structure	89,100 lb.
Seven fixed and seven expansion shoes, cast steel	1,750
Asphaltic mastic floor covering	56,000
Total dead load	146,850 lb.

Table 5

ESTIMATED WEIGHTS & COST OF WELDING

SIZE	CLASS	FIELD OR SHOP	TOTAL LENGTH	WEIGHT LB. P.L.F.	COST ¢ per Ft.	TOTAL WEIGHT LBS.	TOTAL COST $
FILLET WELDS							
3/16	Intermittent	Shop	395	.15	44.2	59.25	174.59
1/4	"	Shop	57	.20	48.7	11.40	27.76
3/8	"	Shop	8	.28	51.0	2.24	4.08
3/8	Continuous	Shop	223	.25	46.4	55.75	103.47
		SUB-TOTAL				128.64	309.90
1/4	Intermitt.	Field	20	.20	73.0	4.00	14.60
1/4	" Vert	Field	12	.20	150.0	2.40	18.00
3/8	Intermitt.	Field	79	.28	76.5	22.12	60.44
3/8	" Ov. Hd.	Field	9	.40	230	3.60	20.70
161 lbs. of fillet welds.		SUB-TOTAL				32.12	113.74
BUTT WELDS							
1/4"	on 3" Pipe	Shop	7.3	.25	85±	1.82	6.21
5/16"	Curb Pl	Shop	24.0	.27	86.7	6.48	20.81
3/8 "	Girder	Shop	12.7	.48	94.0	6.10	11.94
3/4 "	Fl. Bm. Conn	Shop	7.6	1.8	250	13.68	19.00
1 "	" " "	Shop	10.0	3.10	414.8	31.00	41.48
7/8	20 TF 67	Shop	13.4	1.61	277.8	21.57	37.23
1½ "	20 TF 109	Shop	13.4	3.84	762.6	51.46	102.19
		SUB-TOTAL				132.11	238.86
½ -	Stringer Fl.	Field	4.7	.82	190	3.85	8.93
5/16	" Web	Field	4.5 (Vert)	.27	250	1.21	11.25
1/4	End Fin- Fl.	Field	17.7	.25	120	4.43	21.24
		SUB-TOTAL				9.49	41.42
* { 3/8 OR (3/8	20 TF to Web	Shop	484	.48	94	232.32	455.00
	20 TF to Web	Shop	484	.20	31.10	96.8	150. +)*
374 lbs. of butt welds.		GRAND TOTAL				534.68	1158.92
	*(GRAND TOTAL				_	312.04	853.92)*
	*(DIFFERENCE IN GRAND TOTAL					222.64	305.00)*

*This Item shows estimated cost and savings possible where permission is granted to use a tight, square butt joint for 3/8 " Web Plate Weld using automatic shielded metallic arc method.

= 493 lbs of weld metal req'd for shop welding, 42 for field welding.

Table 6

ESTIMATED UNIT COST OF STRUCTURAL STEEL ~

	ITEM	$ PER TON	% OF TOTAL
1.	Base Price $3.25 per 100 lb.	65.00	26.60
2.	Warehouse extra delivered (2.25 per 100 lb)	45.00	18.44
3	Sales Tax 3 %	3.30	1.35
4	Cambering Girder $2 per T × 36T ÷ 60T	1.20	.49
5	General Handling	1.00	.41
6	Hauling to Site (1.00 + $10 ton mile) 100 mi Av.	11.00	4.50
7	Erection Crane plus Power	10.00	4.10
8	Shop Overhead = 40% Total Cost (Item 1 to 5)	46.20	19.0
9	Flame Cutting $176.30 ÷ 59.41 Tons	2.97	1.22
10	Shop Fillet Welding $309.90 ÷ 59.41 T	5.23	2.14
11	Shop Butt Welding $238.86 ÷ 59.41 T	4.02	1.65
12	Field Welding $(113.74 + 41.42) ÷ 59.41 T	2.61	1.07
*13	Flame Cutting 3/8" Web Pl. $93.70 ÷ 59.41 T	1.58	.64
*14	Butt Welding Flge. to 3/8" Web $455 ÷ 59.41 T	7.65	3.14
15	Field Overhead 25% (Items 6+7 = 21.00)	5.50	2.25
	TOTAL $	212.26	87.0
	15 % Profit	31.84	13.0
	COST PER LB. = $.122 ←→ COST PER TON $	244.10	100%

* If a tight square butt weld can be used for welding Flange Sections to 3/8" Web Pl. Then Item 13 above will be eliminated and

		203.03	86
14	Butt Welding Flge. to 3/8 Web $150 ÷ 59.41 T	2.52	1.0
	AND TOTAL WOULD BE	205.55	87.0
	AND 15% Profit	30.83	13.0
	COST PER LB. = $.118 ←→ AND COST PER TON	236.38	100%

Saving for tight square butt flange to web weld would be $7.72 per ton = $458.64 = $3.79 per foot of deck

NOTE: Overhead on Items 9, 10, 11, 12, 13, 14 included in estimated unit cost.

Estimated Cost Shop Welding = 6.93 % of Total Cost
and Field Welding = 1.07 %.

Estimated Structural Steel Weight = 118,820 lb. ⎫
Weight One Coat Shop Paint = 450 lb. ⎬ = 119,400 lb
Weight of Fillet Welds (Shop) = 130 lb. ⎭ Shipping Wt.
say 120 Tons

He had 48,700 ft. of butt weld and 11,400 ft. of fillet weld using ⅛ in. electrodes. For the butt welds, the recommendations were 400 amperes, 24 volts, and 100.12 in. per minute, and for the fillet welds were 100 amperes, 14 volts, and 14 in. per minute.

The cost of steel was broken down into the following percentages:

Materials delivered at shops	45
Drawings	5½
Templates	3
Laying out the work	¾
Shearing	½
Straightening	¼
Assembling	3
Milling	5
Casting	3
Welding	20
Painting	7
General expense	7
Total	100%

Mr. Jennison tabulated his costs as follows:

Structural steel	53,900 lb. @	$ 0.18		$ 9,720
Reinforcing steel	17,650 lb. @	0.15		2,650
Temporary rods, etc.	1,000 lb. @	0.25		250
Bronze expansion plates	78 lb. @	1.00		78
Bolts	53 lb. @	0.50		26
Concrete (structure)	144 cu. yd. @	50.00		7,200
Redwood timber (railing)	1744 fbm @	0.35		610
Bolts for railing	417 lb. @	0.30		125
Total				$20,659

Of the 53,000 lbs. of structural steel, 47,055 lbs. were rolled shapes, 4,960 lbs. were plates, and the remaining 1,899 lbs. were bearing plates and expansion rockers. An alternate railing of structural steel weighing 4,211 lbs. could replace the timber railing.

For their two girders with the two-way concrete slab, Messrs. Bleich and Schwarting listed the following quantities:

Total structural steel	115,120 lb.
Spiral shear connectors	1,120 lb.
Reinforcement bars in deck	22,320 lb.
Total steel weight	138,560 lb.
Concrete in roadway slab and curb	120 cu. yd.
Total weight of shop welds	580 lb.
Total weight of field welds	11 lb.

Each of the three triangular trusses Mr. Ullman used weighed 25,830 lbs. giving a total structural steel weight of 77,490 lbs. The reinforced concrete deck contained 93 cu. yd. of concrete and 21,000 lbs. of reinforcing steel.

The quantities for the bridge designed by Messrs. Hadley and Johnson are shown in Figure 11. As indicated in this figure, all welding was done in the shop. They estimated their costs as follows:

4000 lb. concrete	84.6 cu. yd. @ $65.00	....	$ 5,499
Reinforcement, in place	11,640 lb. @ 0.11	....	1,280
Structural steel	97,000 lb. @ 0.20	....	19,400

Total cost $26,179

Messrs. F. W. Cox and L. W. Cox gave elaborate tables of weights but summarized them in the following manner:

Rails and rail posts	5,195 lb.
Steel curb	8,280
Expansion device and bearings	4,220
Floorbeams	19,934
Girders	106,697
Cross frames	14,260

Total for bridge, less steel grid floor	158,586 lb.
Steel grid floor	51,810

Total of all steel................................210,396 lb.

The total weight of welds was 1219.7 lbs. for 15,909 ft. with 934.7 lbs. being shop welds and 285 pounds being field welds. Of these totals, the steel grid floor required 205 lbs. of the shop welds and 43.6 lbs. of the field welds.

Mr. Pimenoff computed his costs as follows:

Structural steel	59 tons @ $250	....	$14,750
Deck concrete	71 cu. yd. @ 50	....	3,550
Deck reinforcing steel	10 tons @ 170	....	1,700

Total cost $20,000.00

The tied arch bridge that Mr. Gilbert designed contained 222,714 lbs. of steel. The arch ribs (3 ft. in diameter) weighed 45,240 lbs.; the tension tie bars weighed 17,000 lb.; the deck plates weighed 66,930 lb.; the floorbeams weighed 24,220 lb.; the curb plates weighed 18,320 lb.; and the remainder was distributed between the details, except for 1,912 lb. of weld metal.

Messrs. Cassidy and Otto had 80 tons of supporting structure, including end connections, girder, floorbeams, and stringers. They considered that their concrete filled, I-Beam-Lok floor had 3464 sq. ft. of area which with the wearing surface would cost $12,055. This assumed the steel floor to cost 17 cents per lb., the concrete to be $62 per cu. yd., and the wearing surface at 35 cents per sq. ft. The estimate for structural steel was 16 cents per lb. in place.

246

Mr. Miller used 31.1 tons of steel for the trusses and shoes at $350 per ton, 75.6 tons for deck and bracing at $260 per ton, 240 lineal ft. of railing at $6 per ft. and 350 sq. yd. of bituminous concrete surfacing at $2 per sq. ft.

The bill of materials and the list of welds that Mr. Lazaro prepared are shown in Table 7. For each weld, he listed size, kind, description, length in feet, weight in lbs. and cost in dollars.

BILL OF MATERIALS

Item	Size	Weight (lbs.)
MAIN GIRDERS (2 units)		
Web plates	2 - 15/16" × 56" × 121'-0"	43,200
Bottom flanges	2 - 2" × 27" × 48'-0"	17,600
	2 - 2" × 45" × 34'-8"	21,200
Top flanges	2 - 5/8" × 40" × 121'-0"	20,600
End stiffeners (web)	4 - 1/2" × 8" × 2'-6"	140
(flange)	4 - 1/2" × 6" × 2'-6"	100
Fl. beam brackets (web)	14 - 3/8" × 28" × 2'-5"	1,200
(flange)	14 - 1/2" × 10" × 3'-8"	870
Shoe plates	4 - 3" × 9" × 1'-4"	490
	TOTAL	105,410
FLOORBEAMS (7 units)		
Bottom flanges (WF Tee)	7 - 12" @ 42# × 20'-1"	5,900
Top flanges of temp. fl. beam	7 - 1/2" × 4" × 19'-0"	910
Vert. " " " " "	14 - 1/2" × 4" × 1'-4"	130
Webs	7 - 1/2" × 17" × 21'-0"	4,250
	TOTAL	11,190
CANTILEVERS (14 units)		
Webs	14 - 1/2" × 28" × 4'-4"	2,890
	14 - 3/8" × 13" × 1'-10"	430
Flanges	14 - 1/2" × 12" × 1'-6"	430
	14 - 1/2" × 6" × 6'-1"	870
	TOTAL	4,620
Y-STRINGERS AND FLOORINGS		
Stringers (Y-beam)	13 - 11" @ 28.6# × 121'-0"	45,000
Floor plates	2 - 5/8" × 7'-0" × 121'-0"	43,200
	1 - 5/8" × 6'-0" × 121'-0"	18,500
Backing strips	2 - 1/4" × 3" × 19'-0"	100
	58 - 1/4" × 2" × 0'-11"	90
	2 - 1/4" × 3" × 121'-0"	620
	TOTAL	107,510
FOOTWALK (2 units)		
Floor plates	2 - 5/16" × 49" × 121'-0"	12,600
Stiffeners	12 - 1/4" × 13" × 4'-4"	580
Curved plates	12 - 1/2" × 8" × 1'-6"	250
Wheel guard (light angle)	2 - 3" × 3.7# × 121'-0"	890
	TOTAL	14,320
RAILINGS (2 units)		
Posts (I-beam)	22 - 4" @ 9.5# × 3'-6"	730
Posts at splice (I-beam)	8 - 4" @ 5.4# × 3'-6"	150
Hor. members	4 - 2½"φ @ 5.8# × 121'-2"	2,820
	2 - 6" @ 8.2# × 121'-2"	2,000
End stiffener plates	4 - 5/16" × 7" × 2'-1"	60
Vertical bars	336 - 5/8"φ @ 1.33# × 2'-9"	1,230
	TOTAL	6,990
EXPANSION PLATES		
For roadway	2 - 1/2" × 14" × 26'-0"	1,240
For footwalk	4 - 5/16" × 14" × 2'-8"	160
	TOTAL	1,400
BOLTS		
For railings	8 - 5/8"φ × 2"	10
(Can be re-used)	60 - 5/8"φ × 3"	30
For floorbeams (Can be re-used)	56 - 5/8"φ × 3"	30
Expansion plate	136 - 5/8"φ × 3"	60
	136 - 1/4" × 3" × 4"	120
Anchor bolts	136 - 5/8"φ × 12"	170
	TOTAL	420
FIXED BEARINGS (2 units)		
Base plates	2 - 2" × 9" × 2'-1"	260
Anchor plates	2 - 2" × 9" × 1'-4"	160
Vertical plates	4 - 5/8" × 7" × 0'-7½"	40
	8 - 5/8" × 3" × 0'-3¼"	15
	2 - 2½" × 6" × 1'-4"	140
Bolts	4 - 1"φ × 10"	15
Anchor bolts	4 - 1½"φ × 18"	50
	TOTAL	680
EXPANSION BEARINGS (2 units)		
Base plates	2 - 2" × 9" × 2'-1"	260
Roller plates	2 - 2" × 7" × 1'-4"	130
Vertical plates	4 - 5/8" × 6" × 0'-6"	30
	2 - 2½" × 6" × 1'-4"	140
Dowels	4 - 1"φ × 2"	-
Anchor bolts	4 - 1½"φ × 18"	50
	TOTAL	610

TOTAL GROSS WEIGHT OF STEEL = 253,150 lbs.
ASPHALT CONCRETE WEARING SURFACE = 25 cu. yrds.

WELDS

SIZE	KIND	DESCRIPTION	LENGTH (ft)	WT. of WELD (lbs)	TOTAL COST
FIELD:					
3/16"		overhead	11	1	1.60
1/4"		overhead	11	2	1.60
		vertical	57	8	8.50
		flat	65	11	2.60
5/16"		flat	157	33	24.20
		vertical	39	12	6.30
1/2"		"	20	26	4.90
		flat	8	10	1.80
5/8"		"	282	483	84.30
3/4"		"	11	26	3.60
(SAY $ 150)			TOTAL	612	$146.40
SHOP:					
3/16"		automatic weld	480	51	68.50
1/4"		" "	968	155	143.20
5/16"		" "	3388	1525	586.00
1/2"		" "	968	784	204.00
5/8"		" "	242	315	62.20
(SAY $ 1100)			TOTAL	2830	$1063.90
3/16"		flat	281	30	40.00
1/4"		hor. & vert.	861	138	128.00
5/16"		" "	1526	305	233.00
		" "	115	36	18.90
3/8"		hor.	23	8	3.90
1/2"		" & vert.	86	46	16.10
		" "	19	25	4.70
11/16"		flat	154	170	37.70
1"		"	18	53	7.40
(SAY $ 500)			TOTAL	811	$489.70

TOTAL COST $1750
TOTAL WEIGHT OF WELD.... 4253 lbs.

NOTE: Cost includes electrodes, power, labor, & 100% overhead at 15 ft. fl. to fl. speed.

Welded Bridges of the Future

120-Ft. SPAN STEEL DECK GIRDER 2-LANE BRIDGE

PLATE 4

Table 7